# Discovering Ourselves

*Third Edition*

# DISCOVERING
# OURSELVES

*A View of the Human Mind
and How It Works*

EDWARD A. STRECKER, M.D., Sc.D.

AND

KENNETH E. APPEL, M.D., Sc.D.

IN COLLABORATION WITH

JOHN W. APPEL, M.D.

*The Department of Psychiatry
University of Pennsylvania*

THE MACMILLAN COMPANY
NEW YORK

*Eleventh Printing, 1967*

*Earlier editions:* Discovering Ourselves *by Strecker and Appel, copyright, 1931, 1943, by The Macmillan Company.*

*Library of Congress catalog card number: 58-5132*

*The Macmillan Company, New York*
*Collier-Macmillan Canada, Ltd., Toronto, Ontario*

*Printed in the United States of America*

# PREFACE TO THE THIRD EDITION

*Discovering Ourselves* IS AN ELEMENTARY BOOK OR PRIMER ON THE psychology of motivation, behavior, and human relations. It continues to sell 27 years after it was first published. This must mean that it fills a real need. Perhaps this is because, while not a textbook, it offers a brief guided course of reading without being complicated, rigid, or dogmatic. Problems, psychological mechanisms, and the dynamics of personality are discussed. These are important for ordinary people in the United States in 1958 and for their leaders to understand. In brief fashion it points out some "causal" relationships or factors in ineffectiveness, discontent, unhappiness, discouragement, depression, and many important psychosomatic illnesses. It offers questions that we should ask ourselves when we are not getting along well or finding satisfaction, either physically or mentally. It does not "make" all illnesses psychological. It does not try to sell one point of view. It should help patients who are not too sick, but of course it is not a substitute for doctors, psychiatrists, or the clergy. It does not claim that psychiatry is a panacea for the discontents, failures, disappointments, and threats to survival of present-day civilization. Nor does it pretend to be a substitute for religion, education, the laboratory, the general practitioner, and the surgeon.

It does, however, attempt to offer some elementary information about behavior and moving forces in human nature and society and some of the underlying feelings, motivations, and directions in civilization today. These matters concern all, whether they are teachers, parents, nurses, physicians, or clergy. It may be of interest to legal experts who are trying to organize life in balanced and orderly ways.

Literature widely illustrates many of the principles discussed, whether in Tolstoy, Dostoevsky, O'Neill, or Al Capp's *Lil Abner*.

This is a distillation of years of psychiatric practice—of helping people with adolescent, parental, vocational, marital, medical, mental, and religious difficulties.

The junior author would be delinquent if he did not emphasize his conviction, as the result of over 30-years' experience, of the constructive value of identification, empathy, and inspiration in human relations and psychotherapy. They are forces often greater than reasoning or any particular form of therapeutic procedure. The Existentialists have recognized the limitations of reason, set formulas, and stereotyped thinking—from Nietzsche to Jaspers, from Kierkegaard to Maritain and Tillich. St. Augustine and St. Thomas years ago were aware of this. It is important to recognize spiritual and inspirational forces at a time when civilization with its atomization often appears to be approaching the brink of annihilation. Materialistic foundations laid down by the seductive scientific formulations of the nineteenth century, which seemed to assure progress, have not made it possible to build a world which is firm and secure, as was so fervently hoped. Instead we have the Age of Anxiety and the reality of Sartre which is supposed to substitute for culture and religion. James and Bergson had much to say about all this, but that would carry us too far afield. The fruits of science, great and important as they have been, have not always contributed to the constructive in health, human and international relationships. Not that we should have less science, but we should develop new uses and concepts of science and culture. Without new visions, understanding, and rededications, science which can help people to live more fully and abundantly will contribute instead to their destruction. Pursuing the patterns of the past may very well bring disaster. There are visions that can lead to survival, well-being, and life that is more gratifying to more people.

It is hoped that the new edition of this book, with its important additions, will increase understanding of some of the basic factors underlying behavior and human relationships, and enable them to become more effective, constructive, and satisfying.

Grateful acknowledgement is made to Dr. Henry T. Kleiner for his contribution to the chapters on "Personality Development" and "The Superego." We wish to thank Alfred A. Knopf for permission to quote from *Facts and Theories of Psychoanalysis* by Ives Hendrick.

Our thanks are also due to Mrs. Elma L. Harper who has contributed most generously of her time in the work on the current revision.

# FOREWORD

THERE SEEMS TO BE A GENERAL NEED FOR A MORE INTELLIGENT understanding of mental hygiene.

Many people, psychologically interested through the medium of gigantic advertising campaigns, have wholeheartedly adopted programs of physical hygiene. Numerous books and periodicals, innumerable pamphlets and magazine articles, and countless placards, signs, and posters all blazon forth in word and picture the doctrine of the prime importance of a sound body. There are milk and spinach with their respective vitamins for the children; ornate ultraviolet sunrooms for club members; reducing exercises for the ladies. On any fair day the many golf links of the country are alive with tens of thousands engaged in healthful exercise and recreation. The object of periodic health examinations and life extension institutes is understood, and their benefits are reaped by many. Dentists are busier with prophylaxis and prevention than with extractions and repair work. Dietary experts are having well-attended innings. World War II brought to our attention anew the tremendous importance of the physical health of our people. Organizations have been developed to cultivate and increase the physical fitness of our youth.

By and large, the public has intelligently grasped the aim and scope of physical hygiene. If the body is neglected, not exercised, not rested, not scientifically fed, then its organs and appendages will begin to deteriorate. There will be discomfort and suffering which will interfere with happiness and success. If the neglect continues, serious organic disease may make its appearance, and life is unnecessarily shortened. The stakes in the care of the body are health or disease; life or death.

In view of such intelligent foresight, it is strange that the mind has been given only haphazard attention. Just as the brain is the supreme organ of the body, so is the mind the mechanism which expresses the soul. Even a perfectly developed body is useless unless it is directed by a well-balanced and capable mind. Once we saw a boy who seemed to be physically perfect. He had beautifully proportioned limbs, a magnificent torso, and a head that looked as though it had been shaped by a great sculptor of ancient Greece. But his movements were awkward and incoordinated; his speech was childlike; his laugh a silly guffaw; his eyes were vacant and expressionless. His wonderful body meant little or nothing to him. It would have been better if it had never been. There was no directing intelligence— no mind. He was an imbecile.

If the stakes in the game of physical hygiene are health and life, then the stakes in the game of mental hygiene are even higher. Here we play for adjustment or maladjustment; efficiency or inefficiency; success or failure; happiness or unhappiness; replete, satisfying, and worthwhile lives or empty, unsatisfactory, and pathetic existences; mental health or mental illness.

It is to the realization of the constructive potentialities of the human personality that this book is dedicated.

Its aim is to present in readable and nontechnical language commonly accepted concepts of the newer psychology which have been found useful, helpful, and understandable by patients in our daily practice. Our indebtedness to numerous writers will be obvious to those familiar with the subject. In such a book as this frequent footnote acknowledgments have been deemed unnecessary. All psychiatrists today owe much to Freud, Jung, and Adler for their pioneer work in psychological analysis. We acknowledge special obligations in the preparation of this book to Bernard Hart's *The Psychology of Insanity;* and T. A. Ross's *The Common Neuroses.* We are indebted also to the following: *Principles of Mental Hygiene* by W. A. White; *Just Nerves* and *Intelligent Living* by A. F. Riggs; *Outline of Abnormal Psychology* by William McDougall; *Instincts of the Herd in Peace and War* by W. Trotter; *The New Psychology* by A. G. Tansley; *The Logic of the Unconscious Mind* and *Psychoanalysis and Its Place in Life,* both by M. K. Bradby.

January, 1943

# CONTENTS

*xi*

PART II

*Psychology of Everyday Life:*
*The Conflicting Urges of Thought, Feeling, and Action*

PART III

*The Nature of Emotion, Anger, and Fear*
*Contributed by John W. Appel, M.D.*

PART IV

*Mental Mechanisms Which the Personality Utilizes to Meet Conflicting Urges and Difficulties in Everyday Life*

PART I

# Concepts of Modern Psychology

*Chapter 1*

# QUESTIONS PSYCHOLOGY
# HELPS TO ANSWER

*In which are propounded a few of the important and interesting questions that psychology attempts to answer.*

HUMAN PSYCHOLOGY IS THE STUDY OF THE HUMAN MIND AND THE way it works. The behavior of man is considered with particular reference to its mental or psychological aspects. The motives and driving forces of thought and action are analyzed and interpreted; their mechanisms and effectiveness are considered. Dynamic psychology is an attempt to understand why we behave like human beings.

Why does the child rush toward the stranger who is walking down the street, in the mistaken belief that it is his father returning from work? When we are anxiously awaiting the doctor, why do we interpret the toot of every automobile horn as indicating his arrival? As youngsters when we were deep in the jam pots or stealthily trying to smoke, why did every creak of a loose floor board or any chance sound mean to us the approach of nurse or mother? Why do we forget certain engagements, such as dental appointments, and readily remember others? When we bungle a piece of work, why do we so often blame our tools and so rarely ourselves?

Frequently the disappointments and dissatisfactions of the office are visited upon wife and children. The wife suffers for the stupidities of the stenographer. The efficient secretary draws down upon her innocent head, bottled-up wrath really due to the culinary shortcom-

*3*

ings of a new cook or the extravagances of the employer's wife. Why is this so?

Why do upright citizens praise a rascally political bedfellow? Why do we become heated and hurt when our political ideas and religious beliefs are opposed? A discussion about physics or mathematics is not nearly as likely to upset our equilibrium. Once we turn from a consideration of facts that may be verified to the realm of beliefs, opinions, bias, and prejudice, then we are in another world in which emotions boil readily, and obviously are surrendered only after the most stubborn struggle. This is the world we are about to study.

Why do some contestants in an athletic contest lose their heads, while others remain calm? In the heat of argument, dignified Senators may behave like naughty children. It is said, that, in the White House, there is a place on the red carpet of a certain room where a former President of the United States threw himself and kicked and screamed like an hysterical schoolgirl, because a group of Senators succeeded in setting aside his will. Sometimes, when we are hard pressed in an argument, we do not retreat or attack anew, but suddenly begin to give irrelevant replies or raise questions not at all related to the point at issue. Why?

One man waxes enthusiastic about his ideal of womanhood. She is cool, sedate, gracious, dignified, and blond. Another will have naught of this type. He worships at the shrine of a jolly, vivacious, lively brunette. What is the explanation? Why are some of us sensitive about certain matters that come up in casual conversation? Why do some of us blush readily and others not at all? One person is afraid of darkness; another is more at peace when the shades of night have fallen, but is terrorized by thunder and lightning. Why? Crowds depress some but stimulate others. Why could one of our patients, a girl of eighteen, ride a dangerously wild horse with perfect control, ease of mind, and much enjoyment but could not bring herself to walk along a city sidewalk unattended?

Why does failure stimulate some individuals to renewed and successful effort but paralyze others into hopeless inactivity? What are complexes and inhibitions? What do we mean by projection and identification? What are the causes of nervous breakdowns?

When we try to answer these and many other questions and

problems, we begin to think *psychologically*. We learn to use psychological concepts in understanding our own troubles, worries, fears, distractions, irritabilities, sensitivities, and peculiarities. It is the purpose of this book to help us to reach the goal of clear and honest thinking. It should enable us to see a little farther into our inner selves. It should permit us to manage our minds better. If we are "nervously" inclined or happen to be passing through a so-called "nervous breakdown" we should be helped toward a realization as to how the condition developed. It should assist us toward adjustment and recovery. Finally, we should come to understand that "nervous breakdowns" are not inevitable and in many instances may be prevented. It is indeed no more necessary to have them than it is to have smallpox or malaria.

*Chapter 2*

# THE INTIMATE RELATION
# OF BODY AND MIND

*In which there is pointed out the intimate relation-
ship that exists between our bodies and our minds.*

WHAT IS THE HUMAN BODY? IT IS A PHYSICAL OBJECT CONSISTING
of material substances. We can see it. We can point to it. We can
touch it. We can measure it. We can weigh it. During surgical operations our innermost physical secrets are exposed to the gaze of the
surgeon. The penetrating eye of the x-ray can reproduce pictures of
bones, blood vessels, and other parts of the anatomy. Through the
agency of the fluoroscope it is possible to observe the heart in action,
contracting and expanding. But no surgeon or x-ray or fluoroscope
can reach the mind. We can *tell* others our mental experiences, but
they cannot directly observe these experiments. They may *infer* our
mental attitudes from physical or bodily expressions (pain, joy, sorrow, etc.), but this is not direct observation, and it is an uncertain
and often misleading method.

What is the human mind? It is not the brain, since the brain is a
material structure visible to the naked eye, and under the microscope
it is further revealed in its finer details. The mind, on the other hand,
is something nonmaterial. It cannot be seen or touched or measured
or weighed. It is something spiritual, if you will. Spiritual, however,
does not mean the mind is not *actual* and *real*. Far from it! For instance, a man of spirit is very real. In our thoughts of him we emphasize this side of his make-up rather than his body. The spirit is the
important and vital thing. It is truly *the very essence*. The spirit of a

6

school, of a business organization, of a family, and even of a nation is the real and the essential. Yet, it cannot be seen. What do we remember of a beloved one who has died? His body? No. We recall more clearly his "spirit"; his tendencies and his enthusiasms; his likes and dislikes; his ideals and his conflicts; the things he struggled for and the things he fought against. When we think of the mind of another we think of his thoughts, feelings, and impulses, his ideals and his will. In short, we think not of his toes or fingers or nose or heart or lungs but of his *personality,* which is nonmaterial and is the sum total of his behavior with reference to mental factors.

Nevertheless, nerves, the spinal cord, and the brain, which are a part of the body, are necessary. Without them the mind cannot function. The brain is essential for conscious behavior.

## THE RELATIONSHIP BETWEEN
## THE BODY AND THE MIND

How are the body and mind related? This subject has provided endless material for the discussions of philosophers and scientists through the ages. There is no universal agreement. Common sense, however, tells us at once that there is an extremely close and intimate connection. This is readily verified by our own experiences.

Often, the body influences the mind. The effect of disease is a typical example. Let the fever of influenza, pneumonia, or any infectious disease mount beyond a certain degree and there is delirium. Certain diseases primarily affect the brain and hence the mind. In encephalitis or sleeping sickness, the brain is inflamed, and the patient is overcome by an uncontrollable desire for sleep. Children who have been the victims of this disease frequently exhibit conduct which is not far short of atrocious. One of our little encephalitic patients was discovered just in the nick of time. Equipped with a box of carpet tacks and a hammer, he was about to begin driving the tacks into his infant sister's head.

Even small and transient bodily disturbances may temporarily upset the mind. If we eat something that disagrees with digestion, we may find the whole day is ruined. We may become curt, snappy, irritable, and difficult. Our judgments are poor and hasty; we are unfair and inconsiderate. Sometimes, particularly at luncheon, we may dine well but not too wisely. If we have eaten too much, we may feel uncomfortably full and heavy and stupid. Then our whole attitude changes. Interesting work, friends, family only seem to intensify the ill humor. A stranger would think us anything but affable. Our outlook on life is "bilious."

Likewise, alcohol and other drugs may degrade a sociable, reliable, pleasing personality into its opposite. Alcoholics are proverbially unreliable. Morphine addicts are accomplished liars and cannot be trusted. Blood vessel disease, syphilis, kidney and thyroid affections, tumors of the brain, etc., may alter the mental outlook to the degree of complete transformation. Even such a small thing as the wearing of badly fitting glasses may be enough to cause physical discomfort which is sometimes translated into mental peevishness.

It is obvious that the body can and does affect the mind deleteriously. The reverse is also true. A sound healthy body, whose various systems are working harmoniously, is usually the bearer of a cheerful, buoyant disposition. The words sanguine, phlegmatic, melancholic, choleric, and bilious indicate the dependence of mental attitude and disposition upon the state of the body.

## THE INFLUENCE OF THE
## MIND UPON THE BODY

The mind has a potent and far-reaching influence upon the body. This effect may be either harmful or beneficial.

Everyone is familiar with the deep sense of power and strength which seems to radiate from that human being who has reached a state of moral serenity in life. Peace of mind, contentment, satisfaction are reflected in quiet, orderly functioning of the body. After a serious mental or moral struggle is over, we can feel relief and relaxation in our very muscles. Before an important examination there may be anxiety and a higher blood pressure. With the sense of completion that follows a strenuous task well done, the pressure falls to a normal level.

If a cat is frightened by a fierce dog, there is an outpouring of adrenalin into the blood stream far in excess of the usual amount. The majority of the members of a famous varsity football squad show sugar in the urine on the eve of the important game of the season. It has been authoritatively related that on one of the South Sea Islands where voodooism is practiced, strong, healthy, young natives died a few weeks after they had been told that a small tree gum image of themselves had been fashioned by the voodoo priest, thrust through with a sharpened twig, and melted in a flame. If this is true it is an example of emotional death.

Pleasant environments influence the physiological processes. Beauty soothes, quiets, relaxes. Surroundings in which truth, goodness, and kindness predominate foster happiness and peace of mind. Digestion may be aided by attractive surroundings at meals. Good food tastefully served in quiet, pleasant places goes a long way toward preventing indigestion. This is not merely poetry but actual fact which can be demonstrated in the laboratory.

After we have solved a difficult problem there is a sense of well-being and elation which has definite bodily components. The body of a human being whose mind is occupied with satisfactory work *feels* and functions better than it would if the mind were continuously idle. If the mind is not engaged with the concrete problems of daily life, it turns in upon itself and is occupied with certain physical activities which attract its attention and with which it was never meant to be concerned.

The body functions more harmoniously when love dominates the mind than it does when hate rules. Similarly, when tenderness, joy, happiness, and the warm feelings of sympathy and comradeship prevail in our minds, unquestionably the physical mechanisms work more easily and more satisfactorily. These feelings and emotions are at once reflected in the organism. Compare appetite and digestion when dining alone or with a group of friends; after a walk or game with congenial companions or an unpleasant session with someone we dislike and distrust.

The lighter side of life, play, laughter, amusement, and even occasional childish silliness are as important for the proper working of the body, as are more serious pursuits. They oil the bearings of the body through the mind, decrease friction, and make the machinery run more smoothly. We find that we must teach many of our patients how to play.

Jog on, jog on, the footpath way,
And merrily jump the stile, boys;
A merry heart goes all the day,
Your sad one tires in a mile, boys.

One of the functions of art in general is to produce favorable bodily reactions. Think of beautiful strains of music, a perfect painting, immortal poetry, sublime sculpture. Surely, we are physically better for having heard and seen. Finally, it may be added that attitudes of reverence and worship before the great mysteries of life have a wholesome effect on the body; antagonism, bitterness, distrust, and fear are harmful.

All of us have experienced the physical expression of unpleasant and harmful mental influences. Fear furnishes a conspicuous example. The heart starts thumping and seems to jump into the throat. We breathe rapidly and may feel cold. Apprehension may be accompanied by a "gone feeling" in the pit of the stomach. After such an experience we are exhausted. Living under conditions which entail anxiety for a considerable length of time may have the same effect as sudden fear, and we not only *feel* but *are* actually exhausted. When an animal is subjected to frightening circumstances, a substance which stops digestion is rapidly poured into the blood stream. The same thing may happen to any human being. Digestive disturbances result. Often "nervous" patients dwell upon their "indigestion" and demand the kind of medicine that comes in a bottle or box. They fail to recognize that anxiety, trouble, and worry are the primary causes of the frequent nausea and stomach upsets. The medicine they need is mental peace and freedom from worry. Psychic pain, the conflict of opposing desires, may make us lose all interest in food. If this continues for a long period of time, we lose weight, color (anemia), and strength. Some patients complain bitterly of constant and unconquerable fatigue. They, too, want medicine, as if the body were the cause of the fatigue, instead of being merely the agency through which it is expressed. They do not understand that the fatigue is only the reflection in the body of a mental struggle which has not been satisfactorily settled.

Intense anger is another emotion that readily induces sensations of exhaustion. And just as anxiety plus anxiety plus anxiety equal *fear,* so does irritation plus irritation plus irritation equal anger.

Disgusting sights are apt to make us feel nauseated. If we live continuously in an environment that brings us into contact with people we scorn or with objects that are repulsive to us, we find that scorn and repulsion plus scorn and repulsion plus scorn and repulsion equal *disgust,* and it is easy to develop a so-called "gastric neurosis."

Mental overwork is even more pernicious than physical overwork. We become restless, and the slightest and most casual occurrences readily irritate us. We become aware of the beat of the heart in the chest, the throb of arteries in head and neck, the movements of the stomach and digestive tract. These are normal sensations, so normal that ordinarily we automatically ignore them. Here is needed, not sedatives, but the inauguration of a more balanced and wholesome physical-mental regime.

Social isolation results in too much restriction of the outlook— a mental myopia. It is a question of degree, loneliness, homesickness, nostalgia. Too prolonged separation from home and loved ones may cause loss of joy and cheer, even of appetite and ability to sleep. There is something physically stimulating in social intercourse.

Inferiority feelings may inhibit free social relationship with our fellow human beings. If these feelings of inadequacy are allowed to evolve unduly, the mental horizon is seriously shortened, and those social contacts which are so fundamental for the balanced development of the normal human being are lost. After a time the sense of ineffectiveness may be reflected in poorly developed muscles, delicate appearance, and lack of vigor.

If aroused to a high pitch, shame, distress, hate, envy, jealousy, all strike to the very core of our being. They leave us worn, tired, incapable, and almost helpless. The blush of shame, the haggard countenance of distress, the consuming burning of envy and jealousy, and the facial and vocal expressions of hate are striking testimonials of the deteriorating effect of these emotions upon the body. Surprise has its physical reactions. It stimulates. Again, we may jump with joy or droop in sorrow. If we are confused as to which plan of action to follow, food may escape attention, and faintness and indigestion may appear. Many people lose their appetites just before commencing a journey. The lawyer dines lightly before an important argument in court. The meals skipped by surgeons and, perhaps, even by psychiatrists in their anxiety for their patients would feed an army.

Driven by curiosity, which is simply another name for science, workers may labor too persistently over favorite projects and problems. If this tendency is followed too intensively, other channels of activity gradually become blocked. We have all met people who are

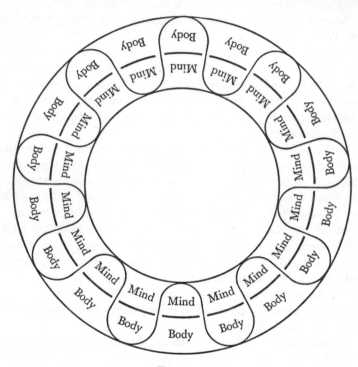

Figure 1

so closely engaged mentally that they become absent-minded, exceedingly careless of dress, and forgetful of even the ordinary needs of the body. It is not long before the abused body begins to show signs of protest—hollow cheeks, dark circles under the eyes, bent shoulders, pale skin, loss of weight.

It is clear that the relationship between body and mind is continuous and very intimate. It is not within the province of this book to discuss it in all its manifold and intricate details. Just as a treatise on physical hygiene, while it does not ignore the mind, nevertheless is chiefly interested in pointing out ways and means of promoting and safeguarding the health of the body, so are we in this book primarily concerned with feasible methods of procuring the maximum of mental health, comfort, and efficiency. It suffices to repeat that mind and body are so closely connected that not even a single thought or mood can come into existence without being reflected in the physical organism. Perhaps this relationship may be graphically expressed in a diagram.

In spite of this intimate body-mind contact we still assert that the structural nervous system (that is, the material brain, spinal cord, and nerves) is not per se the cause of "nervousness."

## Chapter 3

# NERVOUSNESS IS NOT A DISEASE OF THE NERVES

*Wherein it is demonstrated that in spite of the close relationship between body and mind, "nervousness" is not caused primarily by disease of the physical nervous system.*

A COMMON ERROR OF EVERYDAY SPEECH IS THE USE OF WORDS "nerves" and "nervous" interchangeably, as if they meant the same thing. "Mrs. X. is just a bundle of nerves." "It is nothing but nerves." "My wife is so nervous." "Doctor, I am nervous. My nerves are shot to pieces." These expressions are familiar. We all know what they mean. But they are being incorrectly applied. They are figures of speech and must not be taken literally and scientifically. For instance, when we say that our nerves are high strung or taut we scarcely mean to imply that, like violin strings, they are stretched to a high degree of tightness and tension. When we are extremely "nervous" we may feel as though the nerves of the body were actually taut, but, of course, they are not.

Paradoxical as it may seem, *the cause of nervousness is not our physical nerves.* If a patient is nervous even to the extent of a serious and disabling neurosis (hysteria, neurasthenia, psychasthenia) and the nervous system could be exposed outside the body, the most careful examination and minute dissection would fail to discover anything abnormal. Even the microscope would reveal only normal nerves. We must look elsewhere for the cause of the nervousness.

Actual organic disease of the nervous system is readily discovered by the microscope. We are able to observe directly the structural changes. The nerves look different, just as a house which has been gutted by fire looks very different from what it did before. If a nerve has been severely injured and degenerated, instead of presenting the normal appearance of a straight, dark line or wire, it may appear to be irregularly broken into small pieces, much like a telephone wire that has been shattered by a storm.

Again if a nerve is injured, the resulting symptoms are not the symptoms that indicate nervousness. The telltale signs depend on the location of the nerve and the nature of the injury. For instance, if we "catch cold" in a nerve, we may feel pain and tenderness along the course of the nerve. The doctor tells us we are suffering from neuralgia or neuritis. He does not say we are nervous.

If it is a *feeling* or sensory nerve, there may be burning or tingling in the skin which is supplied by the affected nerve. Should the injury or infection be more severe, there may be numbness. If the process goes farther, the skin in that area may become entirely insensitive to touch or to the prick of a sharp needle. Then we say the skin is anesthetic, i.e., without sensation or feeling.

If the main nerve running to a muscle is severed by a knife or bullet, it does not produce nervousness but does result in inability to move the muscle. In other words the muscle is paralyzed. Infantile paralysis, for example, is not a nervous disease but a nerve disease. That is, it is an infectious disease which does not make the patient nervous, but does damage motor (muscle) nerves and their cells of origin, and consequently paralyzes various muscles, particularly those of the legs.

Trauma, i.e., injury, infection, or drugs (such as alcohol and lead), frequently damages nerves. The symptoms which ensue are pain, tingling, numbness, anesthesia, weakness, and paralysis, but there is no indication of that group of emotional disturbances which comprise nervousness.

We have the contradictory situation, therefore, of nervousness in the presence of a nervous system which is apparently normal, and actual disease of the nerves without nervousness. In fact, disease of organs which are not properly a part of the nervous apparatus, such as the heart and arteries, kidneys, thyroid gland, etc., is somewhat more likely to be a factor in nervousness than are affections of the brain, spinal cord, or nerves.

Sometimes before important examinations students feel nervous, and complain of palpitation of the heart and odd sensations in the stomach. Of course, they do not have organic disease of the nervous system. After the examination is over, especially if a passing mark is obtained, the symptoms rapidly disappear. If such sensations and others come into consciousness frequently, the individual may have what is termed a psychoneurosis, or he may have thyroid disease, or he may be in love. The first step toward checking the trouble is to trace it to its causative source. A fire may start from a short circuit in the attic or from a defective flue in the cellar. Likewise nervousness may have various origins. This is why psychiatrists hesitate to prescribe medicines. It is often futile merely to give drugs—this medicine for the headache; something else for restlessness; still something else for this or that odd sensation; an endless assortment of sedative and hypnotic drugs for insomnia. It is much more important to find out why the patient has headache or twitching or insomnia. The correct answer will frequently lead into the realm of conflicts, problems of life, emotional upheavals, maladjustments, and the like. The net result will not be a prescription for bromides but the teaching of self-understanding and emotional control.

## CLASSIFICATION OF NERVOUSNESS

Four types of "nervousness" have been described.

1. MOTOR. This is the type in which there are frequent, uncontrolled movements of various parts of the body. There are muscular twitchings which are irregular and do not seem to have any foundation in disease. They seem to be nothing more than restlessness and motor irritability. These jerkings are rather like those that occur in St. Vitus' dance and sometimes in sleeping sickness. Then, too, there are the uneasiness and slight overactivity which overflow into the body in states of anxiety and fear. Here, too, belongs the individual who never relaxes, cannot sit still, is never in repose. Sometimes there are repeated contractions of the same set of muscles, and this is called a habit spasm or tic. In goiter, there is a fine trembling of the hands.

In very old age, or as a result of disease of the arteries, there may be continuous shaking movements of the head and hands.

2. SENSORY. Often nervousness is used to describe marked sensitivity to the stimulations which reach consciousness by the route of the special senses—hearing, sight, smell, taste, and touch. Some people shudder and say the "blood runs cold" if a fingernail is drawn across the surface of a blackboard. Others are startled at the slightest noise. If a door is sharply banged they feel as if they were going to "jump out of their skins." All sounds seem very loud and sharp and make them feel tense. Still others insist on having the room darkened. Ordinary daylight is intolerably glaring. Another group is nauseated by odors not usually regarded as unpleasant, or is sickened by tastes which do not bother most of us. We had a patient who "simply could not stand" the contact of nylon underwear with the surface of the body. All these are examples of undue sensitivity.

3. PSYCHIC OR MENTAL. In this type it is ideas and situations and conflicts which call out the "nervousness" and produce mental irritability. Everything, even the very casual, suggests frightening or disgusting trains of thought with their accompanying emotional reactions. There may be constant worry, apprehension, sensitiveness; feelings of suspicion and ideas of reference; loss of self-control, a sense of unreality, inferiority, and the like.

4. VISCERAL. This is "nervousness" referred to some organ of the body. For instance, the heart is felt to palpitate, or the "liver" is said to be "sluggish." Strange feelings here are attributed by patients, in their ignorance of anatomy and medicine, to the various organs which often have nothing to do with the symptoms concerned. Sometimes these internal sensations are described in a vague sort of way as an "inward quiver," an "inner vibration," or a vague sense of "internal pressure."

Although disease of the nervous system is *not* usually the chief *cause* of nervousness, it is by *means* of the nervous system that we feel "nervousness," just as it is by means of the nervous system that we feel the pain if a finger is cut.

The nervous system, which is a network of nerves throughout the body, is like a telephone system which spans the country. Through sensory nerves, the brain, like central, receives messages or sensations; through the motor nerves, impulses or orders are sent out to the muscles so that action may be executed.

Let us illustrate. A pistol shot is heard. We jump and are frightened, i.e., "nervous." The sound waves came to our ears, traveling as sensory impulses up the auditory nerve; the impulses then divided, some going to the brain, others going via the motor nerves to various parts of our body, to the muscles of our arms and legs, to the heart, lungs, and intestines. Without the sensory nerves which bring us into relation with the world about us, we could not have heard the shot. Without motor nerves we could not have jumped. Without nerves going to our heart, lungs, and intestines, we should not have had a rapid heart, an increased rate of breathing, and alterations in the movement of our intestines. Without sensory nerves from our heart, lungs, and gut, we could not have become conscious of disturbed movements in these organs, which constitute part of what is called emotion. And, finally, if we had no brain we could not have been conscious or aware of all this and could not have told anyone of our experience. We see how important the nervous system is, therefore, but it would have been incorrect to say that the nervous system *caused* our fright.

So too, if an idea which makes us uneasy, or frightens us, comes to mind in *memory* or *imagination,* it would be wrong to look to the nervous system as the cause of these feelings. It is to our experience and to the organization of experience that we must turn in order to account for such feelings. We must learn how experience has been determined or conditioned in order to understand why a certain idea or experience disturbs one person by making him nervous, and leaves another calm and unruffled.

Individual past history and experience are related to the very fundamental causes of nervousness. Analysis of experience—the story of the moving emotional situations of life, the retelling of hopes and fears, desires and obligations—has proved a much more fruitful agent for the control and cure of nervousness than all the drugs of the pharmacopeia. In the example given above, the pistol shot made us nervous. But it made us nervous only because our nervous system was normal. If the auditory nerves had been diseased, we could not have heard the pistol shot. All this cannot be emphasized too strongly.

The most helpful resource in treating nervousness is to have the patient talk over his past experience, understand how the present condition has developed, and reorganize his life on a more healthful basis. An appreciation of psychology is consequently much more important than a knowledge of the anatomy or physiology of the nervous system. What are the "pistol shots" in your experience?

*Chapter 4*

# ELEMENTARY
# CONCEPTS OF PSYCHOLOGY

*In which certain elementary psychological concepts,
such as sensation, perception, thinking, reflex, emotion, habit, and instinct, are defined and described.
If he wishes, the reader need not read this chapter
in detail, but may use it as a reference reading.*

IT IS DIFFICULT TO GIVE A SATISFACTORY DEFINITION OF THE MIND.
There is no general agreement even among psychologists. Some definitions are frankly idealistic and emphasize the spiritual, nonmechan-
ical aspects of the mind. Others are so materialistic that one would
think there was no difference between psychology and physiology or
anatomy. Notwithstanding academic and hairsplitting difficulties, all
of us have a firsthand intuitive knowledge of the meaning of the
words mind and consciousness.

It is not necessary for the understanding of subsequent chapters
to read this one. Those that follow are planned to show how the mind
works. This one is merely an introduction. It is written to help orient
the reader, and to acquaint him with psychological terms, so that he
may the better understand discussions of psychological problems.
This chapter, therefore, may be thought of merely as a sort of glossary
or reference. Just as a watch maker may know how to construct or
repair a watch without being able to define the principles of physics
involved, so we may know intuitively a great deal about the mind without being able to give definitions of it.

Let us enumerate some of the things that occur to us when we think of the mind. They are: ideas, thoughts, feelings, desires, hopes, fears, decision, choices. These, we should say, are distinctively mental experiences. Self-observation or observation of our own conscious experience is called *introspection*—meaning simply, turning one's view or observation inward upon one's own experience. Introspection, therefore, reveals to us our own private individual experience. We can have ideas, feelings, and desires that no one else in the world can know or guess unless we choose to *tell* them. No amount of curiosity, prying, or observation by another person will disclose what these individual experiences are, unless we wish to disclose them. This fact is a serious impediment to the study of the mind and the revelation of consciousness. It can be reached almost solely by introspection. With the body, the situation is different. Anyone, who is adequately trained, may observe our bodies. Even against our will others can examine them, as, for example, when we are delirious with a high fever, or unconscious after an automobile accident. After death our bodies can be examined, but not our minds and consciousness.

Introspection, then, gives us information about mind and consciousness; observation informs us about the body—and only inadequately by *inference* does observation tell us anything about the mind. We emphasize this contrast because the behaviorist school of psychology has attempted to eliminate mind and the various concepts of consciousness from psychology—the only thing worth studying, they assert, is the body and its various responses. Psychology (the word comes from the Greek and means mind or soul-science!) is for them the observation of human behavior. They would reduce all psychology to physiology. But just here we run into contradictions. The flush or pallor of the face is due to the movement of blood in our bodies. In a given case this may be caused by disease, or by emotion and thought. In the former instance we have simply physiological behavior; in the latter, psychological behavior. Merely to strike out the adjectives in the last sentence, and write, we have behavior, and behavior, unjustifiably simplifies the problem in our present state of knowledge, and certainly is not helpful or practical.

Precisely what we desire to know when a person is worried or nervous is primarily: What are his thoughts and his desires, his fears and his inhibitions? (Inhibitions are systems of ideas and feelings

that prevent us from carrying out certain actions or from assenting
to certain thoughts and desires.) Observation merely of the body and
its actions, with our present methods of examination, will yield us
in the majority of cases only meager and unsatisfactory information.
We can reach the mind more satisfactorily through words. It is because of the inadequacy of observation that we must use introspection.
As a matter of fact, the same thing in a lesser degree holds good
for physical disease. A patient may have a pain in the right side of his
abdomen, and the abdomen may be so rigid that by feeling or pal-
pation the doctor cannot determine whether the origin of the pain
is high or low in the abdomen. If he waited for a complete observation
of all the possible facts, the patient might die, whereas a few words
of introspection by the patient may be the clue to the whole situation
and be lifesaving. The patient may be able to tell just where and how
it hurts—also when and where it started. This aspect must be emphasized because of the behaviorist's attempt to rule out introspection.
However admirable this effort is from a scientific point of view, it
is fruitless, as we have seen, in certain practical exigencies of life.

In psychology, therefore, we must continually think of two
aspects or worlds of experience; namely, the world of observation,
which shows us the body (and nervous system), and the world of
introspection, which reveals to us the mind and consciousness. We
must try to avoid confusing the two worlds. There are some words
which refer to both; for example, the word "instinct."

We live in a tangible world. This world in the language of science
is termed environment. If a branch of a tree falls on the foot, we kick
it away. Here there is a disturbance or movement in the external
world, which touches our body and which we feel and recognize with
our mind. As a result of these bodily and mental processes in us, we
carry out an action which does something to the physical world or
environment, which alters the position, for example, of the branch
in the world about us. This disturbance in the environment which
touches us is called technically a *stimulus,* and the action we perform
is called a *response.* The physiological and mental processes that
occur in our experience are often named psychophysical processes,
meaning nothing more than the sum total of bodily and mental experience which goes on at a given time.

The nervous system is merely a grouping of millions of nerve cells and their processes. These cells and their processes (nerves) are stretched out all over the body like so many telephone wires in the country. The brain corresponds to a vast city telephone exchange, which receives messages from all over the body (sensations) and transmits messages to set the muscles into action.

### SENSATIONS, PERCEPTIONS, THOUGHT, REFLEXES

A few definitions are in order. Reading them over will afford sufficient familiarity with them. They are merely signposts in a rather ill-defined and complex field. Definitions should not be taken for the facts of mental experience themselves. The latter are too broad and deep for adequate definition.

*Sensations* are often defined as the ultimate elements of mental experience. In a sense they are units of mental life just as a nerve cell is the unit of the structural nervous system or a liver cell the unit of the liver. Sensations are the most elemental experiences we can picture. They are regarded as the foundation stones of our mental life. Adults rarely have pure sensations unless they experience something absolutely new and unique. For example, the taste of a new kind of wine or a new variety of food, such as snails, might be taken as fairly new sensations. For adults, however, most of our elementary sensations are grouped together and blended so intimately with memories and anticipations that the most elemental experiences of our mental life are usually called *perceptions*. Perceptions may be thought of roughly as groups or clusters of sensations. Let us illustrate. The yellowness of color, the roundness of shape, the weight on lifting, the taste on eating—all these as separate, individual experiences might be spoken of as sensations when we are presented with an orange. But all of these sensations, together with memories and anticipations of what we shall do with it, give us the *perception of an orange as a whole*. It seems all very artificial to divide experience up into such little, artificial pigeonholed entities, when we find such things apparently only in books, where experience is "intellectualized." That is so. We give these definitions for what they are worth and in order that on reading a larger book on psychology we shall know what is meant by these words.

*Thought* is very difficult to define. No definition is adequate, nor will any one be acceptable to many psychologists. Thought and imagination are closely connected. In action we deal with the world in a firsthand way. In thought and imagination we deal with the world in a secondhand way, pictorially, and subvocally, as it were. In other words, everything need not be tried out in practice. This would consume too much time. We close our eyes and picture to ourselves experiences we have had (*memory*), or experiences we plan to have (*expectation—anticipation—choice*). The latter process develops into volition and action. Instead of picturing to ourselves things that were or are to be—some people are poor visualizers—we may talk things over with ourselves without uttering any words. This process is what we mean by dealing with the world subvocally. In either case (and they are rarely separated) we deal with images of the world instead of the actual physical world itself. This affords much saving of effort and great economy in our mental life, and is closely related to the development of language. When images follow one another, determined by factors of similarity, difference, and identity, we have what is called *logical thinking*. When the images apparently do not follow such arrangement, we have *fantasy and daydreaming*. Volition is the desire, resolve, and attempt to carry some plan (image, picture, or talking to one's self) into action. We use it as synonymous with the will.

A few more terms may be defined. An ordinary *reflex* is an action carried out through the mediation of the nervous system but not requiring the cooperation of the brain for its execution. Reflexes are concerned not only with movements of our arms and legs (voluntary muscles), but also with the movements of various organs of the body (involuntary muscles), e.g., heart, stomach, intestines, and blood vessels. If someone sticks a sharp pin into the hand or presses a hot object against it, the hand moves away very quickly. This is a spinal reflex. If, however, a detailed examination should be carried out, it could be shown that the rate of the heart was increased and that the smaller blood vessels were contracting and raising the blood pressure. This is a sympathetic reflex.

If the heart beats very vigorously, we may become aware of it ourselves, feel a bit alarmed, and later quite tired. Then we have had an emotional experience. Physiologists have demonstrated that when we experience *emotional states* the *sympathetic reflexes* are very active in producing movements of the organs like the heart, intestines, blood vessels, sweat glands, and "goose-flesh" muscles, for example. When we are conscious of such activity in these organs we know that the organs must be in communication with the brain through various nerves.

If these reactions are too constant and too severe it is not wholesome, and indicates a needless emotional response on the part of the individual. It is like getting up steam in an engine for a possible emergency, and then, when it is clear that there is no emergency, not using it to run the engine, but merely allowing it to blow off through the safety valve. It is legitimate to prepare for certain emergencies, but when one anticipates too many of them, which never come to pass —whether it is in getting up steam in an engine or in developing unusual emotion—one wears and strains the machine unnecessarily.

There is a proper time and place for everything. There are many concrete situations in which *instinctive actions* are carried out. They should be. They accomplish something in the interests of the individual.

If we are in an automobile and there is an explosion and the car suddenly stops, we (1) instinctively jump and (2) are frightened. The jump takes place through purely reflex levels, and the muscles involved are of the voluntary variety, i.e., those in the arms and legs. Simultaneously, however, (2) the heart starts thumping, the stomach stops its rhythmic movements, the blood vessels contract, and we breathe more rapidly. The state of overactivity of the sympathetic nervous system and of the organs containing involuntary muscles is registered in the brain, and appears in our consciousness as an emotional state. The purely mental aspect of an emotion is sometimes technically called *affect*. Now some people experience such emotional states without reference to any present external factor in their environment. They overwork the sympathetic nervous system and literally waste their emotions. They are then said to be suffering from nervousness. It is important, then, to analyze the emotional experiences of their lives and to discover what factors have exaggerated or overdetermined the emotional life.

Psychologists, for years, emphasized three great aspects of mental life, namely: thinking, feeling, willing. They said with regard to every mental experience that there was the thinking aspect (sensations, perceptions, recognitions, memories), and feeling aspect (emotions and feelings of pleasantness or unpleasantness), and the willing aspect (expectation, choice, volition, action). These three aspects, they said, were irreducible into one another. It happens, however, that whenever we experience *intense feeling* and become *emotional,* our *bodies* internally become *vibrant,* as it were, with sympathetic or involuntary reflexes. Some psychologists have even gone so far as to say that feelings and emotions are nothing more than the experience of these activities. Emotion, then, appears as a sort of bridge between the thinking side of our nature and the willing or doing side.

We have tried to indicate the correlations between the mental and physical spheres, especially with regard to the feelings, instincts, and emotions, because nervousness, as we shall see, in the majority of cases is so intimately bound up with these sympathetic reflexes. So much so is this the case that thousands of people daily consult physicians in the belief that something is wrong with various organs of their bodies (heart or stomach, for example), when the real difficulty is an emotional one with bodily reverberations or accompaniments. This fact cannot be emphasized too strongly. The main factor in the *treatment* of these cases consists in bringing the patient to realize this relationship. Many *failures* result from attempts by physicians, unfamiliar with the modern treatment of nervousness, to treat these conditions with *medications directed only toward the body.* We see why such treatment is bound to fail.

In all adequate accounts of intense emotion, the bodily reverberations are most important. The following is a description by Dorothy Canfield Fisher in *Rough Hewn.*

But in her life, as by a fatality, there were never any occasions for emotion, for fresh, living sensations. Nothing ever happened to her that could stir her to anything but petulance and boredom—nothing! nothing! If anything seemed to promise to—why, Fate always cut it short. Those wonderful afternoons when Sister Ste. Lucie had taken her to the convent to talk to Father Elie! From the first of her Bayonne life she had felt it very romantic to know real Catholics, who used holy-water and believed in saints, and she had loved to go round with Sister Ste. Lucie in her long black gown and frilled white coif, just like a picture out of a book. But this was different. When the dark, gaunt, hollow-eyed, old missionary-priest had given her one somber look and made the sign of the cross over her, she had felt her heart begin to beat faster. And as he talked to her afterwards, in the bare, white-washed parlor of the convent, with the light filtering in through the closed shutters, he had made her tremble with excitement, as he himself had trembled throughout all his thin, powerful, old body. His deep-set eyes had burned into her, as he talked, his emaciated fingers, scorched brown by tropical suns, shook as he touched the crucifix. How he had yearned over her as he told her that, never, never would she know what it really was to live, till she cast out her stubborn unbelief and threw herself into the living arms of her true Mother, the Church of God. Flora had not known that she had any belief in particular to cast out—she had never thought anything special about religion at all, one way or the other. She only wanted him to go on making her tremble and feel half-faint, while Sister Ste. Lucie clasped her rosary beads and prayed silently, the tears on her cheeks!— *

This literary account of emotion has spoken of the thumping heart, the trembling, the burning, the sensation of faintness, the tears —all bodily processes controlled by sympathetic reflexes. These are all symptoms that we meet very frequently in patients who are suffering from nervousness. The only difference is that in nervousness these emotions are almost continuously with one, while in literature as in normal everyday life they are intermittent and temporary.

## EMOTIONS

To understand human behavior it is essential to consider emotions, for emotions have the vital role of supplying the energy which motivates human behavior. Emotion is the energy, the force which causes man to do things. It is emotion which activates man, which transforms him from a vegetable to an animal, so to speak. To survive, a man must breathe, digest his food, and expel waste material, and oxygen must be conveyed from his lungs to his various organs. But this is not enough; he must also hunt food, build shelter to protect himself from cold, fight, run away, and procreate in order to survive. Emotions provide the energy which enables him to do these things. In addition to these fundamental activities of life, emotions vivify and

* From *Rough Hewn* by Dorothy Canfield Fisher. Courtesy of Harcourt, Brace & Company, New York, 1922.

beautify life and create the very joy of living. The painting of a masterpiece, the conversion of a block of marble into a figure of enduring beauty, the writing of a great novel, in fact almost every great achievement in the arts is emotionally and not intellectually inspired.

Emotions enter into the decisions great and small of the individual, and the masses of the people fall strongly under their sway. Revolutions are awakened; bloody and costly wars are fought; potent historical documents are brought into existence; kings and queens lose their crowns and their heads; ordinary men are elevated to high places in response to the electrical current of feeling which sweeps through the mob.

It is clear that emotional energy may be used for good or ill. If it is to be a force for good it must be guided by the intellect, by thought. Mental hygiene tells us that at a given time we cannot help (foresee, prevent) the feelings which arise within us. We have to recognize their existence and accept them. But we can determine what we do with our feelings. Our actions can be controlled, guided, and directed by thought and will. Thinking thus lends direction and plan to emotional energy, switching it into channels which may be effective or ineffective, constructive or destructive. Personality and character are terms used to describe the patterns and channels this energy *habitually* follows. However, both thinking and personality would themselves be lifeless and static without the driving force of the emotions which activate them—like wires with the electricity turned off.

The emotions, then, are mobilized energy, energy the purpose of which is to enable us to do something—run away, fight, take care of somebody, or make love. Just what we do and how we do it is determined by our will, thinking, habits, and personality patterns.

The way we usually detect the presence of an emotion in us is by "feeling" it. We talk about "feeling" a strong emotion. We "feel" the emotion fear, we feel afraid. We "feel" the emotion anger, we feel angry. Thus, the words "emotion" and "feeling" frequently are used interchangeably. We refer to our emotions as feelings. A person of strong emotions is a person of strong feelings. But in both cases we are referring to energy, we are "feeling" the presence of energy. When we say our feelings impel us to do something, we mean, in most cases, that emotional energy impels us.

Because of its importance, emotion will be discussed in further detail in Chapter 11, as well as the specific emotions of anger and fear (Chaps. 12 and 13).

## HABIT

There are certain terms which have not yet been defined. The word *habit* is one which is somewhat ambiguous in that it may be used in speaking of either bodily or mental processes. Thus we have habits of work or play, and habits of thinking. We should always try to have clearly in mind in which sense we use the word. When we use the word habit several ideas arise. In the first place there is the *notion of repetition*. When we have a habit of a certain way of putting in golf, or sewing as a seamstress, or operating as a surgeon, or hoisting a heavy load as a laborer—the implication is that we do things *repeatedly* as we have done them before. If we took a motion picture of various habitual acts, we should see that the acts were repeated according to the same pattern. Habits of thought mean the same thing. We think repeatedly in similar, customary ways.

There is another notion that the word habit implies, namely that of *automaticity*. If one says we are creatures of habit, he means that we do things or form ideas and judgments almost without thinking about them. If our daily job requires us to hoist frequently heavy barrels from the ground, we develop a knack of doing it, which we acquire without thinking of it. After having learned to play tennis or swim, we go through the movements with very little thought. If we are ardent Republicans in politics, or Quakers in religious belief, we can make certain decisions in politics and religion with very little thought, because we have habitual ways of thinking about these matters. In this sense, habits give us certain ready-formed decisions. Customs are habits of thinking and habits of doing which society gives us ready-made. Life, from one point of view, consists in the learning and formation of habits. This is important not only from the physical, but also from the mental and moral aspects. For if one has formed good habits of work or thought or morality, he is relieved of a great deal of trouble and effort when he meets situations which can be solved summarily by habits already formed. And the time saved can be used for more constructive efforts in facing situations that cannot be handled on habitual levels. The process of becoming skillful means the acquisition of habits—whether in the bodily or mental spheres.

Clever and successful people have formed helpful habits of thinking and doing. Many people inadequate emotionally, or nervously upset, have not formed good habits of dealing with problems. They meet situations with immature or primitive types of reaction. Each difficulty is a fresh occasion for emotion and indecision instead of merely a transient situation that is easily mastered by good habits. A child hearing a fire alarm stops his play, becomes excited (emotion), imagines all sorts of things (fantasy), and does not return to his play (action) for a long time, and then perhaps only with difficulty. A normal healthy adult may leave his chair momentarily, but as soon as he has determined that the fire is not nearby he will return *by habit* to the task on hand. The neurotic or nervous person, on the other hand, will behave much as did the child—not merely with regard to fire alarms, but emotional matters in general. An emotional situation will cause a neurotic to suspend effective action for a much longer time than a normal person. Successful, stable people are not torn from their work by mild emotional stimuli, or if so, they return to their jobs through force of habit with little time lost.

This brings us to another implication of the word habit, namely, that it is something which is learned. This will be clearer if we contrast habits and reflexes. Reflexes are actions carried out through the mediation of the lower nervous centers. But one of the most interesting things about them is that reflexes do not have to be learned —they are present at birth. If you wash the eyes of a newborn baby, its eyelids will automatically close. He will suck at the breast immediately after birth. Similarly he will swallow if water is placed in his mouth. But he must *learn* to hold a bottle, to walk, and to talk. We might say, therefore, that *reflexes are inherited but habits are learned*.

*Instinct* is a word that one will meet frequently in psychological reading. By instincts we mean fundamental types of activity that we perform more or less spontaneously, and when we perform such actions we experience certain feelings or emotions. Unfortunately there is confusion in the use of this word. Sometimes it is used as if it referred to the sphere of the body and sometimes as if it referred to the mind. For example, the sex instinct has been described as purely physical or psychological, while the gregarious instinct (the tendency to associate with people) might be thought of as belonging to the mental sphere. Some instincts are supposed to be present at birth (reflexes), and others are held to be learned or developed (habits). An example of the former would be the instinct of self-preservation or the food instinct; of the latter, the instinct for race preservation or the sex instinct. Those who deny the mental aspect of things, as the behaviorists do, would say that instincts are nothing more than groups of reflexes or habits.*

* McDougall, who has written extensively on instincts, defines an instinct as an inherited "innate disposition which determines the organism to perceive (to pay attention to) any object of a certain class, and to experience in its presence a certain emotional excitement and an impulse to action which find expression in a specific mode of behavior in relation to that object." The following list of instincts and emotions is arranged from material found in William McDougall's *Outline of Psychology*. (Charles Scribner's Sons, 1923, p. 110, by courtesy of the publishers.)

## ON INSTINCTS

| INSTINCTS | EMOTIONS |
|---|---|
| Parental—protective | Tender emotion—tenderness, love |
| Pugnacity—combat, aggressive | Anger—fury, rage, annoyance, irritation, displeasure |
| Curiosity—inquiry, discovery, investigation | Wonder—feelings of mystery, strangeness, or unknown |
| Nutritional—food seeking | Appetite—craving, gusto |
| Repulsion—repugnance | Disgust—loathing, nausea, repugnance, creepy, snakeish |
| Flight—self-preservation, avoidance, danger instinct | Fear—terror, fright, alarm, trepidation |
| Gregarious | Feeling of loneliness—isolation, nostalgia, love of kind |
| Suggestion—imitation | Sympathy |
| Self-assertion—self-display | Elation—positive self-feeling, superiority, masterfulness, pride, domination |
| Self abasement—submission | Depression—subjection, inferiority, devotion, humility |
| Sex-mating, reproduction, pairing | Love—lust, jealousy, coyness |
| Acquisition—hoarding instinct | Feeling of ownership—possession protection, property |
| Construction | Feeling of creativeness—making, productivity |
| Appeal | Distress—attachment, helplessness, negative self-feeling, trust, excitement |
| Play—laughter (minor instinct) | Amusement—jollity, carelessness, relaxation |

The psychologists who emphasize instincts in their writings try to find some instinct that lies at the foundation of all forms of human activity and experience. It amounts practically to a *classification* of human activity. It is as if we should let a circle represent all forms of activity and divide the circle into little wedge-shaped sections which would represent different types of activity. The wedge-shaped pieces then would symbolize instincts.

Treating experience in this way has some value, especially in the consideration of complexes. But it is quite artificial as we can see. Furthermore, psychologists place varying emphasis on and insist on a different list of instincts. It is not profitable, therefore, to memorize any single table. The important thing is to be familiar in general with the concepts involved. It also enables one to check up on himself and to realize whether any one field of activity is receiving undue emphasis in his own life.

We can thus determine whether there is a balance in different forms of activity. Dr. Richard C. Cabot, following Tolstoi in viewing life as a whole and not merely as a problem of instincts, has written that a well-balanced, normal personality must divide its activities into four great fields, i.e., love, play, work, and worship. It is worthy of note in passing that very often people suffering from nervous breakdowns have not shown a proper balance of activities in these four fields. They frequently are deficient in several of them.

*Chapter 5*

# ACTION AS THE GOAL
# OF MENTAL PROCESSES

*The ultimate object of sensation, thought, and feeling is to produce* Action. *This chapter discusses the need and importance of* following through *with proper action, the balance or distribution of human activity, and the selection of suitable types of activity.*

THIS BOOK IS MEANT TO BE ENTIRELY PRACTICAL. IT IS NOT WRITTEN for psychologists or psychiatrists. It does not aim to discuss theoretical questions. Abstract discussions are introduced only insofar as they throw light on the practical problems of nervousness and teach how they may be dealt with and solved. In the midst of this account of the way the body and mind work, let us indicate directly several practical points. They refer in a general way, first, to the degree of activity; second, to the distribution of activity; third, to the type of activity of a given individual. It is of the utmost importance to realize that *the normal end and object of nervous system function and conscious experience is action.*

The nervous system has for its purpose the adjustment of man or of any organism to its environment. It is an instrument of adaptation. It is by means of nervous system activity that the turtle withdraws its head from danger when we touch it with a stick. By a similar correlation of the nervous system we kick away the branch of wood that falls on our foot. The nervous system enables us *to do something*

to the environment in which we live, to protect ourselves, and to pro-
long our life and security. Man adapts the environment to his needs,
and this accounts for his evolutionary progress. The nerve cells and
their filaments have the same function, whether they are in the
structure of a jelly fish or in the brain of man. The intricate structure
of the brain of more highly developed species merely allows more
complicated activity to result, and removes the possessor from the
tyranny of the present. That is to say, the possession of a brain allows
one to store up experience and to act by its lights. But we must repeat
again that the brain and nervous system are given us in order *to act*.
We may act at once, as we do when we find ourselves in the path of
an on-coming automobile. The action may be delayed, as, for example,
a tax bill received this summer may not be paid until next winter.
The prompting to act remains and *ultimately* there is *action*.

The same thing is true of consciousness. Consciousness itself
is an instrument of adaptation. Sensations are not ends in themselves.
They are merely occasions or signals to inform us when it is proper
to *do* certain things. The orange color, the roundness of shape, the
weight, would have little interest for us as sensations per se if they
were not signals to us that this object (orange) in front of us was
worth *opening* to satisfy our hunger and thirst. The blueness of the
sky would have little meaning for us were it not associated with memories of glorious days *spent* in field and stream, or were it not a temptation to leave work and *go* to the mountains or sea.

The same may be said of the feelings and emotions. We are
frightened so that we may run faster, fight harder, or endure the contest longer. We are thrilled that we may love harder. Emotion without
action is an artificial state of things and is unwholesome and sterile.
This is what William James meant when he said that we should never
allow ourselves to be moved by emotion at a symphony concert without working it off doing something after the concert was finished.

As to memory, thought, and imagination, it should take little
arguing to persuade oneself that they are for the sake of action. That
is the meaning of the trite saying, "Knowledge is power." Power for
*accomplishing* something. We have memory to *avoid* our mistakes
and *repeat* our successes. We have science to help us *conquer* nature.
We have imagination to reach beyond our confines in time and space,
and try out plans of action which otherwise we should never test.

Even the most abstract thinking of a philosopher, which may apparently be far removed from practical considerations, has for its ultimate purpose that he and his fellows may *act* more wisely and *live* more happily.

In certain states of nervousness this ability to "carry through" to action things perceived, felt, or thought, is distinctly impaired. They

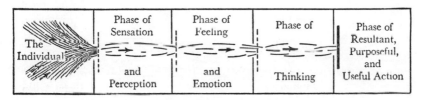

| The Individual | Phase of Sensation and Perception | Phase of Feeling and Emotion | Phase of Thinking | Phase of Resultant, Purposeful, and Useful Action |

*Figure 2*

"cannot make the grade." The *amount of activity* of these people is unusually limited. The process of consciousness may stop at the sensation-perception stage, the feeling-emotion stage, or the thinking stage. For example, in *neurasthenia* the person is "stuck" at the sensation-perception stage. His experience consists almost exclusively of sensations relayed from various parts of his body. Sensations of fullness, tightness, distention, warmth, or cold irritate and annoy him. Patients with *anxiety states* are distracted by feelings and emotions. There is tension and strain. Things are dreaded. Often there is palpitation, breathlessness, tenseness, and faintness. The individuals who cannot "get across" the thinking stage—who are continually harried by doubts, speculations, and apprehensions—suffer from what we call *psychasthenia*. They stop at the level of possibilities, none of which are acted out.

A simple diagram may help to illustrate these stoppages or blocks to what should be a continuous stream ever leading to purposeful and useful activity (Fig. 2).

In normal, adjusted mental life there are no "blocks." Sensations, feelings, and thinking lead continuously to purposeful, useful action (Fig. 3).

The problem with all these persons is to get them *to use* their sensations, feelings, and thoughts *for actions*. Often merely pointing out these fundamental psychological laws is enough to set them on the path to renewed health and happiness. If the mirror shows the hair is uncombed, we should comb it. The psychiatrist often needs to be little more than such a mirror for the patient.

That wholesome, normal activity has a balancing function with regard to our mental and emotional life is shown by the effect of a sojourn at a well-organized spa or sanitarium. Here people are put

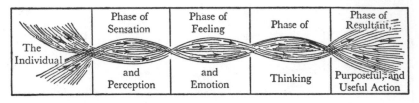

*Figure 3*

through a course of routine *activities*. They are set to play, assigned to work, required to rest, and sometimes asked to think—at carefully selected intervals. Medicines are the least important part of such cures. After a certain time people with nervous breakdowns, through the sheer force of well-balanced activity, find themselves restored to health. The lesson to learn is that the well-ordered personality carries through to the *action stage* and does not permit itself to stop at any of the previous stages. It is by action that we test the fitness and health of sensations, emotions, and thoughts.

The second problem of mental hygiene we plan to discuss here concerns not the amount but the distribution of activity. Here it is not a question of lack of action. The people we consider in this section *can act*. It is a question of division or dispersion of activity. In what fields do they spend their efforts? These individuals are better adapted and happier than those we discussed in the last section. For activity itself, even if ill-advised, indicates effort and partial adjustment.

Let us use a diagram. Let it, as a whole, represent the globe of our mental life. Lines running around it may then stand for the latitudes of our life. Just as life at the equator is different from that at the arctic circle, so in our mental life there are certain circles of activity that stand out (Fig. 4).

## LEVELS OR LATITUDES
## OF MENTAL ACTIVITY

The normal, well-balanced individual is the one who can move from one circle to another at the instigation of his will. Like the hale and hearty mountaineer, he is at home in every climate. We should school ourselves to be like the mountaineers. They know when it is safe and

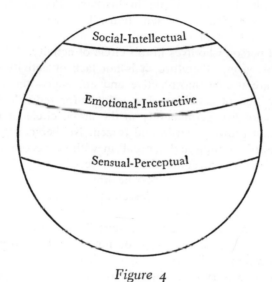

*Figure 4*

profitable to take their families and cattle up to the cooler regions, and when to descend. They do not remain all year round at one altitude. So with us, we should know when to change the latitude of our mental life.

There are people whose lives are almost completely filled with social, moral, or rational activities. They are concerned almost entirely with ideal problems. They do not know when to descend and take life on a more physiological level. They become so involved in vague altruistic or abstract problems that they are exceedingly inadequate when it comes to the ordinary things. Their friends suffer from their lack of the ordinary amenities of life. The family suffers from the absence of affection and warmth which is its very foundation.

Their health suffers from the lack of the usual rubs and contacts of healthful living which maintain a sound body. They do not know how to play.

Certain minds are concentrated on activities associated with the expression of some of the more fundamental instincts. An unfortunate instinctive and emotional experience may initiate a life that remains on that level. The people whose activities chiefly radiate around the feelings and pleasures of sex live in this zone. For some, life seems to be a pursuit of pleasurable sensations. The new, the unusual, the startling, in the form of sensations, spurs them on. The gourmand is the type of person who lives in this circle of activity.

With this group, therefore, it is not lack of activity that is the fault—they are usually most active and energetic—the difficulty is with the partition of activities. The point is for individuals to learn that they cannot live permanently in the arctic circle of intellectual activity without growing sterile and frozen. Neither can they remain in the tropics of emotion and sensualism without becoming parched. Life is not all sex, nor meat and drink, nor yet all ideals. The questions of importance for all of us, whether healthy or nervous, are: At what level am I living? Can I climb or descend to different circles of activity at the proper time?

All this may seem obvious and superfluous to many. But when one sees so many intellectuals who do not know how to play and to live, and yet cannot realize the source of their unhappiness and nervousness, it is necessary to outline their trouble with emphasis. And those whose level is the equator need quite as much to consider the problem from the reverse viewpoint. William DeWitt Hyde has treated this whole problem in his *Five Great Philosophies of Life,* and whoever wishes to pursue it from a scholarly and delightfully philosophic point of view should read his book.

We now come to the third problem, namely, the type of activity with which one feels contented. There is a contrast between routine and administrative work. Broadly speaking, there are those whose work requires originality and initiative in their daily life, and those whose strength and success consists in the effective accomplishment of the routine tasks. Without initiative and spontaneity, life becomes dull and colorless. Without the stability of well-organized activity, life is hectic and uncertain. Society needs both types of activity, but one should know in which he feels happier. One person absolutely detests making decisions and planning. Another is bored to extinction with routine problems. The question is whether we like to meet situations promptly and unreflectively with intuition and habit, or whether we prefer to meet them more deliberately with reason and choice.

This problem is brought up for the following reason. People who wish to find stability, certainty, and permanency in this life must work on habitual levels of activity. Progress and creation take place when the content of consciousness is frequently changing. It is good to know where one finds most satisfaction and to adjust to this kind of activity.

A great deal of discontent and unhappiness can arise from unconsciously trying to work in a manner for which one is not constitutionally adapted. One should not try to perform the impossible task of seeking creation and originality while working in habitual lines of activity. Neither should one attempt to find stability in creative work. There are people who are perfectly happy ploughing the fields or milking the cows. But if they break away from this routine, buy a farm, and try to plan for the equipment and marketing the produce, they are miserable and unsuccessful. Now turn to the manager of a factory. He will be very unhappy if he tries to work as a laborer at a machine eight hours a day. Certain women are content to meet the various problems that housekeeping brings up anew each day. Others find such a life irritating and prefer the routine of office or factory work where things are cut and dried. Some girls are perfectly adequate and contented while living at home with their parents, where life runs along smoothly in habitual channels. When some of them get married, the problem of planning and organizing life, with so much that is new and uncertain, often deprives life of much of its anticipated happiness. When the day is planned for them they are happy; when they must make the plans they are wretched.

Which type of activity appeals more to you? Merely formulating the problem with reference to some of our irritations and dissatisfactions in life will often help us see a way out. None of us can completely escape the necessity of making decisions and forming plans. No one can avoid certain necessary routine activities of life. But we can reduce sources of irritation with regard to these problems to a minimum and reach a more satisfactory balance of these types of activity. Important considerations in "nervous breakdowns" or maladjustments concern suitable types of activity and their proper distribution.

*Chapter 6*

# THE DEGREES OF AWARENESS:
# THE CONSCIOUS, THE SUBCONSCIOUS,
# AND THE UNCONSCIOUS

*Wherein is discussed the Conscious, the Subconscious, and the* Unconscious. *The proper balance between unconscious, subconscious, and conscious is an important criterion of mental health.*

WE HEAR A GREAT DEAL ABOUT THE UNCONSCIOUS, THE SUBCONscious, and the co-conscious. There is no unanimity of opinion as to the exact meaning of these terms. Just as the behaviorists deny consciousness, so do various other schools of psychology wish to dispense with the terms unconscious, subconscious, and co-conscious. But each school must give new synonyms for the old terms.

For the behaviorists, consciousness is, as we have seen, merely talking to oneself, or subvocal talking, or inarticulate movements of the larynx. The realms of the subconscious or unconscious for the behaviorists are merely the realms of nonvocal activity. That is to say, it is roughly the region of the reflexes and habits which are controlled by the sympathetic nervous system. Others might say it is the field of one's instinctive and emotional life.

The word co-conscious is not used as frequently as are the words unconscious and subconscious. We speak of the co-conscious when there are two or more streams of thought or two or more personalities, which have little or no connection with one another. This is the Dr.

*41*

Jekyll–Mr. Hyde type of consciousness we meet in certain hypnotic states.

## THE UNCONSCIOUS

The unconscious has several meanings. When a person has concussion of the brain or is under the influence of an anesthetic during a surgical operation, he is unconscious. When we are asleep we are said to be unconscious. The word unconscious is also often used to indicate types of habitual or automatic action. For example, a person may develop a spasmodic contraction of his face or shoulder (a tic or habit spasm), or a little nervous cough, very irritating to his friends and yet he is almost completely unconscious of it. If an individual is absent-minded, he may unconsciously put on his "Sunday suit" on a weekday—or he may don some shrieking combination of tie and shirt or industriously search for glasses which are perched on his forehead.

Where are our memories when we are not thinking of them? They are said to be in the unconscious. But the unconscious is not merely a passive storehouse of forgotten experiences. For many things this is so. For example, for the arithmetic table it is much this sort of warehouse where figures and their combinations lie rather passively waiting to be used. But when we have forgotten some word that we want to use very much, the unconscious becomes very different. All sorts of similar words or expressions seem to well up (suggest themselves) from the unconscious—there seems to be a veritable struggle, and we are very uncomfortable until the proper word appears. The interesting thing about forgetting, slips of the tongue, and other similar experiences of daily life, is that one can usually discover a conflict of motives with regard to them. That is to say, if one forgets a name that he ought to remember, careful analysis will often show that there is an unpleasant emotional association with that name which tends to keep it from consciousness. We may put off paying a bill that we dislike to pay, until we have lost or forgotten it. Such processes of thinking and dealing with the world and our fellows are often called unconscious. Many examples will be given in subsequent chapters.

## SUBCONSCIOUS

Many writers use the word subconscious as synonymous with unconscious. There is no sharp boundary between them. Neither is there any definition that will satisfy every one. That does not mean, however, that the conceptions signified by the various definitions are valueless. On the contrary, it simply means that the conceptions are more important than the definitions.

The subconscious may be roughly thought of in this book as the realm of vague, not clearly recognized, not fully acknowledged thoughts, desires, and actions. It is the region of uncontrolled thinking. One might say that the subconscious is the domain chiefly of the instincts, emotions and complexes, as opposed to the conscious realm of reason. Or it might be said that the subconscious is concerned chiefly with one's selfish and egotistical thoughts, feelings, and desires, while in the conscious socially minded tendencies are in the ascendant. These contrasts are in part true, but one certainly finds altruistic and rational tendencies in the subconscious, and the reverse in the conscious. As we read through further chapters we shall become increasingly familiar with the subconscious in general and with our own in particular. Suffice it to say that in the usual thinking and communications of daily life we are dealing chiefly with the conscious. In our dream life, however, and in the semi-dream states just before falling to sleep or just after waking, together with the often vague and startling thoughts that come to us "between times" in our waking states, that is, in our periods of daydreaming and revery—it is here that we find the subconscious in full possession of the field.

Fairy tales and myths, as Jung has emphasized, belong to the subconscious of the human race. They are often vague and bizarre dreams or reveries on the origin and explanation of things. So, too, in our own fantasies and dream life our subconscious tries to work out and resolve problems that we meet in everyday life. They are often reminiscent of infantile desires and ways of meeting difficulties that were employed in childhood. These solutions are often highly symbolic or allegorical, but that is the language of immaturity and emotion. Our clearly conscious life uses symbolic mechanisms also. Love and patriotism are replete with symbolisms even for the most intellectual. The realm of the subconscious often appears as absolutely foreign to us. The thoughts do not seem to be our own. We do not feel responsible for them. Symbolisms transform thoughts so that they can be considered without any sense of responsibility. Freud introduced the conception of the censor in discussing the psychology of symbolism. A sort of guard or censor was supposed to stand at the threshold between the unconscious (or subconscious) and the conscious. Unacceptable thoughts or desires could get by the censor when dressed in more acceptable or symbolic clothing. The concept of the censor is much more complicated than appears at first sight. The important thing to recognize is that there is a sort of censor mechanism (whether we call it censorship or not matters little) in our mental life. There are certain thoughts that we (the censors) approve of, while there are others we try to disown, suppress, or drive out. And on the relationship between these two great planes of mental activity depends much of our mental health. If there is continual strife between the unrecognized and the recognized, the unacknowledged and the acknowledged, or the unconscious (and subconscious) and the conscious, there is unhappiness certainly and probably nervousness in that personality. Happiness and health may often be regained by exploration of the relationship of the various aspects (both pleasant and unpleasant) of a personality. All psychotherapy (psychoanalysis and other brands) attempts this. Psychoanalysis has introduced, for the exploration of the unconscious, dream interpretation, the analysis of daydreams, and free associations. It has attempted to make use of a wealth of material that was formerly looked upon as irrelevant, meaningless, and bizarre. In the process of analysis the analyst tries to become a mirror for the patient and show him to himself as he really appears to an impartial observer, and then he tries to help the patient make a satisfactory adjustment. Theories (sexual or otherwise) are not necessary for such analysis. The requisites are a knowledge of the working of the unconscious and subconscious, and a personality on the part of the analyst which includes a large share of common sense.

One hears a great deal about the word *transference* and how this is necessary for a successful analysis. It is also said to be dangerous in depriving the patient of his own will. It is only necessary to say that by transference is meant a definite feeling of trust or confidence in the analyst or physician, due to his reputation, personality, ability, and position of authority over the patient. Without this an analysis is impossible. This is saying nothing more than that if the patient will not trust the analyst and expose the intimate problems which come out in his dreams and fantasies, the analyst cannot fully understand the unconscious. This kind of investigation is an important part of

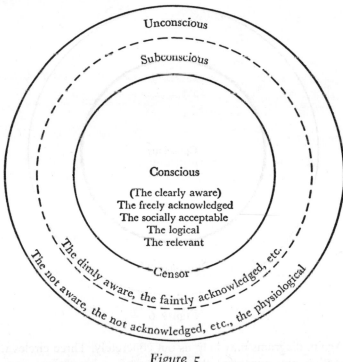

*Figure 5*

the process of psychoanalytic therapy. The basis of this transference may be one of parent-child relationship or a deeper one of love and affection. Theories will make little difference as long as the analyst is well trained and thoroughly imbued with the principles of science. *Resistance* is the opposite of transference. If a person will not reveal his subconscious, he is said to show resistance and an analysis is impossible.

Otto Rank has emphasized the fact that a successful analysis should from the start build up a certain independence on the part of the patient. An excessive transference leaves a patient weak and ineffective when the analysis is over, and he no longer has a director. Therefore, from the very start the patient must be encouraged to assume his own directorship, separation and independence.

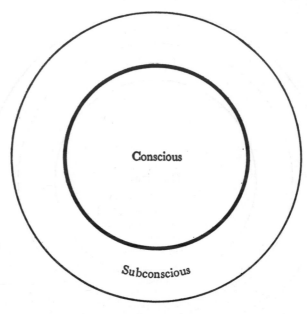

*Figure 6*

Again, diagrams may help us out concretely. Three circles within one another may represent the unconscious–subconscious–conscious relationship. The censor is represented as being on the threshold between the subconscious and the conscious (Fig. 5).

The dotted line between the unconscious and subconscious shows that these borders are ill-defined. For the practical purposes of our diagram we may include the unconscious under the subconscious.

If we are well and happy these two circles have a normal relationship in which the central one covers more territory (Fig. 6).

Let us think of our diagram with reference to the everyday problem of work and attention and distraction. For a healthy person

at work the central circle includes a larger area than the more peripheral one (Fig. 7). It is filled most of the time with problems and
activities connected with our daily work. Our attention is concentrated on them. We are not too readily distracted. They are clear to us.

During the greater part of the day an individual can keep at his

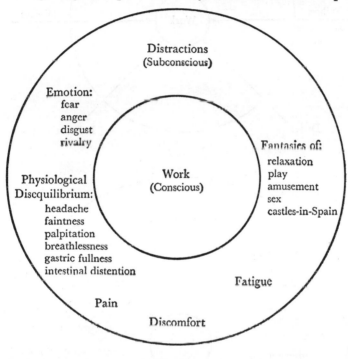

*Figure 7*

work with little distraction from the troubling thoughts and feelings
which lie on the periphery. Only for brief instants do fantasies, daydreams, and unpleasant sensations or emotions enter his mind.

Illness, exhaustion, worry, unhappiness, faulty habits of living
and thinking, drugs, defeat, all may change the relative size of the
circles (Fig. 8).

As a result of these disturbing influences the various factors represented in the periphery of Figure 7 assume larger proportions
(Fig. 9).

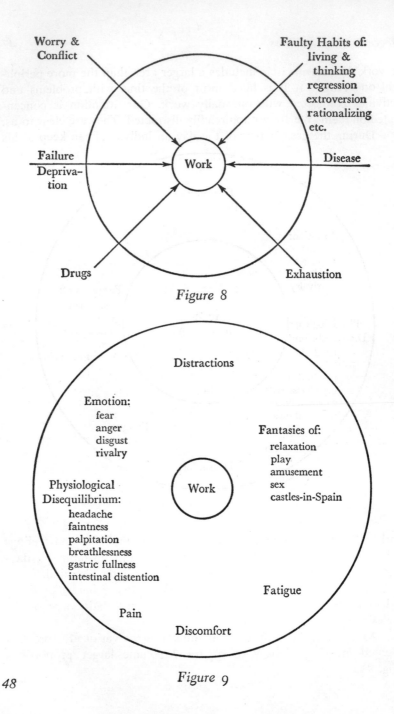

Figure 8

Figure 9

The central circle becomes very small and the outer one is the more important. The central one may become so small that work is even impossible. The central circle may be filled only with eating, sleeping, and the most elemental functions of life. This is what happens in severe cases of nervous breakdown. These diagrams then show

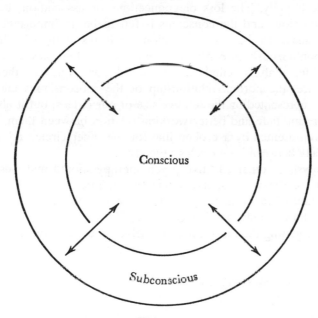

*Figure* 10

that it is the outer circle (the subconscious) and the arrows (environment and past history of the individual) which are the important aspects to investigate and analyze the nervousness (Fig. 10).

Analysis, therefore, tries to make clear to the patient these "peripheral," external, and apparently irrelevant factors of history and the subconscious. It delves into things we have usually considered unimportant, unpleasant, and bizarre. It makes us focus our attention on things that we have been in the habit of ignoring. It is obvious, therefore, how difficult it is to adopt this new approach at the beginning of an analysis. Instead of the clear, we are told to consider the not clear. Often we are forced to face the unpleasant instead of the pleasant. And we are urged to consider our intuitions as opposed to our reason.

As a result of these considerations we are said to establish a clearer and more balanced relationship between our conscious and subconscious. We understand ourselves better, act more wisely, and live more happily. The loss of connections or associations between the subconscious and the conscious is felt to be an important cause of nervousness. In the free associations or trains of thought that are set up spontaneously in considering our dreams, fantasies, and problems in life, analysis refinds these connections. Analysis, then, not only restores the normal relationship of the subconscious and conscious as represented by the relative size of our circles; but it also sets up a more intimate and better working relation between them, which may be represented by a broken line for the inner circle and arrows going freely between both circles (Fig. 10).

Analysis or other effective psychotherapy should make us more conscious of the weak spots in our personalities and enable us to take account of them more adequately. An athlete can play better if he knows how to manage his weaknesses. The same holds true in the "game" of getting the most out of ourselves and our minds.

# PART II

# Psychology of Everyday Life: The Conflicting Urges of Thought, Feeling, and Action

*Chapter 7*

# THE COMPLEX, OR THE EMOTIONAL WEB OF IDEAS. LOGICAL VERSUS EMOTIONAL THINKING

*Wherein the Complex is identified and described, and the differences between logical and emotional thinking are illustrated. The conditions which make a complex "bad" are discussed.*

IN SPITE OF THE TREMENDOUS OUTPUT AND INSATIABLE APPETITE for the written psychological word, one may still find without much difficulty many contradictory and erroneous opinions concerning the nature and complexion of the so-called complex. It has been mysteriously mentioned as an obscure, rare, and unusual phenomenon. We have heard the complex described as though it were of necessity a skeleton in the closet of the mind. Again, it has been maligned as something which might undo a respectable citizen and degrade him into a marauding thief or murderer. In reality, as may be gathered from a simple definition, the complex is neither uncommon nor disgraceful, nor does it very often lead to criminal behavior.

A complex is an idea or a group of ideas, closely bound together by a strong emotional bond. When we *feel something very strongly,* we are usually dealing with a complex.

It is obvious that every human being with the average amount of mental capacity has many emotionally toned ideas. These are subjects about which he feels deeply and strongly and concerning which

*53*

he often expresses himself vehemently, quite forcefully and occasionally even violently. Such ideas relate to the greatest variety of subjects: religion, war, politics, the length of women's skirts, the correct club to use for a certain golf shot, and so on. It is clear, too, that anything as common as the complex could scarcely always, or even very often, be shameful and disgraceful. If this were so, we should perforce condemn many of those we now number among our friends, for instance, the stamp or coin collector, the golf or baseball enthusiast, and we might even damn the entire younger generation which is mad about a current fad in dancing. Let us understand then that the mind of each one of us is literally filled with complexes. We begin to imbibe them almost with our mother's milk and have continued to gather them unto ourselves ever since. Often they accomplish much that is good and constructive. Only under certain conditions do they become harmful and destructive.

## THE CHARACTERISTICS OF COMPLEXES

What are the chief identification marks of complexes? How may we recognize them in ourselves and others? Why recognize them? For one thing their recognition adds zest to life. It is at least interesting to know why John Smith, the noted corporation lawyer, can argue in court with cold, clear-cut, unimpassioned logic for hours, and yet act like a sulky, spoiled child if the meat for the evening meal is a trifle overdone. And there are better reasons than this. They relate to self-understanding which may involve the peace and happiness and integrity of the mind.

Perhaps the chief characteristic of the complex is that it leads to emotional as contrasted to logical thinking. There are groups of ideas which do not induce strong, moving feelings. Usually such subjects as arithmetic, geometry, algebra, chemistry, physics, astronomy, and logic may be discussed fairly coolly and placidly. History, too, is generally a more or less neutral subject. When differences of opinions arise, they can be settled by resort to authoritative references. *Personal feelings will not change the result.*

Now let us turn to a group of schoolboys discussing the merits and advantages of their respective schools. Or to business men emphasizing the virtues and altruism of *their* business methods. Or let a conversation drift toward governmental policies with regard to labor relations or taxes! At once we are on different ground. The facts are no longer neutral. Our feelings rise rapidly to the surface and not only reinforce but overwhelm our thinking.

Let us go a step farther. We are now considering, let us say, candidates for public office. Or a question of family or personal honor. Or the best way to serve God. Now see how positive, how intent, how vehement, and how heated we are in what we say and how we say it! *We unconsciously act as if violent emphasis and heat of conviction would decide the issue.* Sometimes we even become "hurt" and "injured" in an unconscious effort to force agreement.

Whenever we abandon the cool considerations of logic we may be sure complexes are active. Rational thinking binds ideas together on the basis of identity and difference, similarity, coherence, cause and effect, and correlation. Nonrational thinking links ideas together through feelings and emotions which are variously stirred into activity according to the previous life experiences of the individual. Nonrational thinking, therefore, means emotional or "complex" thinking. If our attitude toward an idea or situation is surprisingly emotional, then one of our complexes has been touched. The difference between the two modes of thinking is obvious. The results have very different values. One is logical; the other, emotional. Yet we assert emotional conclusions as if they had been arrived at by cool, mature, and logical thought. This is not true. For some reason human beings are ashamed of and disown emotional thinking and make strenuous efforts to maintain the fiction of logic.

When ideas are associated together emotionally, the connection is a purely personal and relative one. When ideas are grouped together logically because of similarity and difference, cause and effect, and the like, they are accepted by everyone. The ideas I associate with John Jones up to the point of having arms and legs and being a taxpayer are identical with those you or anyone must associate with him. But our varying experiences with John Jones may lead me to think him a good neighbor and you to believe that he ought to be run out of the neighborhood. Or, a surgeon meets John Jones and after an examination removes his appendix. The surgeon may think of him as having been rather difficult to anesthetize, as having a somewhat thin abdominal wall and a badly inflamed appendix. He is comparing him with other patients. But later he meets John Jones socially. He finds that he is *foolish* enough to think that labor could do without management, or *narrow-minded* enough to think it is wrong to play golf on Sunday. Now, the surgeon is no longer logically *comparing* John Jones, but is *criticizing* him by the emotional criteria of his own likes and dislikes. It is a well-known fact that most of us during the greater portions of our lives think emotionally or through the drive of our complexes, although we usually succeed in making ourselves believe that we are thinking rationally.

The second trait that distinguishes the complex is the ease with which it makes associations. All is grist that comes to the mill. In its activity the complex eagerly reaches out in all directions, and somewhat illogically it lays hold of all sorts of associations very distantly related or even not at all connected with the central theme, and willy-nilly weaves them into the emotional pattern. We know a physician who is "wrapped up" in his youngest child. No conversation can proceed very far without quotations from what Rose Marie said or did. One day we tried to discuss with him the functions of the frontal lobe of the brain, particularly as to its relations to intelligence. We had anticipated an interesting exchange of opinions. But after a few opening remarks, we were interrupted by our friend, who said, "Yes, yes, that is very true, it reminds me of what Rose Marie said the other day." Then he was launched on his favorite topic and no doubt he would have continued for hours, had we not at the first opportunity relieved him of his audience. He was merely airing his complex and to his emotionally engrossed mind there was no doubt the closest relationship between the functions of the frontal lobe and the "cute" sayings of his offspring.

Finally, the complex may be recognized by its very insistence. It constantly demands expression in our conscious everyday life. It can no more be stilled than can our breathing. Consider the young male of the species who has a love complex or is in love. Almost his every act is given to the expression of his devotion to the young woman of his choice. The blue of the skies leads him to write verses to her eyes. The sight of the postman stimulates him to send her a special delivery letter. A flower shop reminds him to order roses for her. The telephone is utilized chiefly for one purpose, to speak with her. He is shunned by his friends because his conversation is restricted to descriptions of her charms. And so on. In other words his conscious life is employed more or less constantly as the medium to express his complex. And to some extent this is more or less true of every complex.

We should now be in a position to visualize the complex. It is *common*. It denotes *emotional thinking*. It *readily makes associations*. It *insists on expressing itself*.

*Figure 11*

Perhaps, the mind with its vast content of ideas might be represented by many incandescent bulbs. A few are small and burn with a steady and coldly clear light. They might represent our logical thoughts. Other larger bulbs are in great majority. They give a rather flaring light. In this illumination objects are somewhat distorted and are readily mistaken and confused. The larger lights represent complexes (Fig. 11).

## "GOOD" AND "BAD" COMPLEXES

Somewhat arbitrarily we should like the reader to think of complexes as "good" and "bad."

A "good" complex is one which accomplishes something helpful or useful. If the world depended solely on cold, logical cause-and-effect thinking for its progress it would soon be in a sorry state. Although it is illogical, emotional thinking is warm and active, since enthusiastic momentum is produced and, often, civilization moves forward. Thus, the thrill of patriotism is wholesome when it helps to realize more effectively the ideals for which a country stands. The fervor of politics is helpful if it puts good candidates into office. Family honor is constructive when it maintains and justifies itself. Religion is splendid when it leads to honorable, fair, and decent living.

Even when complexes concern much smaller things such as amateur stamp or coin collecting or interest in sports they are not without their uses. Even at the minimum they give the individual a mentally or physically healthful interest or hobby.

A "bad" complex is one that has a destructive effect on the individual, which is necessarily in some degrees reflected in the environment. Serious bias, prejudice, intolerance, and injustice are a few of the harmful by-products of bad complexes. In the milder manifestations, perhaps no great harm is done. We must expect to "put up" with the person who perpetually "can't stand that" or "can't bear that person." In more serious manifestations we are brought face to face with resultant behavior which indicates maladjustment, unhappiness, and even worse for the individual, and which, in given instances, may delay the forward march of human progress. In this book we are chiefly concerned with possible damage to the hygiene of the mind.

Why do not all complexes proceed as helpful interests or, at least, as harmless hobbies? In other words, what makes a complex "bad"? Probably a complex may be suspected of harmful potentialities when it cannot be openly, freely, and naturally expressed in consciousness, as can, for instance, an enthusiasm for golf. The reader will remember that a complex cannot be simply squelched or suppressed. It insists on recognition and expression in our everyday life. Why is it not possible for every complex to obtain simple, direct, and open release in our daily behavior?

There are at least two reasons why this cannot always occur. Each of us has in his inner mental life a self-erected ideal. It constitutes a criterion, a measuring rod of what we should like to be and how we should like to act. If, therefore, a complex falls too far short of this ideal or is too much at odds with it, then at once there is placed

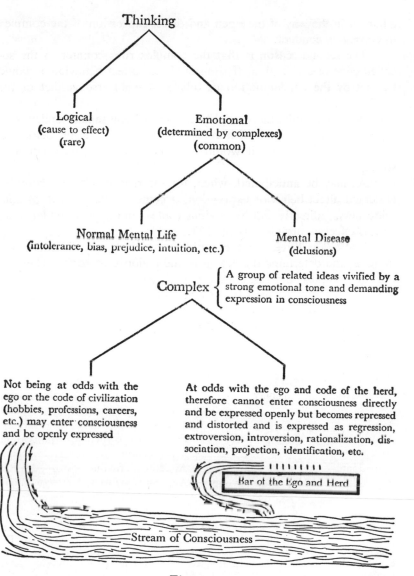

Figure 12

a barrier in the way of the open and direct expression of the complex in conscious conduct.

The second reason is that the complex runs counter to the so-called code of civilization. If translated into direct behavior, it would be met by the condemnation of others—the adverse verdict of the herd.

As an example, there might be cited a homosexual tendency or complex. In the majority of human beings it would fall far below the self-ideal. Furthermore, it would have to face the condemnation of society.

As may be anticipated, when, for the reasons cited, a complex is denied direct behavior expression, it comes to the surface of consciousness, indirectly and by devious routes, and appears under more or less effective disguises (Fig. 12).

There are three great complexes which chiefly dominate the thinking and determine the action of the majority of adults. They are the ego complex, the sex complex, and the herd complex.* The instincts and emotions may be grouped under these three complexes. The serious *conflicts* that arise in our lives usually may be traced to the opposing claims of these three complexes.

## EGO COMPLEX

| INSTINCTS | EMOTIONS |
|---|---|
| Self-assertion—self-display | Elation—positive self-feeling, superiority, pride, mastery, domination |
| Aquisition—hoarding, property | Feeling of ownership—possession, protection |
| Nutritional—food seeking | Appetite—craving, gusto |
| Pugnacity—combat, aggressiveness | Anger—rage, fury, annoyance, irritation, displeasure |

---

* Freud has introduced a tripartite division of directing forces in the human personality which he calls the ego, the id, and the superego or ego ideal. The superego is the unconscious or automatic incorporation of the attitude of society (parents, teachers, friends, religious advisers) as a controlling or determining force on conduct and belief. The id stands for the great mass of primitive and instinctive urges and strivings unmodified by social considerations. The ego is the personality in its practical, executive aspects and as it appears to others.

| INSTINCTS | EMOTIONS |
|---|---|
| Construction | Feeling of creativeness—making, productivity |
| Curiosity—inquiry, discovery, investigation | Wonder—feeling mystery, strangeness, or unknown |
| Play—laughter | Amusement—jollity, carelessness, relaxation |
| Self-abasement—submission | Depression—subjection, inferiority, devotion, humility |
| Flight—self-preservation, avoidance, danger instinct | Fear—terror, fright, alarm, trepidation |
| Repulsion—repugnance | Disgust—loathing, nausea, etc. |

## SEX COMPLEX

| INSTINCTS | EMOTIONS |
|---|---|
| Sex-mating, reproduction, pairing | Love—jealousy, coyness |
| Parental-protective | Tender emotion—tenderness love |

## HERD COMPLEX

| INSTINCTS | EMOTIONS |
|---|---|
| Gregarious | Feeling of loneliness—isolation, nostalgia |
| Suggestion—imitation | Sympathy |
| Appeal | Distress—attachment, helplessness, trust |

Note: In adopting this grouping and terminology we have been guided by the concepts of Professor A. G. Tansley.

*Chapter 8*

# THE MAJOR STRUGGLES BETWEEN THE HERD, THE EGO, AND THE SEX COMPLEXES

*This chapter treats of the location and nature of the conflict. It discusses everyday behavior traits which arise from unrecognized conflicts, and describes the inevitable clash existing between the ego, sex, and herd complexes.*

WE ARE SURE THAT IT WILL BE READILY APPRECIATED THAT NO ONE can possibly have a mind and a mental life which is completely and entirely in harmony. In other words one could scarcely have complexes which lead only to a type of conduct which is single in its purpose, wholly pleasing to the remainder of the personality, and meriting always the approval of the herd and its social code. We may picture the mind as an orchestra consisting of many instruments. It would be too much to ask that never should there be played a false note by any of the instruments.

In fact, it is very doubtful if such uninterrupted mental harmony would be constructive for us and our fellow human beings. Never meeting obstacles, never experiencing any conflict between the things we desired to do and the things we felt we ought to do, it is probable that our minds would "soften" and deteriorate. Life would become monotonous and filled with boredom.

It may be assumed that not only are complexes very numerous, but that it is inevitable that often their respective claims must be flat-footedly opposed to each other. They *clash*. Frequently the mind becomes a veritable battleground with the conflicting forces drawn up in armed array. Conflict means struggle. Mental conflict, therefore, refers to the clash or struggle between the various tendencies of the mind.

## LOCATION OF THE CONFLICT

Where does the conflict take place? Do we realize there is a conflict? Do we ever appreciate it clearly? Are we ever entirely unaware of the conflict? A diagram (Fig. 13) may help answer some of these questions.

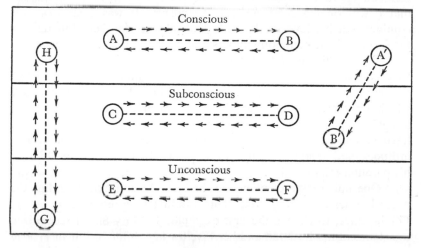

Figure 13

The upper third of the diagram may be taken to represent the conscious part of the mind of whose content we are clearly aware; the lower third the unconscious. We are not aware of its content. The middle third is an intermediate (subconscious) zone. It contains material which is more or less at the threshold of conscious appreciation and it is in some sense accessible. Let us say we are partially aware of it. It cannot quite escape the light of consciousness.

A conflict may take place at any of these levels. For instance A-B may be taken to represent a conflict fought out in consciousness. Mary Smith is married and has small children. She falls in love with John Jones. Clearly she comprehends that she no longer loves her husband but is deeply in love with another man. Her wish is to consummate her love with him. Clearly, too, she recognizes her love for her children, her desire not to lose them. Likewise she is aware of her obligations to her husband. With practically all of the elements of the conflict spread out openly before her on the table of her mind, she finally decides the issue.

Or, one may imagine a similar conflict, C-D, transferred to the intermediate zone. We know of many such instances. A married man was obviously in love with a woman not his wife. Consciously he was troubled (partial recognition) but he tried hard to insist to himself that it was only a deep and fine friendship. It was clear from his conduct that his love for his wife had all but vanished, but he was far from a clear, conscious understanding that this had occurred.

The conflict may take place in the unconscious, E-F. It is at least conceivable that occasionally some odd mannerism of conduct or some obsessive act may represent the blurred outlines of conflicts which were enacted far back in the now-dim history of the early struggles of our species for its survival. The difficulties a man may have with an employer may be due to an unconscious struggle against attitudes and tendencies that were primarily disturbing to him in his parental relationships.

One unit of the conflict may be clear in consciousness but the other less frankly recognized. This would be represented by A'-B'. For instance, to change the first example: If Mary Smith recognized the claims of her husband and her love for her children, but succeeded partly in blinding herself to her love for another man, even though the truth of this fact was revealed by her everyday behavior. Or again, as happened so frequently in World War I, there was a bitter conflict between the deeply buried instinct of self-preservation (G) of which the soldier was not aware and (H) a complex consisting of a group of ideas, made up of soldierly ideals, desire to serve one's country, to bring honor to the regiment, to be admired and praised by the people at home, etc., etc. Many soldiers recognized these ideals consciously. The conflict may be visualized concretely, by remembering that in the battle zone it was impossible to serve these ideals completely without endangering life, and, therefore doing violence to the instinct of self-preservation.

Thus, many variations are possible. Generally speaking, if the conflict can be brought into consciousness and faced openly and frankly it is not apt to cause serious nervous difficulty. Certain methods of psychotherapy are designed chiefly to accomplish a conscious recognition of conflicts.

### FURTHER CONSIDERATION OF THE EXPRESSION OF CONFLICTS AND THE LESSONS TO BE LEARNED

We repeat that conflict means struggle and friction. Mental conflict implies a struggle between opposed tendencies of the mind, grinding away at each other, much as do two pieces of wrongly placed machinery.

We are clearly conscious of some conflicts while of others we are wholly ignorant. We may pretend to ignore conflicts. Each one of us is occasionally guilty of certain conduct reactions, of which we are not directly conscious, nor do we frankly acknowledge them. Finally, the stepchild tendency may become so apparent in some gross act, that we are brought face to face with something we had not realized belonged to us. And future behavior should be modified.

Frequently, we do things and wonder why. The driving motive is hidden. In all of us there is blindness or at least very much impaired vision in regard to our own peculiar and selfish inclinations. It is humorous and sometimes pathetic to observe the unconscious tendencies of an individual manifesting themselves so obviously while the actor himself remains in blissful ignorance of the real state of affairs. There is the "pusher and shover" who crowds himself to the very front of a line waiting to buy theater tickets, apparently unconscious that many have been standing in the queue long before he arrived. He may not see that he is trampling on the right of others. There is the lover, only conscious of what he wants and unable to realize that there are other things in the world besides the young woman of his choice. Many examples could be given but they would all testify to the same fact: Often we fail to see ourselves as others see us, and then, usually, we are acting in the service of some complex.

Just as a complex may lead us into more or less unconscious behavior, so may a conflict of complexes go on below the surface without being viewed in the revealing light of conscious consideration. Patients frequently complain that they do not know what is upsetting them; why they feel so tense; why their thoughts are so gloomy. The answer is that their difficulties are situated outside the realm where things are clearly recognized.

One of the foremost admonitions of mental hygiene is contained in two words: "Know thyself." At least it is important to penetrate into the motivations that are back of serious actions. When there are nervousness, unhappiness, worry, and maladjustment, at least some degree of such self-understanding becomes imperative. Too often such troubles are rooted in conflicts that have not been faced. This is the reason for talking things over. We try to look beneath the surface; to uncover the very beginnings. Just as the machinery beneath the water line is important for the ship's ability to navigate the seas, so is the machinery of instincts, emotions, complexes, and conflicts (which may be mentally invisible) vital in meeting the stresses of life. Instincts, emotions, complexes—broadly desires—may be thought of as units of thinking and behavior. But, if a man follows his desire for self-assertion, self-display, and superiority to an extreme, he must forfeit the social approval which he also desires. If his desire for food makes him piggish, he is ostracized. If he is too "close" and his desire for acquisition leads him to forget to return articles which he has borrowed, society looks askance at him. If he is so aggressive that he continually antagonizes others, then he is left severely alone. Overdeveloped curiosity becomes rather tiresome. Excessive feelings of awe and mystery signal one out as an abnormal dreamer. Society has numerous reprisals for too crude manifestations of the self-preservative instinct. The herd does not take kindly to having its feelings ridden over roughshod. Exaggerated sex instinct is taboo. If the parental instinct leads to inordinate tenderness toward the children, the parents are regarded as oversentimental and the spoiling of the child is disapproved. If sympathy runs away with head, and the person is too socially anxious, too concerned about the morals and justice of humanity, he is tolerated as "well meaning but one-sided."

Thus, there are mutual checks which attempt to counterbalance our various impulses and desires. In this way a balanced personality should result. The happy person is the one who has these conflicts reduced to a reasonable minimum, for conflict is painful. The successful individual is the one who has his conflicts adjusted to such a degree that, instead of wearing himself out in the unsuccessful handling of personal problems, he may apply his physical and mental energy to the creative problems offered by the world. We all know those unfortunates whose mental adjustments are so painfully inadequate that they never decide even small problems; never are able to proceed to the concrete problems awaiting them in the external world; never assert the will to believe. They should read Osler's *A Way of Life* and *The Will to Believe* by William James.

The major conflict of life, and the frequent cause of nervousness, is the lack of balance among the three fundamental complexes: the ego or self complex, the sex complex, and the herd or social complex. The conflict of the first (ambition, pride and self-assertion) with the second (sex, in all its implications) and of either or both of these with the third (the rules, requirements of society, and the desire to be freely accepted as a member of the herd), these three broad drives and their conflicts form the basis and the motif of most of the dramas of novels—and of life.

The herd complex—the wish or the urge to be a recognized integral member of society—is very powerful in most human beings. The loneliness, the helplessness, and the utter distress of the social pariah and outcast often force him to comply with the beliefs and rejoin the activities of the herd even against his own private judgments. "Being one of the boys" or a "real fellow in school" or a soldier in the service of his country or even a saint in the service of humanity, all have, at least in part, the same dynamic driving force, i.e., the herd instinct. Even the individual who has apparently rebelled against some part of society often may be found to be following the dictates of another fraction of the herd.

The desire to be one of the herd is represented in us by the demands of religion, morality, and patriotism. These demands become

our desires. We then speak of them as duties and moral obligations.
It is clear that these conflict in many ways with our own desires for
self-assertion, self-aggrandizement, or sex satisfaction. A very frequent
conflict in modern life involves sex and morality or religion. When
love ceases between a married pair and religion and morality tell
them to "live together in happiness," then we are dealing with a

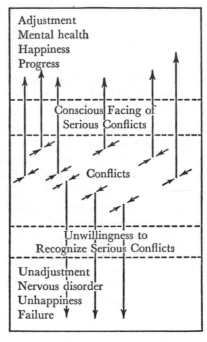

*Figure 14*

situation in which there are seemingly opposing and irreconcilable
tendencies of thought and action. Another common conflict which
we have often witnessed may arise in one of the daughters of an in-
valid mother who feels the obligation to remain at home to nurse the
mother, and yet, there is the pull toward mating, marriage and
children.

Must we have conflicts? If we cannot hope to escape complexes,
so, too, must we expect to encounter conflicts almost from the cradle

to the grave. A preliminary consideration is this: the less the impelling motives are faced and acknowledged, the more difficult it becomes to reach a solution. Even when the opposing claims of the conflict are equally strong, there is still an advantage for mental hygiene in knowing and realizing. It is the difference between being able to improvise at least some kind of shelter or being tossed about mercilessly in a violent storm whose warring forces are not at all understood (Fig. 14).

If a conflict is so serious that it is producing nervous symptoms, the first effort should be to understand the nature of its component parts—to face it in the daylight of consciousness.

*Chapter 9*

# PERSONALITY DEVELOPMENT

*Wherein is discussed the personality, the character-
istics that not only are distinctive in man, but also
identify each man apart.*

PERSONALITY HAS BEEN DEFINED AS THE TOTAL PATTERN OF PSY-
chological and social reactions. Some acquaintance with the contributions of Freud and psychoanalysis is today indispensable to the
understanding of the development of the human personality. Personality is the sum or totality of our habitual way of behaving, feeling,
thinking—attitudes and responses characteristic for each one of us.
It is highly individual or personal. It is what is typical of John Jones
as a unique *individual* as distinct from John Jones as a human being
and a member of the human race. The sum total of individual life
experiences, especially in infancy and childhood, stamp upon one
certain distinguishing characteristics or ways of responding which
differentiate John Jones as an individual person from him as a man
typical of the species. Hence the essence of what characterizes us
as individuals is what we have lived through—our experiences, our
processing, our development. Psychology speaks of this process as
"conditioning." It could be likened to the athlete. His experience or
training may be good or bad, and he will hence be in good or bad
condition. The body, too, and its functioning or physiology enter into
the concept of personality. The stocky, muscular individual is more
apt to be athletic and interested in the world about him—his environment. The thinnish, less well-muscled person is more likely
to be reflective, introspective, and interested in his thoughts. The

rapidity of responses may be a factor in personality: there is the quick, alert, reactive individual; and the slow, casual, phlegmatic personality. Personality is thus not merely mental or psychological. It includes certain bodily, physical, or physiological aspects of the individual, some of which are constitutional or hereditary, while others are developmental and the result of experience.

How many of us are really aware of the developmental or formative forces in our personalities? Psychology speaks of these forces as motivations, whether they are needs, drives, expectations, attitudes, preferences, disinclinations, avoidances, or denials. How many attach proper importance to the early years of our lives and understand that, "The child is father of the man?" Or, "As the twig is bent the tree's inclined." Most human beings upon reaching adulthood look back on their early years with mingled emotions. Most attitudes involve feelings or emotions that are mixed—yes, but; no, but. All of us tend to see childhood rather dimly as a pleasant vista blurred and softened by time. We cling to an idealized conception of childhood, ignore the pain and bitter experience of growing up, and as adults feel longing or nostalgia for what in retrospect appears to be the most carefree years of our lives.

But if it were possible for many of us to relive our childhoods, some might decline. Some would recall and know that the process of *growing* up, of *maturing,* of relinquishing childhood pleasures, of adjusting to hard reality is, by its very nature, a painful experience. Then, too, who can deny the helplessness that is attendant upon childhood, the discomfort that goes with being weak and dependent upon adults for sustenance, care, and one's very existence?

Behold the newborn infant! This tiny human being is utterly and completely dependent upon its mother, nurses, or relatives for life. The newborn can do nothing to help itself beyond breathing, swallowing, excreting. It is completely helpless; in fact, so much so that were it not for its mother, nurses, relatives, or friends it would perish. In most respects the newborn in fact is remarkably like a newborn animal. But newborn animals in a short time are better off than newborn humans. In the animal world, at the most, there are only a few weeks of dependence. After this time, animals detach themselves from the protective care of their mothers, evolve, attain independence, and go along their way without need of further help.

If they lag, the animal mother forces them to become self-sustaining. It is very different with human beings. In human infancy and childhood we live in parasitic dependence upon our mothers for many years. We need protection during these years because we cannot alone maintain ourselves; we do not know how to procure food for our bodies, nor do we know how to avoid or protect ourselves from danger. Indeed, the evolution of the human being to independence is so prolonged that, perhaps, fifteen years must pass before he can in some measure dispense with the protection of adults. Many people need help, and many come to psychiatrists because they have never succeeded in severing the emotional ties of childhood, and this latent condition causes the development of inferiority, ineffectiveness, resentment, irritability, tension, and anxiety.

We have but to observe the newborn infant to note that, during the first weeks of life, food has one of the top priorities in his life. Because of this, the infant's mouth and everything connected with it are most important parts of his body. Since the newborn human centers his needs and interests about his mouth, esophagus, and stomach, this early or *initial* period in the child's life is called the *oral or mouth phase* of personality development. The taking in of food, being fed, being made comfortable, through the nursing process, are some of the most important factors that make possible the continuation of life, growth, and well-being. The infant's world is small, and he has only the most elementary sense of time experienced in certain physiological rhythms. He has no access to the processes of reasoning and logical thinking. Because of this, he "knows" nothing about postponements and putting off satisfaction of his needs until later. He feels only tensions and rhythms. He lives only in the present and when he is frustrated and deprived, he squeals and cries in discomfort. The ability to endure the tension of hunger, for example, is at a minimum during this period. Since he cannot reason (control, defer, inhibit), he reacts only to the rhythms set up by his physiological apparatus or body mechanisms.

The taking in of nourishment serves another purpose for the infant besides stilling the discomfort and tension of hunger—it gives him an opportunity to suck. He enjoys the flow of milk into his mouth, down his esophagus, and into his stomach. The childs finds sucking at his mother's breast or at the bottle and getting the flow of milk into his mouth very pleasurable. He wishes for the continuance and repetition of this enjoyable activity even when he has satisfied his hunger. The child learns how to repeat and obtain for himself this pleasant gratifying feeling independently of food and the person who suckles him. He discovers that he can suck his own fingers. The pleasure derived from sucking, which was originally satisfaction only incidental to the taking of nourishment, becomes a satisfaction in itself. Indeed, the gaining of pleasure is an emotional force that dominates the child's life throughout his early years. We say that he lives by the *pleasure principle,* because there are pressures ("he wants to") to relieve tensions and desires, *irrespective* of limiting factors, oppositions, and conditions.

The pleasure-giving activity of the mouth is by no means confined to food and sucking. When the child is approximately six months old, he acts as if he would like to become acquainted with the whole world within his reach by means of his mouth. He bites, he licks, he chews and tastes almost everything near him. Everything is important as it relates to his mouth or his oral region. The mouth, during this time, is one of the most important places and instruments of means of testing his environment. For at least a year the mouth plays this pre-eminent role in the personality development of the infant. The child uses his mouth to express feelings and passions which he will express in camouflaged or substituted ways as an adult. It is likely that, even in adulthood, the original pleasure attached to oral activities still remains, and is seen in kissing, smoking, gum chewing, and the like.

It is agreed today that it is of *paramount* importance in healthy personality development that the oral period should be a time during which the infant secures satisfaction, sufficient nourishment, and opportunity for an adequate amount of sucking. When, for some unfortunate reason, the child's nursing, hunger, and sucking desires are frustrated, then he remains constantly unsatisfied and under tensions. This sets up a vicious psychological pattern which can persist into adult life, showing up as character traits in the personality. When we are frustrated and deprived, we react by feelings indicating that we have been cheated, and we want more of what has been withheld from us. The child who is *deprived* in the oral period of his life may develop into an adult who is never satisfied and always feels cheated. He may feel that his just deserts have been withheld from him, and we may observe that no matter how well things turn out for him he is *never satisfied*. On the other hand, the individual who has been nursed longer than the optimum time and for whom the breast was a ready pacifier for any discomfort will develop opposite adult reaction patterns. This type of individual goes through his life implicitly believing that no matter what happens, things will turn out for him the way he wants them to, that he will get what he wishes with the minimum of effort. Characteristic social relations, reactions to others, may thus get their start in the early months of life. The discontented, demanding, irritable pessimist or the carefree, irresponsible optimist may have their origins in childhood experiences or conditioning. Love and hate may be related to feeding habits through acceptance, comfort, well-being; or rejection, dissatisfaction, illness. Gastrointestinal functions (digestion, indigestion) may express feelings toward others. Social attitudes or feelings may be expressed early in life by these physiological processes or activities. In later life as adults, disturbances of digestive functions may be the earliest manifestations of unsatisfactory, uncomfortable feelings, and relationships with others, before one is intellectually aware (conscious) of these unsatisfactory relationships.

During the first year then, the mouth holds a most significant place in the development of the individual. However, normally, the interest of the child in this region is gradually displaced and focused upon another body zone—the anal-urethral area. Grown-ups view this interest with discomfort, disapproval, misgivings, and oftentimes less than tolerance, even with condemnation and punishment.

If children are observed between the ages of one and two and a half, we are struck by the fact that at this age they are not only interested in and curious about, but may be preoccupied with, excretory activities and products. The *child* displays an extraordinary interest in his own feces and urine. He shows *no* signs of *disgust* and shame regarding his excretions, and tries to touch them, smell them, play with them and, repugnant as it may appear to grown-ups, the child, if not restrained, may even attempt to taste them. Judging from the pleased expression on the child's face and the ardor with which he approaches his toilet activities, it would seem that, for the child, these functions afford him pleasure. The sensation of feces passing over the anal skin or the passage of the urinary stream over the urethral lining is enjoyable.

Like animals, children show no disgust, shame, or aversion to their own or other excretions. They talk unrestrainedly and in unabashed fashion to adults or other children about the frequency or size of their bowel movements. The child comes to derive satisfaction from the fact that in large measure he can control the toilet situation. That is, if he so desires, he can excrete wherever and whenever he wishes or, if it so pleases him, not at all. Because of the interest and pleasure that the child displays in his bowel activity at this time, this stage of the child's life is often referred to as the *anal stage* of personality development.

During the oral stage the child demanded a great deal from his mother in the way of satisfaction of body needs. The adult world is very tolerant of the helpless and dependent infant and administers to his wants often without stint, with the exception of insisting on his sleeping and eating schedule.

However, matters are quite different for the child during the anal stage. Now, gradually but inevitably, there enters into the child's life a new and important factor—*training* in cleanliness. This is a matter of no small moment. It ushers in the next step in the personality development of the child. His parents endeavor to "break" him of the habit of wetting and soiling himself. Toilet training is initiated, and the parents insist that the child *give up* his *excretory pleasures*. He is asked to desist and refrain from excreting wherever and whenever the pressures come; that is when he wishes. They demand that he give up the pleasure of being dirty, frowning upon the child's practice of withholding his urine and feces to secure maximum anal and urethral pleasurable sensations. *Control* and conformity are *external pressures* put upon the child, *demanded* and *expected* of him.

Human beings never seem to give up any pleasurable activity without doubts (later, maybe, obsessional conditions) or resistance— without some degree of struggle. The child is plunged into a *conflict;*

for every child needs and loves his mother (if there has been a normal development and relationship), and wishes to please her. The mother urges and insists that the child be clean; but, for the child, acceding to such a request means sacrifice of the pleasure he enjoys. Therefore an inner *struggle* takes place. The child vacillates between his *desires* to *please* his mother and *avoid* her *displeasure* and his desire to *retain* his *excretory enjoyment* (indecision, ambivalence). Eventually, because his mother's love is vital, her wishes prevail. The child learns to control his excretions. But with control there may be involved doubt, fear, and resentment toward the control and the parent's urging in trying to force control.

As toilet training proceeds the child's attitudes and feelings toward his bowel productions undergo modifications. Whereas, formerly, he felt no repugnance towards his excretions, he now, like his mother, views them with dislike and gradually with disgust. The process of toilet training is ended when the child's own feelings of disgust and shame can now be depended upon to act as a *barrier* or *restraint,* and control is established. They will restrain and hold in check activities which once were considered enjoyable and were indulged in without reserve.

The toilet-training period has psychological importance, for out of its conflicts and struggles arise certain attitudes and character traits that help form the final emotional make-up of the adult. If, for some reason, the toilet-training period has been distressing to the child, or his mother angers him, he has a *retaliatory* or revenge weapon —he can soil anywhere he so desires, and the adult is almost powerless in the situation. Attempts to *manipulate the environment* by such anal activities may become a ready tool that the child employs during this time. If there is a struggle over toilet training, the child will pit his anal and urethral sphincters (bowel and urinary expulsion muscles—just like the muscles of the arms and legs in resisting or fighting) against his mother's prohibitions and demands. In the ensuing conflict he may come to feel that he can master, be more powerful, and overcome his mother's restrictions through his excretory activities. In this situation, anal and urethral processes become fused and intertwined with feelings of aggression, anger, hate, and destruction. It is as if the child were saying to his parent, "Because you do not love me, I am angry. I will annoy you and hurt you by depositing my feces wherever and whenever I choose." This feeling of mastery and power by anal-aggressive expression is pleasurable for the child. For the first time in his life he is *no longer defenseless against grown-ups* and he enjoys these anal-destructive feelings. We say then that the child at this time is *sadistic* because he derives pleasure from feeling that he can injure, master, and destroy by bowel activities. Parents' attitudes toward excretory functions are of prime importance. It is common to hear mothers boast of the early and rigorous toilet training that they administered, not knowing that the achievement or victory is psychologically pyrrhic or has disadvantageous aspects. It is true that the child may conform rapidly if the mother shows intense pressure, domination, disgust, or anger at his toilet activities; however, that is so only because children are exceedingly sensitive to any threat that may deprive them of their mother's love. Therefore the child becomes clean, but it may be that henceforth any form of disorder, disarray, and dirt is a source of discomfort, fear, anger, or threat to him, with similar *demands* and expectations made *by him on others.* Such a child may develop into an extremely overclean and meticulous adult who becomes dismayed at any imperfection or muss.

The child may bow to his mother's wish to be clean in another fashion. He will retain his excretions because he senses his mother's discomfort and disgust when he has a bowel movement. The child may develop constipation and feel better because he is clean as his mother demands. However, on a psychological level, he is filled with a sense of power and control—no one can force him to give up anything he really does not want to. Such a child may become an adult who is *stubborn,* retentive, and hoarding, who will passively resist problems he meets.

If the relationship between the mother and the child is healthy and the child feels securely loved, he seldom will have recourse to soiling. His attitude toward his mother will be: "Because you love me, I desire to please you. I will give up my feces wherever and whenever you wish me to." Thus, excretory acts become a way by which the child can *express hatred or love* or both. It is because of the conflicting feelings surrounding bowel movements that the groundwork is laid for the emergence of opposing emotions. The child can feel love and hatred for the same person at the same time—that is, he is *ambivalent*. Feelings are rarely undiluted. In ambivalency there may be equally strong conflicting trends which may result in paralysis of behavior. For sound personality growth, ambivalent feelings must be resolved. There must be an integration of conflicting feelings into a satisfactory working balance or proportion so that we can love without hating at the same time and with equal intensity. Aggression should be used realistically to help us make our way in a highly competitive society and to help us protect our loved ones. It is in the toilet-training period that the child wrestles with the problems of aggression and love, trust and distrust, guilt and fear. Here are found many of the bases which determine future feelings, adjustment, attitudes, and behavior both socially (alloplastic) and within the body (autoplastic).

As the average child enters approximately his third year of life, certain changes appear. Oral pleasures no longer assume the importance they did in the nursing period. Then, too, the average child has surmounted the problems and conflicts posed by the toilet-training period. The child now takes an interest beyond the immediate pleasures and desires surrounding his mouth and gastrointestinal tract. He is curious about the world around him and is forever asking *questions* of grown-ups. However, fundamentally the child is still a pleasure-seeking animal, and, as we have already stated, the attainment of pleasure is a goal that rules the emotional life of children. If one form of pleasure is relinquished, then another is sought to take its place. When oral and anal enjoyments are given up, another means of gratification is sought, and the child now normally becomes interested in his genital area and seeks to procure pleasure from his genitals by stimulating them or masturbation. This is a universal phenomenon, and it is now generally agreed that moderate masturbation during the *genital period,* as this phase is now called, is a necessary and natural occurrence—it fixes the child's interests on his genital zone, and, because of this, prepares this area for its future procreational role. It is against such a background as has just been sketched that the three-year-old enters into a powerful emotional conflict during the genital period, which he must master successfully in order to carry out his future human relationships satisfactorily.

Most of us have observed how little boys compete with their siblings (brothers or sisters) for their mother's exclusive affection.

This rivalry often reaches alarming proportions. However, the emotional antagonism between siblings is a comparatively mild prelude to a more potent and intense rivalry relationship. For the little boy knows that a more serious and powerful rival than siblings is present to challenge him for his mother's affection—his father. It does not escape the boy's notice that the father treats her as if she belonged to him exclusively, that his mother seems to prefer to talk to his father, that his father insists on sleeping with the mother by himself. His father, then, is his successful rival for his mother's affection.

This situation arouses resentment in the boy against his father, and the child struggles with a series of hostile thoughts which assail his mind. The boy comes to feel that there is only one way he can enjoy his mother's attention exclusively, that is, if the father were to vanish from the scene forever.

It is about this time that the little boy, in attempting to satisfy his curiosity about himself and the external world, stumbles upon the physical, anatomic, and biological fact that there exist physically different individuals from himself. He finds out that girls lack a penis, an organ which he values highly. This discovery puzzles, frightens, and shocks him, and he struggles for an answer to the enigma. For the child the most plausible explanation appears to be that girls were once endowed with this organ, but, because they were bad, they lost it as *punishment*. Such a fate, the boy believes, can surely befall him since he is *naughty* in having his mind full of *angry* thoughts against his father. Indeed, the child concludes that, if his father knew about these wicked thoughts, the father himself would carry out the dreaded punishment and deprive him of his penis. To *protect* himself against such a frightening eventuality at the hands of his father, the little boy banishes from his mind the hostile thoughts concerning his father. He will make peace with him. *Tenderness* will replace *resentment.* This is not a difficult step normally. If the father is of a desirable character, the boy cannot help but love, admire, and respect him at the same time that he resents him. In such circumstances, the child will conclude that since it is obvious that he cannot best his father in the struggle for the mother's affection, then he will imitate him and someday he, too, will have grown-up privileges. The conflict is resolved, then, when the boy decides that he will be like his father and *not* a *rival* to him. The child begins to pattern himself after the model set by his father, and this process determines in a large measure what kind of man he will become.

The little girl goes through a similar but more complex process during the genital period. Up until this time the female child parallels the boy in her love for her mother and intense jealousy over all rivals for her mother's affection. In the course of satisfying her natural curiosity about herself and others through investigative play, she stumbles across an anatomic biologic phenomenon which astounds her. She learns that little boys possess a penis which she lacks and of which they are quite proud and exhibit unhesitatingly. Disturbed by this discovery, the little girl becomes preoccupied with this phenomenon in an attempt to find out why she lacks such an organ. The most likely explanation the child concludes is that her development is faulty due to neglect by her mother. Otherwise she would be growing up properly with a penis. It is her mother who is to blame for her deficiency. The love the child feels toward her mother becomes mixed with resentment and hate. At this point the little girl believes that her mother does not love her, otherwise she would not have allowed her to be thus deprived. If one has seen the surprise, puzzlement, disturbance, and shock with which a little girl first views the male genitals, one can appreciate the turmoil of her feelings at this time.

Not yet reconciled to her biologic lot in life, the little girl turns to someone in her family whom she believes is more worthy of her love—her father. He possesses the prized organ and perhaps he can fulfill her expectations in some wonderful fashion. If he sees her love for him, perhaps he will present her with the penis that her mother denied her. Such magical thinking and fantasy are very real to a child's mind and do not seem strange and illogical as they do to the mature adult. At this point the child now is drawn closer to her father and resents the fact that she must share him with her mother.

But, of course, there is nothing but disappointment for the little girl in spite of all the expressions of love and attachment to the father. Her father does not respond to her devotion by causing a penis to grow, and she must accept the reality that she will never possess one. Normally, the little girl accepts this fact, for in time she gives up her erotic attachment to her father, and her resentment toward her mother disappears. Instead, she develops a tender regard for both her parents and in time will direct her erotic interests outside the family situation.

Unfortunately, however, due to adverse parental attitudes or circumstances, the discussion of which are beyond the scope of this book, some girls never relinquish their quest and desire for a penis nor do they give up their erotic attachment to their father. Such unresolved conflicts in the girl during the genital period lead to future adult maladjustment. Many of these children grow up into women who find it difficult, if not impossible, to accept normal feminine functions, and experience difficulties in their adult sexual life. Others never marry even if given the opportunity, or if they do marry they are disappointed, and the marriage fails since no husband could possibly live up to an emotionally inflated father image of childhood fantasy. Freud considers unresolved conflicts surrounding the genital period the *sine qua non* in the formation of the neuroses. This is the cloverleaf in the highway of life where, out of the multiple roads open, important directions are taken, determining psychological health, effectiveness, and well-being, or the reverse. Successful resolution of the problems posed by this period is essential for sound adult relationships, because unresolved difficulties emanating at this time later account for a variety of emotional disturbances in the individual's love life.

Thus far in the evolution of his personality formation, the child has been involved primarily with his immediate family group. The early stages revolve in large measure around the satisfaction of certain physiological needs. Later, the child enters into an intense emotional conflict with the parent of the opposite sex, the resolution of which depends mainly on the maturity and adjustment of the parents. Thus this is not a purely biological process of selection and direction. We have seen a turbulence connected with the child's emotional life during these stages which belies the tranquillity and guilelessness of childhood. We have seen the intensity and force of the child's struggles with his needs and desires—struggles which adults rarely consign to the earlier years of life.

A curious event occurs about the sixth year of the child's life; there sets in a period of quiescence and relative calm. No longer is the child engrossed with inner conflicts and desires to seek physical pleasure. The pleasure-seeking impulses have become dormant; they lie latent. Some have been repressed, that is, pushed out of consciousness; others have undergone distortion and modification in a socially acceptable manner, a process called sublimation. Indeed, the name *latency period* has been applied to this time to designate that the pleasure-seeking impulses are dormant and that the child's emotional life is relatively tranquil.

The child now begins to become engrossed in things intellectual —in education. He goes to school. He learns and acquires a larger vocabulary. He becomes acquainted with the legends of the past and the heroes of history. He is exposed to religious influences and Biblical teaching so that he begins to discover and understand the role of morality and ethics in human relationships. It is also during the latency period that the greatest impetus is given to the development in the child of an important part of the personality which we call the superego, or the conscience. The *superego* is the outgrowth of parental prohibitions and training identifications, and later is reinforced by the ideals and standards of education and religion. By virtue of the superego, a child acquires a psychological mechanism which should ultimately keep him from transgressing and erring. During the latency period, there exists a great deal of antagonism and indifference toward individuals of the opposite sex. Boys join gangs and manifest disinterest in girls who cannot play their games. Girls have their coteries and look upon boys with disdain, avoiding their rough-and-tumble antics. Segregation of the sexes is often the policy at this time. This is the situation that prevails between boys and girls until nature intervenes at the time of puberty and adolescence.

Under the physiological impetus of growth and sex gland activity which takes place at the end of the latency period, the individual next prepares to enter the pubertal and adolescent stage of personality development. This is a period distinguished by profound inner struggle, many anxieties, and sharp conflicts with the adult world. It is a time when important decisions and adjustments relating to vocation and sexuality must be effected. This period has come to be synonymous with turbulence and strife. The adolescent attempts to establish his individuality, emancipate himself from his parents and family, break the chains of dependence, and integrate his personality in preparation for entrance into the arena of the adult world and its many responsibilities.

Although there are many problems which present difficulties for the adolescent, the one area with which he is most intensely preoccupied and which causes him the greatest concern is sexuality. The period of relative quiet that prevailed during the latency period is over. The pleasure-seeking impulses which have been lying dormant during the latency period erupt. There is a recrudescence of the sexual impulses related to the parent of the opposite sex. The struggle is brief but intense, and the individual goes through a miniature edition of the problems to which he was subjected during the genital period. Now, however, these impulses come into direct conflict with the individual's conscience which was almost nonexistent during the genital period. In order to avoid feeling guilt and anxiety, the impulses must be deflected away from the immediate family onto other individuals. The adolescent subjectively perceives this as a need to emancipate himself from his parents. He begins to seek the company of the opposite sex. He may attempt to break the ties which hitherto have bound him to the home, and may transfer his loyalties and affections outside his family.

At this time the adolescent also attempts to lessen his increasing sexual tension by resorting more frequently to masturbation. In many instances this leads to guilt and conflict, depending on the severity of one's conscience. Certain physiological phenomena also make their appearance at this time, which may increase the anxiety of the adolescent. The girl begins to menstruate and with this event she must accept with finality the unalterable fact that she is a female. If she still lives in the past and unconsciously hopes one day so secure a male organ and envies and resents the male intensely, menstruation will be disturbing to her and she will have difficulty in accepting her normal feminine role in life.

Unfortunately, many adults only increase rather than lessen the difficulties of the adolescent female. Many mothers surround menstruation with prohibitions and secrecy and impart to the adolescent the notion that she is being subjected to a painful, tabooed, degrading process. Some mothers urge their daughters, under the guise of protection and health, to remain secluded during their period, and withdraw temporarily from social activities. It is no wonder that, after exposure to such harmful influences, many young girls refer to menstruation as "the curse," and their difficulties in adjusting to this physiological phenomenon often take the form of functional dysmenorrhea or amenorrhea.

For many boys, nocturnal emissions constitute a source of concern and anxiety. Fantastic notions that this phenomenon represents a destroying process, a punishment or a disease of some sort, flourish among the misinformed.

The picture then of the adolescent period is one fraught with potential storm and strife, as the individual attempts to adjust himself to his impulses and bring them into reality with the outside world. The depth and severity of the conflicts and the manner in which they are resolved depend on the adjustmental success in the previous stages. This, in turn, is mainly a function of the attitudes and relationship between parents and children. If the parents are reasonably well adjusted, are not threatening, have not made undue moral issues of sexual matters, and have exposed the child to a satisfactory developmental process, then the problems and conflicts of adolescence will gradually and satisfactorily be resolved. In these circumstances the adolescent will direct his interests and impulses in a healthy fashion to the opposite sex, and the antagonism toward his parents will be replaced by a more realistic appraisal of parental ideas and values. Children will finally enter the adult world and deal with the realities of marriage, family, and work in a wholesome, constructive, and mature fashion.

Psychological development, thus, takes place over many years, and is the resultant of many forces and experiences to which we have been exposed. The manner in which the child resolves problems posed by his needs and desires throughout the various stages determines greatly his future adjustment as an adult. Successful resolutions of childhood conflicts make an emotionally and psychologically stable adult. However, this is impossible without an early secure and correct emotional relationship as embodied in mature parental attitudes during the formative years. The child must feel loved, for without love he withers psychologically as a plant does without sunshine or water. Mature parental love sustains the child in his helplessness; later it allows him to reach for independence and self-reliance in order to meet the uncertainties of life with confidence and assurance. Mature parental love is not synonymous with overprotection and overindulgence, since these attitudes only hinder sound personality development, warp our sense of reality, cripple and impede progress to emotional maturity. It is through the relationship with his parents that the child can be expected to acquire the psychological equipment necessary to meet life stresses with a minimum of difficulty.

If, unfortunately, the child feels deprived, rejected, neglected, or is unwanted openly or covertly, then psychological wounds are inflicted which can only be healed, if at all, with great difficulty. A rejected child makes for a maladjusted adult. In our attempts to resolve the unsolved problems of childhood, we are constantly reliving them as adults.

Because of early deprivations in love, there exist many adults who are unable to love anyone other than themselves; they seek out and are interested only in receiving attention and favor, and are seldom satisfied with what they secure. They are dependent and need to lean on others for emotional sustenance. These people are not willing to *give* of themselves because of an early love *deficit*, never corrected, which they constantly attempt to fill unsuccessfully. They are unceasingly trying to collect on an unpaid bill of love. They are often cold, withdrawn, and lack the spontaneity and warmth that goes with a mature, well-integrated personality. As children, they were disappointed in their parents who withheld love from them. Deeply hurt, they avoid close human contacts in self-defense, because the pain of rejection is ever threatening in their minds. They are inadequate and do poorly in their work and marital relationships. In short, they are *psychological cripples*.

At the beginning of this survey we quoted the poet's intuitive line, "The child is father of the man." We have attempted to add substance and reality to this perception. We have tried to show that our approach to the challenge of marriage, family, work, health, effectiveness, enjoyment, and courage depends mostly on the manner in which we have resolved our childhood conflicts. Adulthood is merely the continuation of a road which reaches far back into childhood.

## Chapter 10

# THE SUPEREGO: ITS FORMATION AND IMPORTANCE IN HEALTH AND DISEASE

*Wherein the growth and shaping of the superego, our ethical and moral sentinel is discussed.*

PSYCHOANALYSIS OPENED UP NEW PATHS INTO MEDICAL PSYCHOLOGY. Meaningful insight was afforded into many hitherto baffling psychopathological phenomena. It has thrown light where there was much darkness, ignorance, shadow. It has shown the roots of much frustration, ineffectiveness, disappointment, failure, unhappiness, and nervousness. Freud's classical observations and studies led to the formation of numerous concepts which form much of the basis of modern dynamic psychiatry. While psychoanalysis did not discover the unconscious, it did expand its territory and focused upon its significance. The exploration into the sources of infantile gratification and pleasure seeking and the formulation of a paradigm of personality structure have been among the outstanding contributions in the field of medical psychology. Some of these infantile gratifications become fixed habits or tendencies, and, later in life, interfere with the requirements of the adult world and maturity of action and thought. With the help of psychoanalytic investigation, a new understanding was gained into the emotional ills of mankind, and impetus and vigor were given to curative possibilities.

Intensive studies by medical psychologists are still being carried out on that aspect of the individual which we call personality. Psychoanalysis has approached the study of personality from many points of view or frames of reference. Many of these have become part of standard psychiatry and psychology. That is to say, the ideas on the way the mind works, formulated originally by Freud, have become part of generally accepted thinking by specialists in these fields. Such concepts as (1) the importance of resistance, repression, the rejection of the unpleasant, reaction to threats and frustration, dissociation or disconnection of impulses and feelings associated with ideas and attitudes that are disapproved or dangerous; (2) the unconscious or importance of strivings, or tendencies we are not fully aware of but which appear in dreams, fantasies, everyday mistakes, and symptoms of certain illnesses; (3) the importance of identification, conflict between our childish impulses and adult or social commitments, protestations and directions; (4) transference or displacement of feelings, the meaning of symptoms—these are contributions of psychoanalysis which enter into all thinking about personality and illness by those studying in this field.

There are certain areas where marked differences of opinion exist: over the relative importance of biology and culture; of physiology and psychology; of the past and the present; of individual and racial experience; of the conscious, the intellectual and the will versus the unconscious, the intuitional and emotional; of the material and the spiritual; of drives and goals; of the individual and the social; of the pull of the past and the inspiration or motivation of the future; of the realistic, egoistic, pragmatic, and the idealistic. Various studies have emphasized different perspectives—for example, Adler, the conscious, rational, and intellectual; Jung, the social, anthropological, and religious; Sullivan and Horney, the cultural; Rank, the literary and anthropological; Alexander, the physiological, medical, pragmatic, and therapeutic; Rado, the biologic and rationalistic. Different points of view emphasize various aspects of the function and structure of the personality. Scholars and scientists consider and reflect on all points of view. In this chapter the classical Freudian point of view is presented.

From his painstaking observations of the way he saw the human personality, Freud developed certain ideas or concepts of psychological motivation, function, or dynamics. There were certain repetitions in his observations which he called dynamic or psychological mechanisms. Similarly, Freud believed he found certain sequences in ordinary relationships between childhood experiences, fantasies, and reactions, and adult temperaments, characters, behavior, and illnesses. This kind of relationship, or correlation or sequence, was thought of as causal, etiological, or genetic. The various concepts, correlations, diagrams, or formulations of thinking became psychoanalytic theories. Different schools of psychoanalysis have developed according to their emphases on different aspects of Freud's theories—for example, individual psychology (Adler), analytic psychiatry (Jung), cultural psychoanalysis (Sullivan, Horney, Fromm). Individual psychiatrists incorporate into their thinking aspects of theory from the different schools (frames of reference) which they find helpful in understanding and treatment. In treatment there is not so much difference practically nor in therapeutic results as there appears in the ideological (frames of reference) differences of the various schools. Difference is a challenge which is wholesome and makes for clarification, disputes, and progress.

From his observations of behavior and thinking (interpretation), Freud noted certain ways in which personalities, both sick and well, reacted. He, therefore, formulated statements, theories, and paradigms as to why the human personality in its many varieties acted or functioned as it did. From these observations and reflections, he developed certain ideas about the basic theoretic, conceptual common denominators as to the fundamental forces in the personality. These have been discussed from a different point of view in Chapter 8. There are correlations between these different points of view and those presented in this chapter. Human nature is far too complex to feel that it is adequately represented by any single picture or formulation. William James, the great philosopher and psychologist, long ago pointed out that experience was broader than concepts, and feelings than ideas, and that words are limited and substituted or symbolic aspects of experience.

From the point of view of dynamic psychology or psychoanalytic psychiatry, Freud gave a structural and functional or dynamic description of the basic psychological forces in the human personality. He described the psychological apparatus in terms of three different systems. He called these the id, the ego and the superego.

Freud conceived the id to be an inherited reservoir of the chaotic instinctual impulses which are primitive and unrefined. They are representations of physiologic and bodily occurrences and derive from heredity the genes, constitution, chemistry—and experiences. Impulses that reside in the id are mainly of an erotic and hostile nature. They are unorganized, undisciplined, and are not influenced by morality or fear of external consequences. The id obeys the pleasure principle in that its impulses demand immediate gratification regardless of the limiting circumstances of the external world. The id can be viewed as that part of our personality which avows, "I want what I want when I want it." The id is the neutral, primitive, ancestral, and physiologic strivings of the individual; it is the Van Gogh, Toulouse-Lautrec, or Dostoevsky aspect of the personality. The ego is the rationalistic—Adam Smith, Karl Marx, or John Stuart Mill part of the personality. The superego is that represented by the idealistic and religious heroes of the world from Lao Tse and Confucius to Buddha, Moses, and Christ, to St. Francis, Lincoln, Gandhi, and Schweitzer.

The ego has been described by Freud as the organizing, integrative portion of the personality which attempts to select, control, modify, and coordinate the id impulses and bring them into line with external reality. The ego tries to substitute the reality principle for the pleasure principle. The reality principle, it will be recalled, is the capacity of the individual to forego or postpone an immediate pleasure in order to gain future satisfaction and avoid present pain. It is because of the rational quality of the ego that man is distinguished from the animal and the adult from the child. The ego can be viewed as the "What can I do?" part of our personality, which surveys situations and attempts to arrive at a decision which will best serve the organism. It mediates between demands of physiology and instincts, the ego, and controlling forces of restraint, social strivings, and expectations.

The mind's most recent development is the superego. The word conscience is often used synonymously, but the superego has broader functions than conscience. This part of our psychological apparatus is looked upon as an automatic psychological agency which mediates the "oughtness" aspects of our daily behavior. In it are embodied parental restrictions and taboos, later reinforced by the standards and ideals of education, religion, and the codes of society. These codes, of course, vary with the different cultural milieus and social environments. The superego then is the "What should I do?" part of our personality. Not only does it deal with restrictions and prohibitions in telling us what we ought *not* to do but it also has a voice in telling us what we ought to do. It, thus, in psychological terms, inhibits, inspires, identifies, expects, and requires. It also punishes, makes one feel uncomfortable, sorry, and at times depressed. Here we shall be concerned with the formation of the superego and then with its importance in the genesis of certain emotional troubles and disturbances.

When one observes very young children one sees that they indulge in many activities which to most adults appear unnatural, perverse, and even repugnant. The child is cruel and shows little or no remorse. He is unrestrained or uninhibited in his emotional life; and although he may be violent, crude, and primitive in his behavior, he may show no fear of punishment. Early in life he finds excretory activities enjoyable, and secures pleasure from soiling himself and being dirty. The young child knows nothing about the laws of society and he has no qualms about appropriating another's property; he does not appreciate the meaning of "stealing" nor the consequences attendant upon it. In short, the young child is dominated by the id and lives for the immediate attainment of pleasure with no knowledge of restrictive limitations. Obviously, such a state of unrestrained indulgence can only be tolerated for a relatively short interval. The dictates of family and society intervene shortly in an attempt to set up and reinforce automatic prohibitions that will govern the child's instinctual life.

Children need parental love and are highly sensitive to anything which threatens its loss. It is in those areas of the child's emotional life which deal with training and prohibition that the child feels his greatest danger. It is also in these areas that the rudiments of the superego are first discerned.

Children have conflicts, whether to satisfy a pleasurable impulse and, thereby, incur parental disapproval or to comply with parental restrictions and gain approval and love and restrain resentment. This conflict is especially pronounced during the toilet-training period when soiling pleasures have to be relinquished. Eventually the child renounces these enjoyments, and complies with his mother's demands because he wants to retain her love.

But an astonishing thing occurs during this process—we see that the child begins to behave as he thinks his mother would want him to behave even when she is not present. First, he sets up in his mind an image of his exhorting mother who demands that he be clean and use the toilet for his bowel activities; then he begins to pattern his activities in accordance with his mother's image. "Correct" behavior no longer depends upon his mother's presence. In the beginning the child has constantly to keep his mother's image in mind so as to remind himself of her exhortations to remain clean. Gradually, however, the conscious mother image sinks deeper into the unconscious so that in time the child regulates his bowel habits automatically.

It is in the toilet-training period that the forerunner of the superego is discernible. The child has incorporated into his unconscious automatic function his mother's image forbidding soiling. This has the same effect as the mother's actual presence. He shares his mother's attitudes toward excretory activities so that her prohibitive outlook has now become part of himself. Concomitantly the child feels emotionally secure and pleased—he now feels he is behaving in a way that pleases his mother even if she is not actually present to see him. Ferenczi recognized that the "sphincter morality," or muscle control related to the anal stage of personality development, was an important forerunner in the formation of the superego.

In our discussion of the child who becomes clean after taking over his mother's attitudes toward soiling, a psychological mechanism was at work which is called *identification*. Identification is the psychological assimilation by one individual of some attitude or trait of another person. The superego is the most important product of the mechanism of identification. Although the superego is the composite of many identifications of other personalities, it draws its main force from parental values and standards. Parental attitudes, opinions, and judgments are automatically, that is, unconsciously, taken over by the child's personality and set up intrapsychically or intrapersonally as the superego. This psychological agency henceforth becomes the internal representative of parental teaching and prohibitions. The *superego,* or the internalized parent, becomes the sentinel and policeman of our emotional life. It vigilantly guards our instinctual activity. It says, "I want to do that but it would be wrong." Any impulses that threaten to break loose from the id may meet the superego's disapproval and condemnation.

Shame, guilt, anxiety, disgust, embarrassment, and remorse are all words that we use to note that we have offended our superegos. Guilt is one of the most potent weapons in the arsenal of the superego; its presence indicates that either in impulse, thought, or deed we have offended our conscience by transgression. Guilt can be considered as an attack by the conscience on the individual for having thought or having indulged in some forbidden behavior.

The ego is especially sensitive to the demands of the conscience, and it is often caught between an id impulse striving for gratification and the threat of conscience retaliation, if the impulse is gratified. In order to avoid the painful feelings of an aroused conscience, the ego attempts to control the undesirable id impulse in various ways. A mature and healthy ego tries to compromise between the two conflicting forces by modifying the forbidden impulse so that it is compatible with one's conscience and the external world. This process is called *sublimation*—here the original instinctual impulse has undergone modification and gratifies itself in a way that is now acceptable to the superego and external reality.

If the ego is weak and lacks integrative power, then the above situation may be handled differently. The forbidden impulse may be repressed; i.e., it will be automatically excluded from consciousness and, thus, the threat of superego punishment will be averted. *Repression* is a fundamental defense mechanism of childhood, for a childish ego is weak and its integrative capacity is severely limited. The child represses what he believes to be a dangerous impulse, because he is afraid its fulfillment will bring with it emotional pain at the hands of the superego. The original fear of someone who punished gratification becomes a fear of one's conscience, the intrapsychic representative of one's parents.

The ego then, when it senses a disapproving conscience, institutes repressive measures. Unfortunately, however, if the conscience is inordinately strong, then everything, and anything, that has the faintest connection with the "forbidden" will be excluded from consciousness. This is so because the superego lacks the capacity to make fine distinctions. For example, if the sexual drives during adolescence meet with an especially severe superego which cannot recognize that the impulses no longer are directed toward the parent of the opposite sex (as was true during the genital period), then a general limitation on all sexuality is insisted upon. For the superego, in its shortsightedness or myopia, wishes all sexuality to be repressed even though the object of striving is no longer the same as in childhood.

It is generally considered today that the greatest impetus to superego formation comes with the resolution of the conflicts in the genital (intense family feeling or oedipal) period of the child's life. During this period the child is faced with the hopelessness of his wishes (desire for the parent of the opposite sex), and struggles with his fear of punishment. Eventually the child gives up the ideas of displacing the parent of the same sex; instead he wishes to imitate and be like the parent. He permanently incorporates in himself an image of love and dread, derived mainly from the parent of the same sex. This forms the hard core of the superego which henceforth will watch and, if necessary, punish should forbidden, erotic, and hostile impulses relating to the genital period threaten. This is why Freud termed the superego the "Heir to the Oedipus complex, its derivative and substitute."

By the time the child is ready for school (latency period), a large part of the superego has already been formed. Parental prohibitions have been internalized in the form of the voice of conscience which says: "Restrain these forbidden impulses or else I will punish you." The original fear of punishment at the hands of the parents has been transformed into conscience fear. Henceforth the child can be trusted to conduct himself usually with socially and parentally approved behavior. Now he is automatically controlled in large measure by his own fear of bad conscience, the internal representation of fear of parental disapproval.

However, all of us obey the dictates of our superegos and consciences not only because of fear of punishment but also because conformity with superego standards provides us with feelings of reassurance and well-being. The necessity of being on good terms with one's parents has been transformed into a need to be on good terms with one's conscience. If the superego's demands are complied with, then there is a reward—a feeling of confidence, well-being, self-esteem, and security. These feelings are precise reproductions of feelings that children experience when they are approved by their parents. If the superego is defied and compliance with its standards refused, then feelings of guilt, remorse, discontent, tension and, not infrequently, inferiority are aroused. These feelings are similar to the child's feelings of not being loved any more by his parents.

It was stated previously that the formation of the superego takes place mainly by the process of identification. Although the most fundamental aspects of the superego are formed by the time the child enters school, nevertheless superego development is a life long process. Identifications are constantly being made by the child with his teachers, friends, relatives, clergy, historical personalities, literary and magazine figures and personages, social, labor, and military leaders, and with wishful and idealized modifications of these, with movie and television characters and comic-strip heroes. Religion makes a most important contribution to the identification process of superego formation. It gives purpose to the moral and ethical values imbibed from the mother and father and endows them with far-reaching values. Later in life there are identifications in the realm of political ideologies, art, and philosophy.

Because of diverse backgrounds, it is obvious that the character of the superego will vary from one individual to the next. Since the child, through identification, takes the parents as models in the course of his development and attempts to achieve their standards and ideals, a wide area of difference is possible, for parental values and restrictions vary.

Hendrick, in writing of the difficulties in studying individual variations in the identification process and superego formation, points out that very complicated mechanisms may be at work.

Just how these characteristics of the adults' individuality are related to the love and discipline of the family circle of his infancy, only a very thorough analysis will disclose. For it is not only with those traits which are most apparent in members of his family circle that the child "identifies"; this unconscious process is determined to a great extent by unconscious portions of the parents' superego and even by fantasies of the parents which are real to the child and emotionally experienced, but actually not characteristic of those about whom he is fantasying. Conspicuous traits of any personalities—for example, excessive unselfishness, over-solicitude, etc.,—are often fulfillments in adult life, not of the child's wish to be like the parent, but of his wish to be like the person the child fantasied the parent should be.*

All about us we see many variations in the strength of the superego. There are those individuals in whom the authority of conscience is so strong that the person becomes rigid and inflexible, a prisoner of his unyielding superego. Such an individual cannot make a move without first "checking in" with his conscience. He may be uncomfortable, irritable, hostile, demanding, and dominating if others do not conform with his own expectations and requirements of himself. Perfection often persecutes, punishes, and handicaps others as well as oneself. In another, conscience may be so inadequate and lax that social customs and laws are violated without guilt and anxiety. The latter behavior pattern is commonly seen as a reaction to strict parental training which fosters excessive rebellion against all authority, both external and internal. Harsh training can also lead to great submissiveness in the face of authority. Ernest Jones further points out that it is not always true that only harsh parents produce a harsh conscience. Many times children who are treated leniently by their parents develop an inordinate amount of guilt because such children find it difficult to entertain conscious hostility against lax parents. Other children, because they struggle with strong destructive drives or impulses within themselves, develop a superego which arises teleologically to keep these aggressive impulses in check.

However, by and large, if parental standards are mature and realistic, then the forces of restraint will become well integrated with the rest of the personality and the superego can become a positive and constructive force in adulthood. The superego then can be man's friend as well as enemy. It can be a source of realistic morality or a fountainhead of cruel, irrational judgment.

When we examine certain excessive or psychopathological phenomena, the role that the superego plays in the formation of symptomatology may be clearly discerned. Two of the most common findings that are seen in emotionally or mentally disturbed patients are excessive guilt feelings and the need for punishment. Guilt feelings originate in the parent-child relationship. A child who has already been pun-

---

* Hendrick, Ives: *Facts and Theories of Psychoanalysis,* 2nd ed. Alfred A. Knopf, Inc., New York, 1947.

ished by his parents for doing something wrong will react with fear of punishment, if he repeats the action or, at times, one with the slightest similarity or analogy. Once the child receives his punishment he "makes up" with his parents and harmony is restored. Since the child reacts to a threatened loss of his parents' love with insecurity, punishment becomes a means of restoring harmony and securing parental reconciliation. A recurrent cycle is established—wrongdoing leads to parental disapproval and insecurity for the child; this is followed by parental punishment, reconciliation, and forgiveness.

At first this process takes place in the external world as embodied in the parent-child relationship. Later, after the parental attitudes have become internalized as the superego, the process takes place automatically on an inner plane. If one offends the internalized parent, that is, the superego, guilt is suffered. To relieve these guilt feelings, the individual often automatically or unconsciously punishes himself or seeks punishment from others. In this way reconciliation of the disapproving conscience is brought about by atonement through suffering, and forgiveness is secured, just as formerly the naughty child, after punishment at the parents' hands, felt secure and loved again. The need for punishment in order to relieve guilt and restore internal harmony is a widespread finding in the unconscious of the psychoneurotic patient. Unfortunately suffering often becomes an end in itself and, in time, it may assume a pleasurable function for the individual. One of our patients was much displeased because we would not agree that she was "the worst woman in the world." The attitude here would be: "One must suffer; one may as well enjoy it." This erotization of the need for punishment is called masochism. One sees this in the martyr complex of people, frequent failures at times, mistakes, self-initiated condemnation, accidents, crime, delinquency, and, occasionally, in frequent surgery or chronic illness.

Freud recognized that guilt commonly arises from hostility in some form. The intimate relationship between guilt and hostility is clearly seen in the depressive states. Here the sense of guilt is excruciatingly intense, because a stern and despotic superego cannot tolerate strong hostile feelings that strive for expression. The conscience inhibits the aggressive impulses and turns them in a self-destructive fashion against the individual. The patient subjectively perceives this process as the depressive or feeling affect. At the same time, the suffering from guilt that the patient undergoes serves as punishment for his hostile impulses.

The extreme degree of self-abasement and reproach that the markedly depressed patients manifest represents, in part, a surrender to the superego in an attempt to appease it and secure reconciliation and forgiveness.

It is as if the depressed patient were saying to his conscience, "I am guilty, I confess my crime of hostility, I submit to any punishment if you will just love me and be kind to me." But in many instances the superego is unappeasable. It may be so harsh and cruel that the patient, to obtain relief from its sadism or punishing pressure, may even turn to relief by escape from life in self-destructive thoughts or acts and even suicide.

There are, however, times in which the autocracy of the superego is temporarily overthrown. This is seen in abnormal excitement which is called *mania*. Alien impulses which formerly were restrained by the superego are now allowed free expression. For the time being, the superego has been routed and the id is in control. Clinically, this is revealed in the boastfulness, truculence, and aggression of the manic patient and sometimes profane and indecent language. It appears in his excessive self-regard and insistence (narcissism) and almost complete disregard for others and reality.

There are also occasions when the *superego can be "bribed"* by punishment. Alexander has referred to the *"corruptibility"* of the superego, and he describes a mechanism by which *conscience is bought off with suffering.* Here *punishment* becomes the *currency* with which guilt can be paid off. Alexander relates an anecdote which illustrates this mechanism. A young girl wants to read a book that is frowned on by her parents. She first tells her parents that she has already read it and is punished for it. Now she is able to settle down and enjoy the book with a clear conscience.

The role of the superego is important in the psychopathology of the *obsessive-compulsive neurosis.* In this disturbance the patient also suffers from a strong sense of guilt, due to the presence of unacceptable hostile impulses. To avoid the disapproval of a cruel superego, the patient erects *rituals and ceremonials designed to stave off* the offending impulse. Because of the discomfort of the symptoms, the patient looks upon his illness as *penance and expiation.* The patient is more *fearful* of incurring the hostility of his conscience than in satisfying the aggressive impulses. The suffering and the limitations that his compulsions bring about are preferred to the pain of an aroused conscience. Another psychopathological state in which the superego plays a part is in the paranoid or suspicious and persecutory reactions. The delusions of being watched, criticized, observed, and controlled represent, in part, the *projection* or extension or spreading out to others of a bad conscience. The judgement which one has of himself is attributed to others. "It is not I who am a pervert; it is *they* who for their own vile purposes say I am." The patient, if he is hallucinating, hears voices which frequently criticize and reproach him. It is *just as if severe parents are talking* reprovingly to a naughty child.

It is not only in overt neuroses or psychoses that conscience reactions are important. For instance, Freud described certain *criminals* whose delinquent behavior was modified by a conscious sense of guilt and need for punishment, as we have already described. These criminals commit crimes but unwittingly always leave some clue behind which helps to apprehend them. They are caught repeatedly and punished. Such individuals not infrequently commit crimes to *provoke punishment* and satisfy the claims of the superego. Unconsciously, they want to be caught and punished.

Everywhere we see *conscience* reactions in the form of *self-punishment* and *suffering* that may dominate an individual's entire emotional life. There are those people who seem to be attracted to a succession of mistakes, blunders, failures, accidents, miseries, and hardships. Their relationships appear to be precisely contrived to cause them constant *deprivation* and *sorrow*. There are others whose conscience erupts at a time when they have at last achieved a particular kind of *success* upon which they have been intent. In these cases the individual becomes ill because of guilt. He has envied another's success so that when, at last, he also succeeds in the same endeavor, his conscience will not allow him to enjoy his happiness. This is the law of an eye-for-an-eye, a tooth-for-a-tooth punishment that the superego obeys. "You can't deserve the success since you envied others when they were successful." Severe work inhibitions and incapacitation are the result of such conscience reactions. Freud has applied the term "wrecked by success" in his description of such guilt-ridden individuals.

In thinking of functions or activities in psychology, one should bear in mind that the areas between the psychological and physiological are not sharply defined. The areas frequently overlap in one's thinking. One should bear in mind that a landscape or landscapes look different according to the height and position of the observer, for example, looking down from an airplane. The area of truth or falsehood is not that of a sharp line. One is tempted to think of physics and atomic science as being on solid, generally accepted, permanent foundations. However, the atom is not a permanent, solid thing. It is a series of observations, ideas, conceptions, theories, hypotheses with certain elements accepted by competent observers, and new elements or concepts unconfirmed, remaining in the realm of hypothesis and formulations. Modern physics has seen matter change into energy, and energy into mathematics, and mathematics into systems or organizing concepts or images which are not necessarily and obviously hard, external matter as opposed and external to the curiosity, genius and creative insight of man.

We see, then, that the superego of man, while it represents a great moral achievement, holds within it the seeds of distress, downfall, destructiveness, and disease. It can be a relentless foe that refuses to be placated. It can be hostile, cruel, and remorseless. It is only when a harmonious relationship exists between the superego, the ego, and the primitive urges of the id that the individual's personality can be considered well integrated. A wholesome superego can be and often is a guiding force to health, happiness, and scientific and social progress. It can be a partner in great cosmic or religious affirmations and endeavors.

# PART III

# The Nature of Emotion, Anger, and Fear

*Chapter 11*

# EMOTION—ITS NATURE

*What is emotion? This chapter tells what* Emotion *is, describes its general characteristics, and points out the role it has in the daily struggle for adjustment and survival.*

EMOTIONS AND FEELINGS SUPPLY THE ENERGY WHICH MAKES THE mind work. Without emotion (emotional energy) man, although he could live, would be inert, existing in a vegetative state, not necessarily asleep or unconscious but immobile, almost as in a stupor. Without emotion he would lie prone in bed. Retaining his reflexes, his leg would kick if his knee were tapped, he would swallow if water were poured into his throat, but he would not reach out for food or water at his bedside. He might scratch himself in a reflex way if a fly alighted on his nose, but he would make no attempt to save himself if the building caught on fire. In short, it is emotional energy which enables man to get out of bed in the morning, to dress himself, to eat breakfast, to go to work, to play, to make love, to care for his children, to fight, to build bridges, or paint pictures. Without emotion he would do none of these things, but repose, a breathing lump of clay.

This concept becomes clearer when emotion is considered from a biologic point of view. What is the biologic purpose of emotion in the human organism? Emotion supplies energy, but energy for what? The answer in biologic terms is obvious—to survive. Just as the purpose of the corneal reflex is to protect the eye by covering it with the eyelid, and the gag reflex is to protect man from choking

*103*

or ingesting noxious material, the purpose of fear is to protect him from danger. Fear is mobilized energy available to enable one to run away. The purpose of anger is to provide man with energy for survival by fighting. Maternal love provides energy that the young may be protected and so survive. Sex emotion provides energy in order that the species may survive by procreation.

In everyday life, anger is considered something bad, something undesirable, if not intolerable. That it can be an asset rather than a liability is not generally understood. From the biologic viewpoint, however, looking at man as an organism which has developed by evolutionary stages on the face of the earth, it is evident that anger has important survival value, that it is a dynamic characteristic of the human species. Certainly it is obvious that primitive man, living in the savage competition of the forests and plains, frequently must have encountered situations where the only choice was to fight or perish. Fighting needs a cool head, but it also needs energy. Furthermore, this situation which seems obvious in the case of primitive man is equally true for Mr. John Jones of Bronxville, N.Y. He, too, is confronted constantly with situations where the choice is to fight or perish or at least be hurt. It is anger which supplies him with the energy to meet these situations successfully.

Not a few novelists have recognized the survival value of anger. I quote from Steinbeck in *Grapes of Wrath,* describing the share croppers' reactions to the devastation of their crops by a dust storm.

The people came out of their houses and smelled the hot stinging air and covered their noses from it. And the children came out of their houses, but they did not run or shout as they would have done after a rain. Men stood by their fences and looked at the ruined corn, drying fast now, only a little green showing through the film of dust. The men were silent and they did not move often. And the women came out of their houses to stand beside their men—to feel whether this time the men would break. The women studied the men's faces secretly, for the corn could go, as long as something else remained. The children stood nearby drawing figures in the dust with bare toes, and the children sent exploring senses out to see whether men and women would break. The children peeked at the faces of men and women, and then drew careful lines in the dust with their toes. Horses came to the watering troughs and nuzzled the water to clear the surface dust. After a while the faces of the watching men lost their bemused perplexity and *became hard and angry and resistant.* Then the women knew that they were safe and that there was no break. Then they asked, what'll we do? And the men replied, I don't know. But it was all right. The women knew it was all right, and the watching children knew it was all right. Women and children knew deep in themselves that no misfortune was too great to bear if the men were whole.*

Similarly, fear is a protective device without which primitive man would have been devoured by wild animals and crowded out of existence. It was not healthy for a child to wander in the woods alone at night, and it is good for the survival of the species that he was afraid to do so. In our current civilization, on the other hand, fear, as anger, is more apt to be regarded as a liability. Of course, frequently it is—certainly if we include fear of ridicule, fear of being unloved, shyness, self-consciousness, fear of failure, timidity, etc. On the other hand, are we certain that man would pay his taxes, obey his speed laws or even obey the Ten Commandments were it not for fear? Could society, as we know it, function at all without fear?

As will be described in more detail elsewhere, the emotions of fear, anger, love, and worship are accompanied by profound physiological changes in the body. If a man's face is slapped and he becomes angry, or if a gun is pointed at him and he is afraid, the physiological changes are much the same. The heart beats faster, the blood pressure rises, blood is shifted from reservoirs in the vegetative area to the muscles, the sugar level of the blood increases, digestion ceases, waste material in the bladder or lower bowel may be expelled, the individual becomes alert and irritable. These changes all have a clear-cut biologic purpose: to prepare the body for action, and indicate the mobilization of energy for running or fighting or other behavior tending toward securing survival.

From a consideration of these matters, it becomes clear that the problem of handling emotion and feelings is the problem of handling energy, of handling a dynamic force. This force may be destructive, bringing suffering and unhappiness to the race and to the individual,

* From *The Grapes of Wrath* by John Steinbeck. By permission of the Viking Press, Inc., New York, 1939.

or it may be constructive, bringing peace of mind and survival for the race. The most important function of the mind is to direct this force into constructive channels and divert it away from destructive ones.

## GENERAL CHARACTERISTICS OF EMOTION

Having described emotion, let us now discuss certain general characteristics which appear to be little understood in everyday life, but which are essential to the successful handling of emotions and to adequate comprehension of the way the mind works.

The first of these is the stimulus-response nature of emotions. If a boy stubs his toe and his father says to him, "Johnny, control your temper," there are two ways in which he may interpret this admonition. One, that he should not let himself get angry, and, two, that he should not let his temper run away with him. With the first interpretation, he believes that he is expected to control the *occurrence* of anger; with the second, that he should control the *behavior* of anger. At first glance this might appear to be a distinction without a difference. Actually, however, the boy's self-esteem, his effectiveness, his happiness, and his mental health may depend upon whether he habitually reacts in terms of the first or second meaning. Perhaps there is no one point of more importance to an individual than his attitude toward this simple matter. Mistaken ideas on this subject are among those most frequently observed in individuals suffering from mental or nervous disease, and are the chief reasons why emotions become liabilities rather than assets. Which, then, is the correct way to view this matter? If the boy takes the first meaning and attempts to prevent himself from becoming angry, he has chosen wrongly because he will fail. In choosing the second course of preventing temper from influencing his behavior, he may succeed, but there is nothing he can do to prevent himself from becoming angry if he has stubbed his toe.

That this fact may be stated with such definiteness depends upon a simple point in the mechanism of emotions—that of response to stimuli. If you take a piece of cotton and touch the cornea of your eye your eyelid will blink. This is an example of what is known as a reflex. Its mechanism is relatively simple. When the eye is touched, certain nerve cells of the surface of the cornea are stimulated and an electrochemical impulse is generated which passes along nerves, as though along electric wires, until it reaches the brain. Here the impulse is shunted over to the other nerves which it follows out to the muscles of the eyelid. There it is discharged, causing these muscles to contract and thus the eyelid to blink. The main point to be noted in this phenomenon is its inevitability, if the individual has had no disease which has destroyed nerve cells. Once the cornea is touched, the remainder of the action proceeds automatically. Once the trigger is pulled, the gun goes off. In any healthy person, child, adult male, female, white, black, or yellow, this will happen a thousand times out of a thousand and *there is nothing the individual can do to stop it.* Granted he may prevent the eye from being touched, but once it is touched he cannot prevent the eyelid from blinking. The same inevitability holds true for the other reflexes: if the back of a person's throat is tickled he will gag; if his knee is tapped in a certain position he will kick.

What does this have to do with Johnny and his control of temper? The significance becomes apparent when we consider that an emotional response is very similar to a reflex response. The only difference is one of degree, not of kind. There is a quantitative difference, not a qualitative one. An emotion is merely a complicated series of reflexes. The startling and all-important fact is that the response to the emotional stimulation is just as inevitable as the response to the reflex stimulus. It is just as inevitable for the boy to become angry when he stubs his toe as it is for his eye to blink when the cornea is touched by a piece of cotton. He may try to prevent it, but he will fail. He may say to himself, "I won't get angry!" but he will get angry anyway. His father may shout at him and scold him, and he may fight the anger with all his power, but if the *stimulus* to anger has occurred, anger will inevitably follow. Evidence for this fact is considerable. The reflex nature of the response to emotional stimuli has been elaborated by Riggs, but the more fundamental evidence is to be found in the experiments of Philip Bard on the hypothalamus, of Walter Cannon, Pavlov, and other scientific investigations. Readers interested in pursuing the proof of the statement are referred to their works.

Having pointed out the fundamental similarity between reflex and emotional responses, it is necessary to point out immediately a fundamental difference. It was said that when the boy stubbed his toe he would inevitably *become* angry, but it is not true that he would inevitably *act* angry or even *appear* angry. He would *be* angry, but not necessarily kick the door jamb again or burst into angry tears. In reflex phenomena it is inevitable that the stimulus will be followed by *action*—the eyelid will blink. In emotional phenomena it is inevitable that the stimulus will be followed by an emotional *state*. It is not inevitable at all that the boy will *do* something, but he certainly will *become* angry.

It is important to elaborate this distinction between being angry and acting angry. When Lynn Fontanne, acting the part of Kate in the *Taming of the Shrew,* throws crockery out of the window, shouts in angry tones, curses, and stamps about, even though she may be "living her part," it is very unlikely that she *is* as angry as she *acts*. Conversely, but less obviously, it is possible for Miss Fontanne at least, or any possessor of a good poker face, or, in fact, more people than we quite like to think about, to *act* most pleasant, gracious, and friendly, though they may *be* a seething cauldron of anger within. It is possible to smile in spite of a desire to snarl. It may not be a convincing smile to acute or intimate observers, but it is nevertheless a smile and may conceal the underlying irritation from all except a few.

What has been said about anger applies equally to the emotion of fear. If a boy is suddenly confronted by a snarling, ferocious dog, he will inevitably become afraid. He may say to himself, "I am not afraid of dogs and I refuse to let myself become afraid of this dog," but he will be afraid anyhow. Even if he says to himself, "Only cowards are afraid; I'm not a coward therefore I can't be afraid," fear will not be prevented. Again, because he *is* afraid it is not inevitable that he *act* afraid, or even that he *appear* afraid. He does not have to run away screaming. He may even walk toward the dog with outstretched hand, uttering soothing sounds. Concealing fear is, perhaps, an even more common phenomenon and offers more cultural advantages than concealing anger, though it may be much more difficult to conceal the manifestations of emotion, such as the timid expression, the trembling of the lips, the change in the pitch of the voice, than to avoid performing some action motivated by fear.

Similarly, sex feelings follow the same pattern. As Mr. X. one day is sitting looking out of the window, his eye lights on his neighbor's wife taking a sun bath in the yard next door. His neighbor's wife is beautiful, provocative, sexually attractive, and he detects in himself the arousal of sexual feelings. Mr. X. is a very conscientious, pure-minded man, a good father to his children, and in love with his own wife, so, regardless of the abstract fact that his neighbor's wife is sexually attractive, he feels that for him to be sexually aroused by her is wrong, that failure to prevent such feelings from occurring is evidence of lack of love for his own wife and of baseness of character. Actually having a strong character he says, "I refuse to permit myself to be aroused by this woman!" and opens a determined, even desperate struggle with his feelings. But, since his neighbor's wife *is* sexually attractive and has acted as a sexual stimulus to him, he inevitably responds by having aroused in him the corresponding sexual emotion, and there is nothing he can do to prevent it. This does not mean at all that he must keep his gaze fastened on the yard where she is; if he is wise he will probably turn elsewhere. But just because he detects sexual feelings in himself, even very strong feelings, he most certainly is not compelled to lean out the window and wave or try to make a clandestine engagement. It certainly is within his power to avoid looking out the window when he knows the woman is in the yard, but if he does see her so that a sexual stimulus occurs, there is nothing he can do to prevent the sexual response from following. The belief that he should be able to stifle this feeling may lead to obvious diffi-culties. If, for instance, Mr. X. discovers that even strong will and great effort fail to stop the sex feeling, he may erroneously conclude that the feeling must be a strong one; perhaps it indicates that he has "fallen in love" with his neighbor's wife. Thus a mild instinctive re-sponse becomes magnified out of all proportion to its actual impor-tance.

What has been said in regard to anger, fear, and sexual feelings applies also to the other emotions and feelings; hate, friendliness, jealousy, shyness, tenderness, loyalty, curiosity, all follow the same pattern: once a stimulus occurs the emotion inevitably follows. But because to *act* hateful, friendly, or jealous, is distinct from *being* hate-ful, friendly, or jealous, the necessity for acting according to the emo-tion does not inevitably follow. Even hunger, thirst, pain, and sleepiness come under the same principle. If a healthy man goes sufficiently long without food, he inevitably becomes hungry; without sleep, sleepy. But he does not need to act hungry or thirsty; he does not need to appear to be in pain. Nothing he can do or say, however, will prevent the response from following the stimulus.

There is another general characteristic of emotions which, though very difficult to understand, is, nevertheless, essential to the adequate understanding of what has been said so far in regard to emotion and to the comprehension of the way the mind works. This characteristic has been discussed already in Chapter 6 on the unconscious and subconscious mind. Stated simply, it is merely that an individual may have a strong emotion without being aware of it. In other words, a man can be afraid, sexually aroused, jealous, resentful, or filled with emotion of hero worship or love without being aware of it. Also he may be angry without knowing at whom he is angry. Anger, fear, love, all may be disguised in their appearances so that they occur in forms which are extremely difficult to recognize. For instance, fear may give evidence of its appearance in an individual only by tenseness; anger may assume many disguised forms such as hurt feelings, tears, moodiness, loss of concentration, or insomnia. Surprisingly enough, feelings of depression may be nothing more than camouflaged resentment. The feeling of physical weakness and prostration is a very common disguise assumed by anger, fear, or anxiety. Another matter which adds complexity to the situation is that people frequently call the same emotion by different names and different emotions by the same name. Anger may be called crossness by one person, irritation by another, boredom by another, hurt feelings by another, being upset by another, and a sick headache by still another. All these persons are talking about the same thing, but calling it by different names.

On the other hand when people talk about love they may be referring to sexual love, or the love of a man for his pipe, or the love of a mother for her child, or the love of a patriot for his country—all different feelings but designated by the same label. It is wise for every individual, nervous or nonnervous, to study his feelings so that he will at least be able to recognize them when they occur.

There is another general characteristic of emotions which, though it will be discussed in more detail in later chapters, should be mentioned here. If, for some reason, emotional energy is not getting its proper outlet in outward activities such as work, play, companionship, etc., it may be diverted to the inner organs of the body. As has been described, it is part of the normal process of arousal of emotions, for the heart, blood vessels, and gastrointestinal tract to become active. As was seen, however, this was merely preparatory to the individual's going into overt action. If overt action does not occur, two things among others may occur. First, the organs which would ordinarily have relaxed, if the individual had gone on and performed some overt action, such as running or talking, do not relax, but continue in their state of mobilization. For example: the heart continues to beat rapidly, the blood pressure to remain elevated, the gastrointestinal tract to try to expel waste matter, the liver to pour sugar into the blood stream. Second, the energy designed for the overt action, finding no other outlet, appears able to be diverted to the inner organs of the body.

There is increasing evidence that anger, fear, sexual feelings, the desire to be protected may, as it were, become concentrated in individual organs of the body with the result that coronary heart disease, high blood pressure, asthma, peptic ulcer, colitis, and arthritis are prone to develop. More frequently nonspecific physical symptoms of fatigue, tenseness, lack of strength, indigestion, and insomnia occur on this basis.

Finally, there are certain general conclusions to be drawn from the considerations presented in the preceding pages. As has been pointed out, the purpose of emotional energy is to enable the human animal to engage in actions which will help him survive. In primitive man this meant fighting or running away or making love or protecting his young—all pursuits using muscular activity. In our modern civilization mental activity, willing, talking, and engaging in skilled work have largely displaced these outlets, perhaps not with quite the same efficiency. The stimuli to emotions of all sorts occur constantly to everybody in everyday life, so that emotions are being aroused constantly in everybody every hour of the day. Memory functions so that stimuli occurring yesterday may arouse emotional energy today. If, for one reason or another, this emotional energy is not used in some activity, it will not just evaporate and disappear. It is a law of physics that energy does not just dissappear; it continues to accumulate, to increase in charge, until it may even reach explosive proportions which demand discharge.

An individual may have some success in preventing this accumulation from occurring by withdrawing from civilization and thus avoiding stimuli, although this technique is hampered by the function of memory. Once a person is exposed to a stimulus, however, he is powerless to prevent himself from responding by the arousal of emotional energy. What, then, can be done about it? When he stubs his toe, the boy cannot prevent himself from becoming angry and he cannot prevent this anger from ultimately being transformed into some kind of action. He is, however, able to *choose* which particular type of action shall follow—whether he kicks the door again in retaliation, or swears, or says "ouch" in a loud voice, or says "ouch" in a low intense voice, or whether he hops up and down or whether he stands there silently, fuming and suffering. Practically, in many cases, the *choice* of pattern is not determined by *conscious thought* but by *habit, training, parental attitudes, or impulse.*

Many individuals do not seem to realize that they can develop the ability and freedom to choose their actions. They often consider that heredity determines their behavior. Choice is equally available for the behavior response to other emotional stimuli. Where the boy is confronted by the snarling, frightening dog, he is powerless to decide whether or not he becomes afraid; he will be afraid, regardless of what he decides, but he does have free choice as to what he does about it. He can decide whether, in situations of this kind, to give a shout and take to his heels or to stand his ground and take what comes. He cannot decide whether he will become afraid, but he can decide whether he will be a coward. Similarly in the case of Mr. X., he cannot decide whether he will be aroused by the sight of his neighbor's wife, but he can decide whether to keep on looking at her. The obvious simile is that once the lever has been pulled the water will pour over the dam; and there is no choice, once the lever has been pulled—the water rushes on inevitably. There are, however, several channels in which the stream may be diverted, labeled: brave, fairly brave, cowardly, stupid, smart, immature; and the individual has the power to direct the stream, so that even though he cannot stem the tide, he can cause it to flow in the channel of his choice.

## Chapter 12

# ANGER

*In this chapter the specific emotion of* Anger *is discussed—what it is, what it does, and what to do about it.*

IN CHAPTER 11 THE SUBJECT OF EMOTION AS A WHOLE WAS DIScussed and certain general characteristics of emotion were described. In this chapter it is our purpose to pick out a single one of these various emotions—anger—show how it follows the general characteristics of emotion and describe the individual characteristics specific to it.

First of all it is important to define this emotion, to answer the question—what is anger? We know that it is an emotion and know, therefore, that anger is a form of energy. Energy present in human beings is usually referred to as an impulse or a desire to do something. Therefore, we can say that anger is an impulse to do something and the question remains—to do what? We have seen that the biologic purpose of anger is to enable man to survive when the alternative which faces him is to fight, be injured, or perish. Thus it becomes apparent that anger is the impulse to fight. However, the purpose of fighting is to destroy or kill, so that, in the final analysis, anger is the impulse to destroy or kill.

At first glance this definition would appear incredible, that every time a person becomes angry he has the impulse to kill somebody or to destroy something. However, it makes more sense if we consider that there is a great deal of difference between impulse and intent. A person may be just a little angry, which would mean that he had just a little impulse to kill, an impulse which would disappear if he merely hurt or injured somebody a little bit. For instance, if Mr. Jones steps on Mr. Brown's toe and Mr. Brown becomes angry, surely Mr. Brown does not intend to kill Mr. Jones; he merely has a slight impulse to kill Mr. Jones which will be entirely dispersed if he says, "Ouch! Say, why don't you look where you are going?" In other words, the impulse to kill must be considered from a quantitative viewpoint. The difference between harming and killing, between damaging and destroying, between forcibly removing and annihilating, is quantitative rather than qualitative. It makes for clear thinking, however, in considering any problem associated with anger, to bear in mind that anger in the final analysis, is the impulse to destroy or kill.

In everyday life the emotion of anger or the impulse to destroy appears in various shapes, quantities, and stages, all of which are called by different names. In order to delineate more clearly just what it is we are going to talk about in this chapter, it is, perhaps, well to list some of these words which usually refer to anger. It is important to state here that the person using these words very frequently does not realize that the feeling he refers to is actually anger; he does not consider that he is referring to the impulse to kill or destroy. It is similar to the case of a person who may talk about a pretty bunny rabbit without realizing he is referring to a member of the rodent family.

Thus, the emotion anger, itself, depending variously on whether it is great or small, acute or chronic, new or of long standing, latent or overt, is called: aggression, resentment, frustration, hate, fury, indignation, outrage, wrath, antagonism, crossness, hostility, bitterness, destructiveness, spite, rancor, ferocity, scorn, disdain, enmity, malevolence, defiance.

When the presence of anger is detected in a person we say that he is mad, bitter, frustrated, griped, fed up, sore, hot under the collar, excited (now don't get excited), seething, annoyed, troubled, inflamed, antagonistic or antagonized, exasperated, vexed, indignant, furious, provoked, hurt, irked, irritated, sick (she makes me sick!), pained (he gives me a pain), cross, hostile, ferocious, savage, vicious, deadly, dangerous, offensive.

Then, since anger is energy and impels individuals to do things tending to hurt or destroy, there is a whole series of verbs which depict actions motivated by anger: to hate, wound, damage, annihilate, despise, scorn, disdain, loathe, vilify, curse, despoil, ruin, demolish, abhor, abominate, desolate, ridicule, tease, kid, get even, laugh at, humiliate, goad, shame, criticize, cut, take out spite on, rail at, scold, bawl out, humble, irritate, beat up, take for a ride, ostracize, fight, beat, vanquish, compete with, brutalize, crush, offend, bully.

Finally there is a group of adverbs also referring to anger—furiously, angrily, etc.

All these words, whether the user knows it or intends it, refer to anger. Some of them are associated with the cause or arousal of anger, some with the threat or fear of anger; but when any of the above words is used, anger or the impulse to destroy is not very far in the offing.

## CAUSES OR STIMULI OF ANGER

The causes and stimuli of anger are so many and complex that no attempt will be made to present a simple formula to include them all. Instead, certain general types of anger stimuli commonly observed by students of human behavior will be described. It may be that merely different words will be used to say the same thing, but this will be an exercise not entirely without value.

One word which is important in the consideration of the causes of anger is *frustration*. This may be frustration of one's wishes, desires, impulses, wants, ambitions, progress, hopes, hungers, drives, instincts, or will. When man or animal is frustrated, he responds by becoming angry. Thus, if a man is hungry and cannot eat, he will become angry. If he is afraid and is prevented from running away, he will become angry. If he is angry and is prevented from destroying something, he will become even more angry. If he wants friends and cannot have them, he will become angry. If he is sexually aroused and is resisted, he will become angry. If he is curious and his curiosity is frustrated, he will become angry. If he desires to worship and is denied, he will become angry. If he cannot get his own way, he will become angry. If his will to survive is frustrated, he will become angry.

If the word frustration is to be used, the student must consider not only frustration *of* what, but frustration *by* what or *by* whom. A person may be frustrated by other individuals—by his father, his mother, his wife, his child, his friend, his business partner, his competitor, his enemy. He may be frustrated by someone who loves him, by someone who hates him, or by a total stranger. He may be frustrated by someone he loves, or someone he hates, or someone to whom he feels indifferent, but in each case, because he is frustrated, he will become angry. This is a point not commonly understood in everyday life, namely, that it is possible to be frustrated by a person one loves or is loved by. And it is even less understood that if one is frustrated by such a person he will become angry regardless of the existing love. Another point to be mentioned here, although it will be elaborated later, is that, if the frustration by someone is unintentional, it is no less a frustration and thus no less inevitably a source of anger. The only difference is that if the frustration is unintentional, the resulting anger is more difficult to deal with. This situation is similar to that where the frustration is intentional, but the motive for the frustration is good. "I am doing this for your own good, dear." Here also the resulting anger is hard to cope with. Not only can a person be frustrated by an individual or a group, or a crowd or a community, but by society as a whole, and, finally, by the representatives of society in his own personality, namely, his standards and conscience. In each case anger will be aroused.

It is important to raise a question here: Does one person frustrate another when he refuses to help that person do something? It is clear that, if Mr. A. wants an apple and Mr. B. pushes his hand away so that he cannot reach it, then Mr. B. is frustrating Mr. A. However, if Mr. A. is a short man, and the apple is on a high shelf beyond his reach, does Mr. B.'s refusal to help him get it constitute frustration? The answer is not simple. However, it is a common observation in everyday life that many people become furiously angry when others refuse to help them get something they want. It would appear that frustration as a cause of anger depends not so much upon the external aspects of a situation as upon how one interprets a situation and whether one *feels* frustrated.

In addition to being frustrated by a person or persons, one can be frustrated by what will be called the laws of nature. For instance, a hungry man can be frustrated by the fact that the refrigerator is empty, or a man can be frustrated in his attempts to climb a wall that is too high for him to climb, or in his desire to play tennis by the fact that it is raining, or in his desire to raise crops by the occurrence of a dust storm. The degree of frustration and anger felt by different individuals under these conditions, of course, varies a great deal and seems to be a function of maturity. It is true that a baby will cry for the moon, but there are many adults who appear to feel that they are singled out for persecution, that rain just comes on the days when they decide to play tennis.

We have seen that a man may be frustrated by others and by nature; he may also be frustrated by himself. Even though self-frustration is one of the most potent sources of anger, it is perhaps the least frequently recognized. If Mr. A.'s desire to eat an apple can be frustrated by Mr. B.'s interference or by the fact that the apple is out of reach, that desire can also be frustrated by Mr. A. himself. The frustration may be on the basis of duty, intelligence, or counterimpulse. In other words, though the apple is sitting there ready to be eaten and Mr. A. would very much like to eat it, he may decide that, since the apple belongs to somebody else, it would be against his principles to take it because that would be stealing; or his intelligence may tell him that apples do not agree with him and it would be unwise for him to eat it; or he may have a counterimpulse of fear that, perhaps, somebody else wants the apple, and would be mad if he took it. Thus a person's sense of duty and principles may frustrate his impulse to eat, to love, to run away, to do what he wants to do, to satisfy his curiosity; and these frustrations are no less productive of anger than frustrations by some outside source. If Mr. A. is frustrated by Mr. B., he becomes angry at Mr. B.; if he is frustrated by himself, he becomes angry at himself.

The concept of frustration could, of course, be elaborated further, but we shall proceed with another term which is useful in thinking about the causes of anger, namely, *harm*. If a person is harmed, he will become angry. Thus he will become angry if he is hurt physically, if pain is inflicted on him, if his feelings are hurt, if his pride is damaged, his peace of mind disturbed, his security threatened, his reputation damaged, his property destroyed, his loved ones harmed, his work belittled, his self-esteem injured, his pleasure destroyed, his chances for success or happiness hurt, his faith destroyed, his defense broken, his home life disturbed, his power curtailed, his credit lessened, his love-life threatened, his ideals shattered, his free-dom destroyed. As in the case of frustration, the harm may be in-flicted intentionally or unintentionally, by a loved one or by an enemy or by the individual himself. Regardless of the source of the hurt, the result will be anger.

And, finally, there is another concept of use in understanding the causes of anger and that is *survival*. Since the purpose of anger is to ensure survival, it is reasonable to expect anger to appear when-ever a person feels his survival threatened. The significance of this concept becomes more clear when we consider that survival means more than just physical, bodily survival, but survival as a person, survival as a sense of being somebody, of being an individual. This explains why an insult so often arouses more anger than a physical hurt, why the implication that one is nobody, why being treated as if one did not exist, or did not matter, or lacked a mind of one's own, often seems to arouse more anger than anything else. It, perhaps, also throws light on why people have so much resentment at being dominated or told what to do or what not to do, or what to think or feel or say. It explains why anger is such a prominent feature of the adolescent struggle to establish an individual personality with wants, likes, ideals, and existence distinct from the family. Thus, if a person feels that the survival of his ego is threatened, he will respond with anger no less than if the threats were to his physical well-being.

We have seen that frustration, harm, and threats to survival all act as provocations to anger. The element of time must also be included before the matter is properly understood. For instance, anger will result not only from an actual frustration in the present, but the threat of frustration in the future, or the memory of frustration in the past. Similarly, the recollection of an insult in the past will often arouse more resentment than was felt at the time. And, finally, though a person's survival at the moment is intact, if an incident occurs which seems to offer a threat to that survival in the future, anger will be aroused.

Individuals vary widely in the frequency with which anger is aroused. Part of this variation is constitutional. Some people from birth are more emotionally reactive than others. Frequently the person referred to as always having "a chip on his shoulder" is one whose interests and purposes are limited and self-centered. If a person's aim is restricted to the pursuit of immediate personal pleasure, and the necessity of demonstrating his superiority, it is obvious that his anger will be frequently provoked. Frustrations will be met at every turn because his desires will constantly conflict with those of others, and his demands will be excessive. A great many situations will prove annoying which would assume less and, perhaps, no importance if more of his energy were enlisted in making a contribution to others or to the social good. Those who accept life as a fight to bring about more understanding and kindlier relationships between people use their emotional energy in a way which expands the ego and makes it less vulnerable to frustration. Furthermore, a person is less likely to have anger aroused if he can see the immediate situation in the perspective of broader and more distant goals. For example, the psychiatrist is not apt to get angry at a patient's irritability and unreasonableness, because he accepts this anger as a part of the working out of the patient's problems.

## CHARACTERISTICS OF ANGER

Several volumes could be filled easily with a description of the various courses anger can take and the different ways in which it can affect the lives of the individuals in whom it is aroused. All that will be attempted in this chapter, however, is to present a few of the more important patterns.

### 1. STIMULUS RESPONSE

A point made in Chapter 11 will be amplified here, namely, if an individual fails to comprehend the stimulus-response aspect of anger, all sorts of difficulties are apt to arise. For instance, returning to the boy who stubbed his toe—if this has acted as an anger stimulus, the boy will respond by becoming angry, and there is nothing he can do to prevent it. However, as a result of his father's admonition to control his temper, he may conclude not only that it is within his power to prevent this occurrence, but that he is expected to do so. Actually a large proportion of people in everyday life believe it to be within their power to decide whether or not they shall permit themselves to become angry.

Now what are the results of this belief? First of all, having stubbed his toe, if the boy believes he can prevent himself from becoming angry, he is apt to try to do so. He may try very hard, exerting great efforts of will power and determination. However, as we have seen, he is bound to fail, and one result of this futile endeavor is to divert large quantities of effort away from the attempt to control his speech and behavior, where it could be successful. A second result is that if the boy possesses a "strong character" and, making a personal issue of the matter, has expended great force of will and determination in the battle to prevent himself from becoming angry, he may become angry at becoming angry, upon detecting his failure in this endeavor. The result is to double or to multiply by many times the amount of anger generated.

Still another thing which may happen is that, if he believes any normal person would be able to prevent himself from becoming angry, he may regard his failure as an indication that he is inferior and abnormal. And if a person believes that it is within his power to prevent himself from becoming angry, he may assume that it is his duty to do so; not only is he able to prevent feelings of anger, it is a moral obligation not to become angry. Becoming angry, then, indicates to him, weakness of character and moral depravity in addition to abnormality. Thus shame and guilt are common concomitants of anger.

Finally, the most frequent danger is that, the wish being father to the thought, the individual, believing that he can and should prevent himself from becoming angry, concludes that he is not angry and either ignores the anger or calls it by a different name—hurt feelings, depression, tenseness. This process usually is not one of conscious intent, and the person may be utterly sincere in the belief that he has been successful in not becoming angry. It is in these circumstances that the mechanisms of suppression, repression, dissociation come into play—mechanisms which will be described in Chapter 20. The result is that the person is angry without knowing it. Such unrecognized anger is no less capable of affecting a person's behavior than anger of which he is aware. Frequently, of course, the failure to recognize the anger is not complete. The person recognizes that he is angry, but fails to recognize how angry. Thus he may believe that he is mildly irritated when actually he is furious. Or he may realize that he is quite cross, but does not understand why, denying that the incident involved is a sufficient reason.

Thus, the first step in the successful handling of anger is the acceptance of its presence. "All right I'm angry—so what?" or "I seem to have become angry, now what am I going to do about it?" perhaps expresses the most helpful attitude. To say, "There is nothing to get angry about, therefore I am not angry," is a statement illustrating erroneous thinking, very common in many people. What frequently would describe the facts more accurately is, "I am angry, so there must have been something to get angry about."

## 2. BODILY SYMPTOMS

A point which will be mentioned briefly, though it is of considerable importance, is that the physical effects of anger not only are frequently mistaken for bodily disease, but anger actually may be an important factor in its causation. It is common knowledge that anger can cause the heart to beat vigorously, the breath to come faster, the hands to tremble. It is perhaps less well known that anger may disturb sleep, inhibit digestion, and cause physical exhaustion. Anger as a cause of insomnia and fatigue is much more common than most people and even most doctors appear to recognize. A point which is very apt to be forgotten is that anger may be chronic as well as acute. Thus, anger can spoil not only a person's breakfast, but his lunch and dinner as well; it can cause not only gas, belching, and cramps for a day, but it can cause chronic indigestion. As long as the anger lasts, the indigestion lasts. The other point most frequently left out of consideration is that a person can be angry without knowing it. A person complaining of indigestion is asked, "Are you angry at anything?" and the startled answer is, "Why, certainly not," and the matter is dropped. But a conclusion can be reached as to the presence or absence of the emotion only by careful investigation: first, to determine whether there is objective evidence of the presence of anger in the person—a feeling or sensation, say, which the person is calling by another name; and, second, to determine whether there is anything in the person's situation that would be apt to cause anger. The person's own ability to recognize it cannot be counted on for diagnostic purposes.

### 3. ACCUMULATION OF ANGER

A characteristic of anger important to know about is its tendency to accumulate. The following case presents an example of this. Miss Y. was recovering from a long illness which had confined her to bed for several months. She had reached the stage where for the past week she had been able to be up for several hours a day, take short walks, and eat her meals at the table. She was cheerful, even optimistic about her recovery. Then one day she was observed to become worse. Her nurse reported that she had become tense, morose, and irritable. The downhill course continued and by the end of the week she was completely confined to bed again, unable to sleep at night, her appetite gone, and she was completely discouraged about her recovery. No cause for this change was apparent. On repeated inquiry the patient had given no reason for feeling badly and the situation was puzzling until suddenly, in the middle of one afternoon, the physician received a message that Miss Y. demanded to see him instantly. On entering her room she was found sitting bolt upright in bed, her hands clenched, her lips trembling, her eyes blazing. "I demand to have that nurse discharged!" she fairly screamed at the physician before he had a chance to seat himself.

This statement from Miss Y. seemed most surprising because the nurse was highly competent, a very pleasant, tactful person toward whom Miss Y. had always seemed most friendly and even affectionate. Actually she had been quite dependent on this nurse for companionship as well as nursing care during her long stay in bed. There had not been the slightest indication during the previous week that her attitude had changed toward the nurse; they were still on the best of terms. Now, out of a clear sky, Miss Y. demanded in no uncertain terms that she be discharged. When asked why, Miss Y. launched into a furious tirade, angrily accusing the nurse of vulgarity, selfishness, incompetence—charges, the unfairness of which, were only too apparent to Miss Y. herself as she uttered them. When pressed for specific examples to substantiate these charges, among further caustic generalities only a single actual item of behavior on the part of the nurse emerged, and that was referred to repeatedly. Incredible as it might seem, when the entire situation became clarified, the only specific charge was that on several occasions in the preceding week the nurse had picked up Miss Y.'s personal nail file from the bureau and used it to manicure her nails while sitting chatting beside the bed. For this one minor breach of good manners, Miss Y. demanded the nurse's immediate discharge. If the loss of a job in this manner had meant a ruined career and starvation for the nurse, judging by the uncontrollable anger of the tirade, it would have made no difference.

Now what can be learned from an analysis of this apparently trivial situation? Upon questioning the nurse an important fact was revealed. At no time had Miss Y. asked her not to use the nail file. And until the final outburst she had given no indication of being displeased in any way. It had not entered the nurse's head that Miss Y. had the slightest objection or she would have stopped immediately, as she was most anxious to please Miss Y. in every possible way. Miss Y., it is true, was a lady of refined sensibilities who would be quick to detect and resent a breach of manners. On the other hand, she was also an intelligent woman with a strong sense of right and wrong and, when she had calmed down sufficiently to consider the situation, was acutely aware of the inappropriateness and gross injustice of her attitude. Added to this, Miss Y. was a very sensitive person who hated to hurt other people's feelings. She was clearly aware of her dependence on the nurse, and the idea of being alone in the hospital room without her company was intolerable, and to hurt the nurse's feelings or run the risk of arousing her dislike was even worse.

With these facts in mind, it is possible to piece together the events which led up to the demand for the nurse's discharge. Obviously, the first time the nurse used the file, angry feelings of resentment were not aroused; at the most Miss Y. felt a minor degree of irritation which would have promptly disappeared if she had requested the nurse to stop. If she had done so, the nurse most certainly would have laid down the file at the time and also would not have used it on subsequent occasions, so that the whole situation would have ended there. However, Miss Y. did not ask her to desist. Two things resulted—one, though she decided to ignore the incident, she was not entirely able to forget it. It continued to pop into her mind from time to time during the day in various shapes and forms: "What right has that nurse to use my nail file—Who does she think she is anyway

—Now am I not silly to let a little thing like that bother me—Well, it's the nurse's job not to upset me, and, if she does things like using my nail file, how do I know she doesn't use my cold cream—I wouldn't put it past her to borrow a pair of my nylon stockings—Oh, I'm tired of the whole subject—I refuse to think about it any more—What kind of a person am I anyhow to let a little thing like that upset me— etc." The second event was that the next day, totally unaware of the trouble she was causing, the nurse used the nail file again. This was adding insult to injury and the minor irritation felt the day before, having grown during the day, was now doubled so that having been minor, it was now moderate. This moderate irritation was even less easy to ignore than the minor irritation, and thoughts of the incident kept recurring in a correspondingly stronger degree during the remainder of that day. The depression and tenseness these thoughts engendered were by that time evident to the nurse who, never suspecting their origin, reported them anyway. When asked that evening by the physician if anything was troubling her, Miss Y. replied in the negative. If the thought even entered her head to mention the matter of the nail file, she immediately dismissed it as childish—"After all, you can't expect a doctor to tell your nurse to stop using a nail file— Why, it would be undignified and ridiculous to take up his time with so trivial a matter." The next day, in spite of herself, Miss Y. waited tensely to see whether the nurse was going to go at it again, but perhaps the nails were well filed by that time and nothing happened. "Well, maybe that's over with at last," she was able to say to herself and felt somewhat more cheerful. The next day, however, though she did not file her nails, the nurse again picked up the file and began to dig at them, cleaning them and clearing away the cuticle. All the resentment of the preceding two days rushed back, now tripled in strength. "Now this has gone far enough—I am going to put an end to it. I'll speak to her about it." And Miss Y. opened her mouth to utter the words, but to her chagrin no words came out. "I beg your pardon, did you say something?" asked the nurse in a friendly voice. Miss Y. found that her mouth was dry, her hands trembling. She became aware that if she spoke her voice would be harsh and strident. If she had spoken the first day, she might have been able to use a calm friendly voice; now she realized that, if she spoke at all, the strength of her feelings was such that she would grossly overdo it;

her voice would not sound calm and friendly, but tense and hateful. She realized that, if she were not careful, her choice of words would be such as to really insult and hurt the nurse all out of proportion to the size of her offense. So she again said nothing, and this time waves of helpless fury swept over her.

Miss Y. had had a hard time all her life; she had been exposed to many injustices and much unhappiness. Her father had gone off when she was a child, and she had been raised alone by grandparents who restricted her behavior far beyond that of other children in her neighborhood. Later she had spent several lonely years in a big city and, during her life, had been subjected to many frustrations beyond her control. The feeling of helpless indignation was very familiar to her. And now again finding herself *helpless* in the face of this humiliating incident, waves of long-standing resentment came flooding over her. Extreme tenseness, restlessness, depression, and exhaustion followed. Memories of former incidents forced themselves upon her and played about in her mind. She began to look at the nurse in an entirely different light—not as a friendly, encouraging companion and helper, but as a threat to her recovery, a cause of the dreadful thoughts she was thinking and the feelings of tenseness, frustration, and despair from which she was suffering—not as a friend, but as an enemy. Yet what reasons could she give to the doctor for her discharge? "You don't discharge nurses because they use nail files, but then you don't become so angry at nurses merely because they use your nail file. There must be other reasons!" And thus Miss Y.'s thoughts turned to a search for objectionable characteristics in the nurse, a search which is frequently successful, even if it is discovered that the most irritating fault of the nurse is that she has no faults. Thus, step by step, a mild feeling of irritation accumulated until it grew into a raging resentment. In the beginning it could have been handled by a few friendly words. At the end the very presence of the nurse had become intolerable.

This case is an extreme example of the accumulation and growth of undischarged resentment. It is obvious that if Miss Y. had been up and around doing things she would have had much less chance to dwell on the incident, could have gotten it off her mind, so to speak. However, she was not well enough to be up and around doing things, and she did try in a determined manner to get her mind off the subject and to think of more worthy things. And, of course, not everybody has been through her degree of misfortune and not everybody has been sick in bed for several months. The important point is that, failing in some way to discharge the irritation, Miss Y. was unable to forget the incident or prevent the irritation from mounting up to explosive proportions where it demanded discharge. This same phenomenon is to be observed constantly in everyday life. There is a commonplace phrase which describes the situation: "It takes a lot to make me mad, but when I do get mad—look out!" We talk about "goading" a person to anger, which means arousing repeated small irritations which finally provoke an outburst af anger. Often the phrase, "That was the last straw," refers to the same sequence of events.

There are several other points to be noted. Miss Y. decided not to mention her resentment at the use of her nail file when it first occurred because she did not wish to hurt the nurse's feelings or run the risk of arousing her dislike. Though, at first glance, this reasoning was commendable, it was actually shortsighted and impractical. An irritation which is not discharged often cannot be forgotten. The person can ignore it and pretend it is not there for a while, but sooner or later the irritation will come out in one form or another, usually so grown out of proportion that the ultimate result is to hurt the other person's feelings to a considerably greater extent than if it had been expressed in the first place. Certainly in this case it would have hurt the nurse's feelings much more to be discharged than to be asked to stop using the nail file.

Another point to be noted is that having failed to take the opportunity to express and thus discharge her resentment at the time it first occurred, when Miss Y. finally did decide to speak, two days later, she discovered she was unable to do so; unable to do so, that is, in a friendly, appropriate fashion. Her feeling had grown so strong by that time that the ordinary means for discharging it were no longer available to her; she was trapped by it. Actually this is the reason why many people in everyday life fail to express resentment and irritation. They fear they will overdo it and thus appear childish or bad-tempered. This, of course, is more apt to occur in people who habitually permit resentment from various sources to accumulate. They carry a constant load of undischarged resentments and thus deprive themselves of the usual channels for the discharge of new resentments. A vicious circle is thus established.

The concept that anger accumulates rests on the fact that anger, once aroused, does not disappear until it has been discharged. It is logical, therefore, to inquire further as to what is meant by the discharge of anger.

If anger is regarded as a force of energy with quantitative aspects, certain requirements for the discharge of this force become obvious. The problem of dealing with large amounts of anger (rage, fury) will be different than dealing with small amounts of anger (irritation, pique). If the boy has stubbed his toe just slightly, the resulting anger will be less of a problem to deal with than the time he stubs it so hard that it makes him very angry. For a person to get rid of anger it is usually necessary for him to *do* something that expends energy. If a person has a lot of anger, in order to get rid of it he will have to do more than when he is just a little angry.

If the way to get rid of anger is to do something, then the next question is—do what? A rather frightening thought presents itself at this point, if it is recollected what anger is, namely, the impulse to kill. Does this mean that anger once aroused in a person will disappear only if he kills somebody or destroys something? Obviously not. Again the quantitative aspect of the problem brings in common sense. If a man is slapped on the face, the anger aroused is not of the proportion necessary to kill in retaliation. It is true, however, that an impulse will be aroused to hurt the person who slapped him. It is a regrettable fact that he will have a tendency "to get even," as the saying goes. Society has long regarded the policy of an "eye for an eye and a tooth for a tooth" with strong disapproval. If such a tendency exists in the biologic make up of a man, however, it is more possible to deal with it intelligently if its presence is recognized. As will be remembered, one of the causes of anger is harm. Anger aroused by a hurt will tend to disappear when a like hurt has been inflicted on the person causing it. If a man is slapped, he will feel like slapping back. If he does not do so, he will continue to feel like it until he has done something which results in a corresponding degree of harm, or until he has diverted the feeling into some other effective channel. If he has been slapped hard, he will feel like slapping back equally hard, figuratively or literally, and to translate this feeling into action will remove the feeling on a quantitative basis. The reason society is quite correct in condemning this means of dealing with anger is that it does not work. It is true that when the man has slapped back he has accomplished the feat of ridding himself of the motivated anger. The trouble comes, however, that in slapping back he has aroused the feeling all over again in the other person. Aggression begets aggression.

The problem of dealing with anger becomes a little brighter when it is regarded from the viewpoint of frustration. If anger has been aroused by frustration, then it will tend to disappear when and if the frustration is overcome. A child having a tantrum because he cannot have a lollipop will tend to quiet down if he is given the lollipop. If a man is angry because he is frustrated in his attempts to enter a certain room, the anger will tend to disappear if he succeeds in getting into the room. If a man bears a long-standing resentment because he is frustrated in his attempts to gain a higher position in his work, this will be removed if he is promoted. Anger resulting from failure to make a point in an argument or discourse will be dissipated if the point is conceded by the opponent. In these situations an important fact emerges, namely, that in order to get rid of anger, it is not necessary to hurt or destroy something; the energy of anger can be used constructively to overcome frustration in the attainment of a goal. Another hopeful thought also presents itself, namely, that of substitution or compensation. Even with the crying child, unless he has been more interested in getting his own way than in actually obtaining the lollipop, a toy or cookie may be substituted. This will tend to compensate for not getting the lollipop, and the child's angry tears will cease. Thus, also, a man who feels bitter at his failure to attain prominence in his business may utilize, and, at the same time, rid himself of the energy of bitterness in succeeding in some other way— through cultural attainment, or by gaining social prominence, or political eminence.

The same means of dealing with anger applies also when the anger has been aroused by a threat to survival. If the biologic purpose of anger is to ensure survival, then obviously anger can best be used to the attainment of that end. In biological terms the reason anger takes the form of the impulse to kill is not that killing is an end in itself, but that, in primitive times, it served the purpose of attaining the greater end of surviving. When early man was threatened by a savage animal, the biological purpose of his anger was not to kill the animal, but to remove it as a threat to his existence—to render it innocuous. If the man could wound or frighten away the animal, the purpose of the anger would be achieved and would disappear. Thus in everyday life, a person who is angry, because he is dominated by another individual, can rid himself of the anger even more efficiently by stopping the domination than by "getting even" with the domineering person. Similarly, if he can regard an insult not as a hurt to his feelings which must be repaid in kind, but as a threat to the survival of his ego, he is apt to be more successful in handling the situation. To attempt to solve the problem by retaliation, returning insult for insult and hurt for hurt, usually leads to even further lowered self-esteem. A more effective and satisfactory attack upon the problem is to regard an insult immediately as a problem in lowered self-esteem, and to concentrate one's efforts upon finding ways to regain that self-esteem.

It has been stated above that the first step in dealing with anger is to recognize and to accept its existence. It has also been pointed out that the policy of "getting even" as a method of discharging resentment usually starts a vicious circle. When a person becomes angry it would seem sensible, then, to heed the old adage about counting to ten. Control of the retaliative impulse will give an opportunity to consider and try to understand the situation. If one can see *why* a person acted as he did, if one can see into his motives and one's own, feelings of anger sometimes fade. There is less danger in a situation which is understood; it is not so threatening and hence arouses less anger. Understanding gives a person more of a sense of being "on top." He can then deal with the situation more intelligently and realistically in some of the ways which have been suggested above.

## 4. MAN AGAINST HIMSELF

This portion of the chapter will begin with a consideration of the captured shark. It is well known among deep-sea fishermen that a shark is a ferocious animal. It is less well known, but there are several recorded instances (*Life* 8–1941) that a captured shark, as he is being hoisted out of the water into the boat, may writhe violently about, then suddenly open his savage jaws and bite into the flesh of his own body. Without presuming too much knowledge of the shark's emotional life, we may hazard the following picture of Mr. Shark. He is swimming along in the deep sea when suddenly there is a tearing pain from a steel hook in the side of his mouth. He lashes about shaking his head, but can find no enemy to attack, no cause for the pain which bites deeper. With fury and pain he dives to escape this unseen foe. His dive is checked not only by pain, but by a relentless pull on the side of his jaw. He is dragged inexorably backward. Again he lashes about seeking in vain a foe to destroy, then starts an ugly, sullen fight to escape, which slowly, inevitably, is lost. Finally he finds himself beside a boat. At last an enemy! But before he can attack, he is hoisted out of the water into the air, where he hangs helplessly. Insane fury overwhelms him, ferocious, uncontrollable rage which can find no outlet but attack; there being nothing else available, the shark attacks himself. Under ordinary circumstances of the competition for survival with other fierce creatures of the deep, the anger would serve to destroy the enemy and save the shark's existence; in this case the force turned in the opposite direction and contributed to the shark's destruction.

This fantastic and almost incredible example is cited for the purpose of calling attention to an important characteristic of anger which is also a feature of anger in human beings. The tendency of a man's own anger to destroy himself is referred to by several commonplace phrases—"man is his own worst enemy," "the will to fail," "ruining his own chances." The general tendency for man to destroy or harm himself, and the part anger plays in that tendency is a complicated and difficult subject. Variously referred to as the death instinct, the need for punishment, guilt, retribution, masochism, it is being extensively studied and written about by students of behavior. Obviously, much remains to be understood of the subject, and no attempt will be made here to consider the matter in detail. All that is desired is to point out that such a tendency exists in mankind, and to describe briefly a few of the more important ways in which it may operate.

The first pattern to be mentioned is, perhaps, the most obvious— it is when direct harm to an individual occurs as a result of his failure to control the influences of anger on his speech and behavior. In this pattern fall the innumerable cases when a man has lost his job by talking back to his boss, or lost a friend by speaking irritably to him, or spoiled an evening for himself by a cross remark to his wife. His behavior invites retaliation. This situation is expressed by phrases such as "aggression begets aggression," "a slap begets a slap," "a blow begets a blow," "a fight begets a fight," and "a war begets a war."

The second way anger may drive a man to destroy himself is more direct and yet less obvious. In the preceding pattern the anger was directed outward so that the self-harm came secondarily as a result of retaliation. Here the anger is directed inward toward the man himself. In other words, in the pattern described above, the individual is angry at something or somebody outside himself. In this pattern the individual is mad at himself; he is the object of his own anger. Thus the anger impulse to kill or destroy is turned inward, and the individual is impelled directly to harm himself.

There are various ways in which a person may become angry at himself, and the particular way in which the self-directed anger is aroused will influence to some extent the form in which it is expressed. A man may become angry at his ineptitude, his stupidity, his carelessness, his helplessness, or his lack of self-control. Thus, on muffing a golf shot, a man may become so angry at himself that he will take his own golf stick and break it on his knee; or, on awakening in the morning to discover that he has badly overslept and will consequently be late to work, a man may curse at himself, call himself a stupid fool, and give other evidences of self-directed anger and disgust. Similarly, a man may literally kick himself or bite his lips for having "spoken out of turn."

Another way in which self-directed anger is aroused is through the operation of conscience. If a man defies the dictates of his conscience either by impulse or deed, vast amounts of self-destructive energy may be liberated. Anger in this form is commonly referred to as guilt, though this term also embraces other phenomena. Under the impulse of guilt, the most varying and complex forms of self-harm may ensue, ranging from the violent finality of suicide to a long lifetime of petty privations and minor suffering. A study of the historical martyrs and ascetics reveals countless instances of almost incredible self-inflicted torture, mutilation, and suffering. Impressive as this list may be, however, it shrinks to insignificance in comparison with the less obvious martyrdom and asceticism of everyday life.

Countless people at every corner unnecessarily deprive themselves not only of pleasure, but actual necessities in order to assuage the goading of a troubled conscience and fulfill a need for punishment. Feelings of unworthiness, of undeservingness, result at every hand in conspicuous neglect of health, comfort, and peace of mind.

The man who, unprovoked, insults his best friend, the man who fails to show up at an important business conference, the girl who refuses an invitation to a party she would very much like to go to, the man who declines to propose to the girl he loves and remains unmarried, the woman who spends endless hours in unnecessary housekeeping drudgery, who "works her fingers to the bone," the brilliant man who insists upon engaging in a petty, monotonous routine, a drab, colorless existence, people who seem to court accidents and have always a tale of hard luck, those who repeatedly make plans which seem inevitably to lead to failure—all may be motivated by guilt, the need for punishment, or self-directed anger. Added to this are countless sleepless hours of worry, of self-recrimination, self-accusation, bitter regret, which also may be traced to the same source.

The third general way in which anger may cause man to harm himself is less obvious than the two so far described, but perhaps even more prevalent in everyday life. Most people, either by looking back at their own childhood or considering their present children, are familiar with the phrase: "You'll be sorry when I'm dead." It is usually preceded by the statement, "I hate you" and is uttered by the child in a moment of extreme anger at what appears to be an outrageous frustration of his wishes on the part of a parent. Occasionally, the threat implied in the statement is also expressed: "I'll kill myself." These phrases represent in pure form a characteristic of anger which will now be described. It depends upon a phenomenon known as identification which will be discussed in Chapter 24. The pertinence to the present problem consists in the fact that a child characteristically identifies himself with his mother. To him, he and his mother are much the same person. In his mind there is no great distinction between what she wants and what he wants, between what he feels and what she feels. Thus what hurts him, hurts her; if he hurts himself, he succeeds in hurting her. That this is a reciprocal relationship is suggested by the time-worn phrase of a father about to whip his child: "This is going to hurt me more than it hurts you." Thus, when a child becomes angry at his parent and, therefore, has an impulse to hurt the parent, a prominent means available for him to achieve this end is for him to hurt himself.

A clear-cut example of this mechanism of harming oneself where it has risen above the level of childish reaction to the status of political influence, is Mahatma Gandhi and his hunger fasts. Here, obviously, this leader was not subjecting himself to the suffering of starvation because of anger at himself, but because he was angry at political frustration of his plans. By hurting himself he caused such hurt to the opposing forces that in more than one historical instance they were forced to capitulate. The power of anger directed in this fashion is obviously great and is used as a threat and punishment to other people by many children, parents, wives, husbands, friends, and employers. The unconscious purpose of functional illness is sometimes to dominate and hurt others, make them feel guilty, and force desired action.

There are many obstacles to the detection of anger when it is operating in the form of self-harm. One of these is that the individual himself is frequently unaware of the anger motive behind his self-denial or punishment. Another is that behavior arising on this basis will have a strong though superficial resemblance to that described in the preceding section, namely, self-denial, self-punishment, martyrdom, and asceticism, on the basis of guilt. The important difference between the two, however, rests on the fact that in one instance the individual is angry at himself, and in the other he is angry at somebody else. When the individual is unaware of the motives of his behavior, there are two main ways in which they may be distinguished. The first is examination of the consequences of the behavior. If the behavior of the individual serves to hurt only himself, then he is more likely to be angry only at himself. If, on the other hand, the behavior brings suffering, unhappiness, and privation to others as well as the individual, further study usually reveals that the individual has cause at least to be angry at those others. The second distinguishing feature is the appropriateness of the behavior. If the degree of self-blame and self-punishment seems disproportionate to the alleged cause for it or any cause that can be found in the individual's history by objective survey, then usually it is revealing to ask the question—"Who is this person mad at?" or "Does this person have cause to be angry with anybody or anything other than himself?"

Actually the detailed investigations of the feelings and life histories of most cases of suicide occurring in this country have revealed that the motive was not, as is usually considered, either hopelessness or suffering but anger and revenge. Either anger at life or the world, or anger at individuals whom the person feels have in some way harmed or frustrated him.

## 5. SURVIVAL VALUE

Perhaps it will be helpful to end this chapter by stressing again the survival value of anger. The destructive, unfavorable aspect of anger is so much in people's minds that the constructive aspect is apt to be forgotten. It is a fact, however, that if it had not been for anger, human beings as a species would have lost out in the struggle for existence and perished from the face of the earth. Equally true is it that Mr. Jones of Bronxville, unless he becomes angry and unless he engages in behavior motivated by anger, is likely also to fail to survive in the present world.

| EFFECTIVE WAYS OF HANDLING ANGER | INEFFECTIVE WAYS OF HANDLING ANGER |
|---|---|
| 1. Accept its presence—face it as something to deal with | 1. Trying to suppress the feeling of anger |
| 2. Exercise control of action | 2. Trying to ignore it and shut it out of the mind, pretending it isn't there |
| 3. Do something about the anger:<br>  a. Try to understand it, its cause, its magnitude, at whom or what it is directed, whether it is appropriate; the other person's motives | 3. Hiding it, not telling anybody about it, bottling it up, harboring it |
|   b. Talk about it to the person who caused it, to a friend, to a stranger; blow off steam | 4. Rationalizing it, projecting it, segregating it, introverting it, using regression, suppressing it (see chapters which follow) |
|   c. Try to remove its cause, if still present or if there is danger of its happening again | 5. Getting even through retaliation |
|   d. Get even with the person who caused it if this seems like a good idea—if getting even won't result in even worse | |

feelings, and if the pressure for emotional expression is very great and such expression will clear the atmosphere

e. Take it out on something where it will do no harm—physical or mental activity—sublimate it, extrovert it, compensate for it, act in a way to increase one's self-esteem

f. Consider whether the adoption of different goals and broader purposes would reduce the number of anger-producing situations

*Chapter 13*

# FEAR

*Wherein the emotion of* Fear *is described and its causes, its effects, and how it can be handled. The distinction between* Fear *and* Cowardice *is made.*

In CHAPTERS 11 AND 12 THE CHARACTERISTICS OF EMOTION IN GENeral were discussed and then the specific emotion of anger was considered. In this chapter another specific emotion, that of fear, is singled out for discussion.

Again the first step is to define this emotion, to answer the question, what is fear? Since fear is an emotion, it can be considered as energy, a dynamic force, and therefore an impulse to do something. What the something is becomes clear, as in the case of anger, when the biologic purpose of fear is considered. In the struggle for existence, when man encountered situations where the alternative was to fight or perish, anger supplied the energy which enabled him to survive. When the alternative was to escape or perish, fear functioned in the same capacity. Thus, it is clear that fear is simply the impulse to escape or run away.

The number of words in common usage which refer to this impulse in its various stages and types are not as many as those referring to anger. It is equally true, however, that the person using the words frequently is only partially aware that the feeling he is seeking to name is fear or the impulse to escape. The list of words presented in Chapter 12, referring to anger, and the list to be presented here, referring to fear, cannot be obtained by looking under "anger" or "fear" in a standard dictionary. The lists were arrived at by familiarity with the characteristics of fear and anger and extensive observation of the actual words used by individuals when they were describing or referring to these emotions.

The nouns which usually refer to fear in one of its shapes or forms, whether the user realizes it or not, are: anxiety, dismay, worry, apprehension, timidity, shyness, dread, fright, alarm, panic, terror, and horror.

When the presence of fear is detected in an individual, it is commonly said that he is: afraid, anxious, alarmed, nervous, apprehensive, worried, upset, disturbed, scared, fainthearted, shy, timid, bashful, diffident, modest, frightened, fearful, or aghast. In comparing the words in the English language commonly used to refer to anger with those words used to depict fear, an interesting fact is encountered, a fact the implications of which may shed light on the power of fear not only over individuals, but over whole cultures insofar as they are reflected in their language. Considering nouns, in the case of anger, twenty-one words are found (aggression, resentment, etc.); in the case of fear, twelve (anxiety, dismay, etc.). Considering adjectives, in the case of anger, thirty-two words are found (mad, bitter, etc.); in the case of fear, eighteen (afraid, anxious, etc.). Finally, and here is a significant point, since anger is an impulse, one would expect a list of verbs in the language to depict behavior motivated by anger, and indeed such a list is found and a long one of forty-four words (to fight, to hate, to ruin, etc.). Similarly fear is an impulse, the impulse to escape and one would expect equally to find a corresponding list of verbs depicting behavior motivated by fear, and what does one actually find? Instead of forty-four, there are only two verbs in the English language to serve in this capacity, namely, the word that has been used "to escape" and the little-used verb "to flee." Of course, "to run away" is a synonym for "to escape," but it is a combination of words and not a verb itself. The verbs to quail, to tremble, to cower, to shrink, to avoid, to hide, to conceal, to elude, to retreat are words which frequently do allude to behavior motivated by fear, but on the other hand do not necessarily imply fear. They could be classified as words frequently borrowed from the language rather than specifically coined for the purpose.

The implications of this disproportion are puzzling. The explanation that behavior motivated by fear is so rare as to need only two words in the language to depict it, will be rejected by anybody who has even glanced at the subject of human behavior. Does it show that there are more ways of expressing aggression and anger than fear and escape? Does it indicate that the social taboo on fear-motivated behavior is greater than that on aggressive behavior? Does it mean that people are more ashamed to show fear than anger? Perhaps we must say that fear has acted on its own impulse and escaped right out of the language. However, this particular point will not be elaborated further here except to note that any discussion of the subject of fear will be severely handicapped by the scarcity of words available to refer to it.

## CAUSES OF FEAR

The next point to consider is what causes fear? What are the stimuli which arouse the impulse to escape in human beings? The word which first presents itself in answer to the question is *danger*. Fear is aroused by danger. This in turn leads to the question—danger to what? Danger to the individual, obviously, but the concept becomes enlarged if we say that a man will become afraid if he detects danger to his child, to his country, to his possessions; danger to his health, his peace of mind, his security, his self-esteem, his liberty, his character, his reputation, his independence, his ideals, his beliefs, his virility, his sense of importance, or his ego. The concept can be enlarged still further if again the biological purpose of fear is considered. If the purpose of fear is to ensure survival, then fear will be aroused when survival is endangered. This makes sense particularly if survival is thought of not merely in terms of physical existence, but survival of the ego, survival of the personality, survival as somebody rather than nobody.

Having used the word danger, further understanding can be reached by considering what this word means. Webster defines danger as the exposure or liability to injury or loss. In this definition, two new words present themselves to assist in understanding the cause of fear. Fear is caused by the prospect of *loss*—loss of love, loss of possessions, loss of self-esteem, loss of health, etc. The second word is injury, for which may be substituted the word harm. Fear is caused by the prospect of *harm*. Here emerges a point of interest for it will be remembered that in Chapter 12 it was said that anger is caused by harm. Thus one derives the statement: anger is caused by harm; fear is caused by the prospect of harm. Actually it appears that the causes of anger and the causes of fear are identical (harm, loss, frustration, threat to survival); only in the case of anger, usually these things have actually occurred, whereas in fear, there is usually merely the prospect that they will occur. From this consideration we arrive at a familiar fact, namely, that fear and anger go hand in hand, are caused by the same thing in different stages, so to speak. One follows on the heels of the other or is transformed into the other. The usual sequence, of course, is fear, then anger, or described more fully, danger causing fear is followed by damage causing anger.

It is true, of course, that the threat of harm can make a man angry even though the harm does not materialize. But here the threat of harm has been a harm in itself by disturbing the man's peace of mind and arousing fear. Another qualifying point is that a person's sense of adequacy also influences the situation. If a person feels adequate to cope with a given stimulus, he will tend to become angry, whereas if he feels inadequate he will tend to become afraid.

The discussion so far has dealt with general causes of fear. It is a strange fact, however, that few people appear to have any conception of the specific causes which actually operate in everyday life to arouse fear in human beings. Most people naïvely appear to think of fear as associated with automobile or train accidents, sickness, starvation, being struck by lightning, being bitten by a dog, drowning, or of being attacked by spiders, snakes, burglars, or sex murderers. Yet, as a matter of fact, these factors are relatively infrequent. Obviously they are things to be afraid of, but as causes for the fear actually encountered in the average man they are comparatively rare. On investigation, fear as it occurs daily in the lives of everybody is usually found to be from an entirely different set of causes. It is far more likely to be: fear of being disliked, fear of ridicule, fear of teasing, fear of being misunderstood, fear of hurt feelings, fear of disapproval, fear of sarcasm, fear of being bossed, of being imposed upon, fear of loneliness. Or there is the "loss" group: fear of loss of love, loss of power, loss of prestige, etc. These are the threats which, far and away, arouse the most fear in everyday life.

Among these causes, there is one in particular which is of such importance that it will be singled out for special comment. As was mentioned in Chapter 12, the psychiatrist is constantly struck with the amount and ferocity of anger produced by domination and coercion. This being the case, it logically follows that the *danger of domination* should arouse the greatest amount of fear in people. And indeed such appears to be the case. The most extreme fear seen in people, the fear that totally incapacitates them, not for minutes or hours, but for months and years, seems to be most frequently traced to this cause. Fear of this type is usually referred to as fear of loss of personality, and, put in other words, it means fear that one's ego will not survive, that one's free will is then lost. As will be seen in the next section on anxiety, one of the chief threats to the survival of a personality comes from the individual himself, but the threat in this respect, it may be mentioned here, comes from the domination by other people. Domination of this sort sometimes occurs in the form of commands or orders, and is a conscious open domination. More frequently, however, it is the domination by suggestion or domination by *threat of disapproval* or *threat of hurt feelings.*

The individual who is threatened feels that he never has a chance to decide things for himself. He either has to do what he is told or he receives so many good suggestions that he is hard put to it to find a course of action that has not already been suggested. Or else he feels that he has to do what other people want him to do, or expect him to do, for fear of arousing their disapproval, or hurting their feelings. For one reason or another, he is so busy doing what other people want him to do that he feels in danger of losing the capacity to have any wants of his own. He seems to be in peril of becoming merely a reflection or an appendage of another's personality and ceasing to exist in his own right. The greater the wisdom of the suggestions which thus assail him, the greater the panic, for if the suggestions have encompassed the entire field of rational behavior, to do something on his own, he may be forced into irrational behavior or into behavior of which he himself disapproves. He thus feels trapped, and the fear may mount to fantastic proportions.

Another source of fear which is important enough to receive special mention is the *feeling of inadequacy.* This is a nonspecific and perhaps vague-sounding source of fear, yet it is encountered frequently. Assailed by a feeling of general helplessness, the person feels he lacks the technique to "cope with things," so that he is in constant fear of something turning up which he cannot handle. He feels inadequate to protect himself from the threats and difficulties of everyday life, and so exists in a state of continuous apprehension and worry. It is the very nonspecific nature of this fear, perhaps, which makes it so distressing, The person is afraid without knowing of what he is afraid. There are thus no checks to his imagination; he has encountered fear of the unknown, which his thoughts may seize upon and pyramid until he is reduced to a state of panic.

Before closing the discussion on the causes of fear, there are two more points to be mentioned briefly. As in the case of anger, the situation is the same whether the threat of harm is intentional or unintentional; fear will occur in either case. Miss Brown may be just as afraid of being unintentionally ignored by certain people as of being deliberately snubbed by them. Going a step further, Miss Brown may be acutely afraid of being teased even if the motive for the teasing is "good"—if, for example, a parent or friend teases her "for her own good." In this way a person may be afraid of someone whom he knows loves him and intends him no harm.

A final point is that the time element must also be considered in relation to the causes of fear. The stimulus may be in the present, in the future on the basis of anticipation, or in the past on the basis of memory. Although no danger actually threatens in the present, a person may be afraid that a danger will threaten in the future. Likewise, though a danger no longer threatens, a person may detect his heart pounding, his hands sweating, his mouth dry at the recollection of a "close shave" in the past.

## ANXIETY

In the preceding section the various dangers which arouse fear in human beings were enumerated. One danger, however, was omitted. It will be noted that the dangers which were described were all dangers from the outside. Of equal, or perhaps even greater importance, are the dangers which threaten from the inside. A nation is even more apt to be assailed by dangers from within, the dangers of internal dissension, than by dangers from without. The threat from inside is no less real in the case of the individual man. As was described in

Chapter 12, each man bears within him forces of self-destruction which comprise an ever-present danger to his survival. This internal danger is no less a source of fear than any outside danger. The fear that is generated in this way is usually called anxiety (though this term also is applied frequently to fear from other sources).

One of the most common examples of anxiety is seen in the case of fear of heights. Why a man perched on the edge of a cliff from which there is a thousand-foot drop should be scared is not difficult to understand, because obviously he is in danger of falling off and being killed. It is not uncommon, however, for individuals to manifest equal degrees of fear when there is a solid railing on the edge of the cliff so that there is actually very little danger of falling off and being killed. This fear is very difficult to understand unless one thinks, not in terms of falling, but in terms of jumping off the cliff. The railing might make it quite difficult to fall off, but would not prevent its being frighteningly easy to jump off. The same situation holds for climbing ladders. It is very easy to hold onto the rung of a ladder and very difficult to fall off as long as one does hold on; but it is also very easy to let go one's hold on the ladder and break one's neck. The danger in these situations lies, therefore, in the individual himself rather than in the situation. The situation is dangerous only in the potential power it delegates to the person's impulses. It is quite true that a person suffering from a fear of heights in this way may be totally unaware of this impulse within him which makes the situation dangerous. All he is aware of is the fear which often seems, even to him, inappropriately great.

These examples are relatively obvious. They both concern danger to an individual arising from impulses within him the pursuance of which would lead to his destruction. It is not necessary, however, to use such an extreme word as "destruction"; the word "harm" may be substituted so that the concept broadens. *Anxiety* is caused by an impulse the pursuance of which would lead to the person's *harm*. The impulses which are most apt to arouse fear in this way are hostile or anger impulses. Obviously, if the anger is directed toward the individual himself, in one of the patterns described in Chapter 12, so that the person has a direct impulse to harm himself, this impulse comprises a real danger which will arouse fear.

Thus, for instance, the feeling of guilt practically always involves both the emotion of anger and of fear or anxiety. The individual is impelled to punish himself, but he also fears that punishment. Stated in different terms, just as a person may fear the criticism of others, he may fear self-criticism. He may be afraid of not living up to his own code, his own ideals. He has a fear of his own conscience. The more strict his standards the more fear he is apt to suffer. He knows that if he does not live up to his standards, his conscience will bother him. If it is a harsh conscience, it may do more than bother him; it may hound and torture him. He is thus afraid that he will slip from the mark and thus afford his conscience a chance to get at him. But at the risk of making the matter too complicated, another point must be mentioned. Not only may a person be in constant fear of not following the dictates of his conscience, he may also be afraid of what may happen if he does follow them. It was mentioned in the section on causes of fear that one of the chief threats to survival of one's sense of being somebody was domination. A person who is being told constantly what to do and what not to do may be in acute fear that he will lose his sense of identity. The same danger may threaten him from an excessively strict and arbitrary conscience. His conscience is constantly telling him what he ought to do and ought not to do so that he feels the same acute fear. Shoulds and oughts so surround him that he feels in danger of being stifled. He feels bound, unable to act of his own free will, and loses a sense of individuality. He is trapped on both sides; he fears to obey his conscience and he fears to disobey it.

Anger directed at objects or persons other than himself may also be dangerous to an individual, though here the danger is indirect. For example, Mr. A. may find that he becomes tense and anxious in the presence of his boss. There is no evidence that the boss is anything but friendly toward him, so that the anxiety appears inappropriate. Its cause is to be found not in the boss, but in Mr. A. himself. Mr. A., for some reason or other, feels angry at the boss. This anger is dangerous to him because, were he to let it out at the boss, he might be fired from the job. In the same way, a woman may detect in herself a feeling of anxiety when she is in the presence of her husband. This fear may not come from any present danger of the husband's hurting her, but from the danger of her hurting her husband. If she is angry at him and, particularly, if she is not aware of this anger, there is the danger that she will hurt him, which is something she does not want to do, because then she might lose his love or he might become angry at her and retaliate. Actually, whenever a person becomes angry, he may simultaneously become afraid because of the danger inherent in the anger.

The concept of anxiety becomes enlarged still further, however, when it is realized that anger is not the only impulse the pursuit of which may be harmful. Sexual impulses, for instance, are a prominent source of anxiety. The impulse to masturbate, if it is believed that pursuance of this urge is harmful, may arouse acute anxiety. Mr. X. in Chapter 11, on detecting sexual feelings aroused by seeing his neighbor's wife sunbathing in the yard, may be afraid that he cannot avoid becoming involved in a scandal that might break up his home.

Even the impulse of curiosity impelling a boy to read his brother's diary, if he is conscientious, may arouse not only fear of the brother's indignation, but his own self-criticism, were he to give in to the impulse.

The emotion of fear itself is also a most common cause of anxiety. If a man detects in himself the impulse to run away, he tends to become afraid that he actually will run away, an act which might be considered cowardly and lead to loss of prestige both with himself and others. Thus there develops fear of fear.

## FEAR VERSUS COWARDICE

This section will deal with an elaboration of the preceding paragraph. Fear of fear is so important in its effect on behavior that it calls for special consideration.

One of the most interesting features of the problem is that fear of this type rests to a large degree upon a misconception, a misconception which is so widespread that it could almost be said to involve an entire culture. This misconception, stated simply, is that fear and cowardice are the same thing. In our language these terms are used almost synonymously: "He is afraid = He's a coward"; "He's scared = He's yellow"; "He's frightened = He's a weakling." Because of the failure to distinguish between fear and cowardice, all the scorn and disapproval of cowardice are commonly also applied to fear as well. Children are brought up to be ashamed of one and of the other without any difference being made between the two. The ideal of bravery and courage is considered identical with the ideal of fearlessness.

Very few children at one time or another are able to avoid such a taunt as: "You're afraid to climb the tree." The usual words used in reply are: "I am not afraid to climb the tree." This statement has two quite different meanings. One is that the prospect of climbing the tree does not engender the feeling of fear. The other is that fear, though present, is not going to prevent the child from climbing the tree. If the first statement is literally true, and the child actually is not afraid of the prospect, even though it is a high tree from which he might easily fall and break his neck, then the child is not a courageous, brave little child; he is either stupid or grossly deficient in the estimation of distances and familiarity with the laws of gravity. To be afraid when there is something to be afraid of is not evidence of cowardice, but of intelligence. Whether the child actually climbs the tree or not, however, is an entirely different matter which *is* specifically related to cowardice. It is not what the child feels that determines whether or not he is a coward, but what he does. No matter how acutely the child is suffering from the presence of fear, it is always possible for him actually to climb the tree, or at least try to climb it. He might even climb it more successfully than if he felt no fear, because he would exercise greater care. And certainly he would be more courageous. Who is more brave, the unemotional boy, apathetic to danger, who climbs the tree without effort, or the frightened boy, acutely aware of his peril, who climbs the tree in spite of his fear, fighting every inch of the way?

The training of children by parents plays an important role in this respect. When the child says, "Oh, Mummy, I'm afraid to go in that room, it's all dark," the reply is apt to be, "Don't be silly, there is nothing to be afraid of, you aren't afraid." This reply is inaccurate because if there were no cause for fear the child would not be afraid. That darkness is not a cause for fear in an adult does not mean that it is not for a child. The reply which would more closely follow the facts and be of more help to the child would be, "of course you're afraid, dear, but let's go into the room anyway." To tell a frightened person he is not afraid, because there is nothing to be afraid of, is like telling a hungry person he is not hungry; he just thinks he is.

The confusion on the subject probably rests to an even greater degree, however, on the common failure to distinguish between the impulse to do something and the actual doing of it. People feel that to be afraid is to act afraid, that to be shy is to act shy, that to feel like running away is not very different from actually running away. The matter is complicated by another factor, that of *appearing* afraid. There are, therefore, three aspects of the situation all of which are quite different: (1) being afraid, (2) appearing afraid, (3) acting afraid. As was described in Chapter 11 on the general characteristics of emotion, it is impossible for an individual to prevent himself from being afraid. He may succeed in avoiding stimuli to fear, but once a stimulus to fear has occurred, there is nothing he can do to prevent the response of fear. He can deny its presence, ignore it, or pretend it is not there, but it will nevertheless occur. Certain individuals may be more successful in not appearing afraid or not showing their fear. This depends upon the strength of the fear and the amount of effort they have concentrated on this problem, but the tenseness of the voice, the dilation of the pupils, the trembling of the hands may be beyond control. The third point, however, offers much more chance of success. It is possible for most individuals to develop sufficient control over what they say and what they do to avoid being overwhelmed and incapacitated by the fear, without diminishing its value in contributing to alertness and hence survival. Certainly fear does not prevent bravery; fright and courage go hand in hand, and the common belief that heroes are fearless is erroneous. The most daring acts of heroism recorded are not infrequently performed by individuals in whom the main motive is to prove to themselves and others, not that they have no fear, but that they can overcome fear. Even severe "stage fright" is not inconsistent with excellent artistic performance. One famous opera singer of our acquaintance, though a professional of many years' experience, a half hour before her cue is invariably assailed with overpowering fear, causing her to tremble, her hands to perspire, and her mouth to become dry. On more than one occasion she has actually engaged the services of friends forcibly to push her onto the stage. When finally there she sings her part to perfection.

Another aspect of the problem is the common failure fully to appreciate the survival value of fear. To do things motivated by fear is considered cowardly and despicable, and yet if our prehistoric ancestors had not constantly escaped, run away, fled, and avoided dangers, the race would not have survived, and we would not be here today to scorn this type of behavior. Those individuals whose self-respect depends upon never flinching, never escaping, never avoiding danger may preserve their self-respect, but they are not apt to preserve their lives, let alone their jobs, their families, or their fortunes. Just as there are some situations when the thing to do is to fight, there are other situations where the thing to do is to run away.

The belief that it is possible to prevent oneself from becoming afraid combined with the belief that fear and cowardice are the same thing tends to produce the following consequences. First, in these circumstances a person is apt to try to prevent himself from becoming afraid. As we have seen, the inevitable result of this endeavor is failure, with the further result that effort and energy thus wasted are diverted from the task of controlling speech and behavior in which their chances of success would have been greater. A second consequence is that in these circumstances a person is constantly trying to do the impossible. He is in the predicament of constantly demonstrating to himself his failure and helplessness. Every time he tries to prevent himself from becoming afraid he demonstrates his inability to do so, with the consequent lowering of self-esteem and self-confidence. Still another consequence is actually to increase the amount of fear. Most people are afraid of being cowards, but a person who believes that fear and cowardice are synonymous will be afraid of being afraid. This person will be afraid not only of being harmed, but of the fear of being harmed. The fear of cowardice may be much greater than the fear of bodily injury, for instance, and people commonly subject themselves to all sorts of dangers and risks merely to prove that they are not cowards. But the confusion of thought here is apparent. People try to prove they are not cowards by trying to prove they are not afraid. If they would concentrate on proving they are not cowards and not bother to prove they are not afraid, their chances for success would be infinitely greater.

In World War I, 110,137 soldiers in the United States Army were incapacitated for service by nervous and mental disorders. In World War II, 380,000 men were discharged for neuropsychiatric reasons. Billions of dollars were spent on veterans disabled because of psychiatric disorders. "Shell shock" or "combat fatigue" were important factors, though, of course, many other conditions were shown to be in operation. A pattern in a very large proportion of them was found to center about the subject under discussion—fear of fear and the confusion between fear and cowardice.

Private Jones, waiting in a trench for the whistle to blow which signals the order to go over the top in a charge at an enemy machine gun nest, becomes aware that his mouth is dry, his hands are trembling, his heart thumping. The thought presents itself—"Am I a coward?" If for him fear indicates cowardice, these physical sensations would tend to answer the question in the affirmative. However, Jones has the type of pride and degree of patriotism which makes it impossible for him to admit that he is a coward. He would rather die than be a coward. And since he cannot admit he is a coward, he cannot admit that he is afraid. He attempts to ignore the physical sensations and to deny the fear. As we have seen, however, he is bound to lose this fight; fear mounts on fear until the resulting feelings and physiological disturbances cannot be ignored. He then is apt to take the step that leads to neurosis. Forced to deny that the physical sensations are due to fear, he attributes them to physical disease, heart trouble ("soldiers' heart"), disease or injury of the nervous system. This natural and unconscious wish to be rescued from his predicament facilitates the belief that he has physical disease, for the latter may mean his release from duty and removal to a base hospital. If this occurs he is removed both from the danger of being killed and the danger of being a coward and yet he can retain his self-respect. He is able to believe—"The reason I did not go over the top was because I was sick, not because I was a coward."

The way out of the dilemma, then, is to accept fear, to accept it as a biological asset in the struggle for survival. To say—"Of course I am afraid, so what?"—"Yes, I am afraid, now what am I going to do about it?"—"Yes, I am afraid, but it is what I *do* about it that determines whether I am a coward."—"I cannot stop myself from being afraid, but I can prevent myself from being a coward."—"I am shy, but I do not therefore necessarily need to *act* shyly." Private Jones should say—"Sure I'm scared, I'm scared as hell! BUT I'm going over the top anyway!"

# PART IV

# Mental Mechanisms Which the Personality Utilizes to Meet Conflicting Urges and Difficulties in Everyday Life

*Chapter 14*

# REGRESSION OR
# EXAGGERATED EMOTION

*In which the various methods of evading the con-
flict are enumerated, and the disadvantages of Regression, the first mental hazard, are considered.*

CONFLICT, AS WE SAID, ALTHOUGH INEVITABLE FOR EVERY ADULT
human being, is a source of dissatisfaction and unhappiness. It is
true that it may be often an incident in progress. When, however,
there is conflict there is tension, uneasiness, and restlessness; frequently irritability and nervousness; and even nervous disorder if the
conflict reaches a certain degree. The conflict need not always be
clearly recognized by us, just as many of our own tendencies, for
example biases, prejudices, and the like, are not always fully realized.
The mind attempts to reach a point of equilibrium by balancing the
elements of conflict. It tries to resolve it. By so doing, it reaches a
working arrangement or compromise of opposing tendencies. Peace
and satisfaction, at least temporarily, are purchased. The wild animal
flees before danger. So does the human being. But he does not necessarily have to flee physically. He may disguise or hide himself or
throw his pursuers off the track by a ruse. So, also with mental dangers,
the mind may employ a certain cunning or stratagem in meeting
them. The mind has certain typical methods of meeting apparent
danger, avoiding unpleasant situations, and solving perplexing problems. They are automatic mental manipulations and compensations of
ideas and tendencies in the face of psychological stresses, just as

automatic as the body's readjustment to maintain its physical equilibrium. There are ways of arriving at this state of security which are common to all of us. They will be easily recognized after they are pointed out. Some are sensible and satisfactory, others are the reverse. Let us enumerate the typical ways of meeting conflicts.

1. Regression
2. Extroversion
3. Introversion
4. Rationalization
5. Segregation or the development of logic-tight compartments
6. Repression
7. Dissociation
8. Conversion of mental conflicts into bodily symptoms: anxiety, neurasthenia, hysteria
9. Displacement or substitution
10. Projection
11. Identification
12. Inferiority and compensation
13. Sublimation

Each method will be separately discussed (Chaps. 14 through 26).

## REGRESSION OR EXAGGERATED EMOTION

Literally, to regress means to go backward. In psychology it signifies a return to a former, somewhat primitive, and rather childish type of reaction. A human being behaves regressively when he is "put out," violently angry, "sore," "loses his head." When desire is blocked, when we are irritated, disappointed, or ashamed, then we are tempted to express ourselves emotionally rather than rationally. A man who is cautiously feeling his way through a dark room and barks his shin against a chair may kick the chair violently and swear fluently. Or he may be in a hurry, find the gas tank of the car empty, and indulge in vehement protests and vociferations before proceeding with the only logical thing to do, namely, go in search of gasoline. Whenever we meet sudden and unforeseen obstacles and checks, we all feel angry. And the anger often results in certain forms of irrational and ineffective behavior. There may be merely much useless and loud talk or there may be kicking, banging, breaking, and slapping. The workman who blames his tools and smashes them when he does his work poorly is showing regression. A noted tennis player made himself very unpopular because, when there was an adverse decision after a hard-played point, he invariably threw his racquet on the ground. A very intelligent woman, from time to time, forgets her intelligence and her usual good judgment and resorts to tears when faced with trivial difficulties concerning the servants.

At one time or another every one of us may lapse into childish or even infantile behavior. Such behavior is not rational. It is surcharged with emotion. In one sense it is instinctive, as distinct from thoughtful. It does not at all help us out of the predicament or trying situation. It only delays right and inevitable action. We may "blow off" steam but after we have "shot off" or "lost our heads" the unchanged problem is still in front of us. The regressive action is ineffective and procrastinating. Often it is humiliating. Later we are, or should be, ashamed that we have so far lost control of ourselves.

We expect to find regression during childhood. Fewer logical reactions are available for the child. The boy wants to go out and play at bedtime. His parents forbid it. He cries—to no purpose, if his parents are sensible. The little girl wants more candy than is good for her. It is refused. She sulks and makes a fuss about going to bed. The youngster in his teens wants to be captain or first batter. His teammates decide otherwise. He won't play—like Achilles.

The adult wants to be chairman of a committee; the vote is against him. At once he resigns and gives up the work which is really close to his heart. The wife wants a new hat. The husband inveighs against "extravagance." She becomes hysterical. The husband wants to spend the evenings at the lodge or club. The wife wants him to remain at home. He raves about the poor cooking, the chilliness of the house, the lack of interesting things to do at home.

In regression there is an inordinate or excessive emotional response. It is out of all proportion to the stimulus and in the long run is not useful. One gains relief and a false and temporary resolution of difficulties and conflicts, but the solution is neither adequate nor permanently satisfactory. Such reactions have their humorous side— if one is not the actor.

There was a young lady of Bicister,
One day when her lover had kissed her
She felt much perplexed,
And to show she was vexed
She gave such a slap to her sister.

No human being may hope wholly to escape regression. In its occasional and not overserious manifestations it does no great harm. If, however, it is employed as a constant method of avoiding conflicts, it leads to maladjustment and unhappiness. There are many stone walls in the life path of every human being, but they cannot be beaten down by puny blows from the childish fists of anger, melted away by a flood of tears, or frightened away by sulking. *The walls remain.* The mental status of the individual is diminished by repeating such emotional exhibitions. His mental strength is a bit decreased. He becomes less capable of surmounting life's difficulties.

We do not intend to suggest that regression may lead to mental disease. In itself, it does not. It is interesting to observe, however, that in the most serious form of mental disease (schizophrenia), the patient regresses to very simple, childish, and even infantile behavior.

The reader may ask this question: "What am I to do about it?— When I am crossed or defeated, I easily become angry or hurt, and before I know it, I am swearing or crying, or I have broken something."

It is true that once the habit is formed, the emotional outburst may follow at once upon the heels of the stimulus. But there should come after-reflection. The intelligence should sit in sober judgment and consider the incident in all its unflattering implications. What has been gained? Nothing at all. What has been lost? The individual feels ashamed before the critique of his self-ideal. He has created a new conflict. Temporarily at least, he has forfeited the respect of those who observed his behavior. Finally, he has not achieved his object. The memory of such a conflict, the recollection of humiliation, and the feeling of shame can in the future act as a safeguarding and controlling stimulus or factor in a new situation which might tend to call out regressive behavior. Such intelligent after-analysis will materially discourage regressive tendencies.

*Chapter 15*

# THE EXTROVERT AND HIS
# PURSUIT OF ACTIVITY

*Wherein is described the* Extrovert, *and the advantages and dangers of his favorite and typical method of meeting the daily problems of life.*

IN CHAPTER 14 WE SAW ONE OF THE WAYS IN WHICH THE MIND seeks equilibrium and harmony in the presence of difficulties and conflicts. The emotional outburst is a relief—it allows one to "blow off" like the excess steam from a boiler. But it accomplishes nothing constructive, just as steam from the safety valve is not used for driving the engine. The expert fireman is the one who uses his fuel and water economically—who develops enough steam to drive the engine but not continually too much. So with the human mind, the efficient person is the one who understands his motive forces (instincts, complexes, conflicts, emotions, ideas) and knows when he is getting up more steam than is necessary. The trouble with most of us is that we get up more steam than is required and then only regret it after it has blown off. The person who continually blows off steam is not an attractive person. It is by not paying sufficient attention to the fires that we suddenly find them red hot. The same applies to the emotions.

But there is another way of resolving difficulties and apparently getting out of trouble which the mind frequently employs. Instead of recourse to emotion it turns to excessive activity. It tries to distract itself by the assumption of feverish activity.

*155*

## EXTROVERSION AND OVERACTIVITY

We might write technically and refer to this method as a flight into
*extroversion*. A frequent example in a mild form is the person who
must continually walk about the room when he is thinking over a
difficult problem. There are businessmen who must pace up and
down when they dictate letters. They find relief in extra activity.
Talking beyond the point is a favorite device of the extrovert. Sometimes in conversation when one is about to be proved wrong, he may
begin to talk rapidly and volubly about a distantly related subject. A
pupil writes profusely about the battle of Gettysburg when asked to
discuss the battle of the Wilderness. A medical student was asked to
describe psychasthenia (which he did not know) and he gave a
splendid description of hysteria (which he knew). The politician is
asked a searching and embarrassing question and discourses elo-
quently on patriotism. A clever joke or humorous reply disarms the
critic. Crowds and mobs may be distracted and swayed by such in-
genuities. Activity is often used personally and socially as a blind or
decoy. It has its extreme pathological manifestations. In acute mania
(manic-depressive psychosis) the patient is in a state of frenzied and
mercurial activity of thought, mood, and act. Psychologically, it is
probable that he is making a desperate effort to keep disquieting dissatisfactions and fears out of the mind.

Naturally, there are varying degrees and kinds of extroversion.
The businessman whose home life is unhappy may fill his evenings
with business engagements and social affairs. By arranging full day
and evening schedules, his mind is kept occupied and he avoids
thinking so much of marital friction.

Women, dissatisfied with the humdrum duties of running the
home, may plunge feverishly into various aspects of community and
social life. Teas, parties, bridge, country-club affairs, dinners, theater,
night clubs follow each other madly, one close upon the heels of the
other during all the waking hours of the day and most of the sleeping
hours of the night. Work, jobs, and even careers may have as their
stimulus a need for diversion. In them may be found a refuge from
the trouble and responsiblity of home and children. Others turn to
women's clubs, charity societies, educational endeavors, in themselves
beneficial and socially wholesome enough, but not to be advised in

excess as an escape from a personal problem in the home. It is often humorous and sometimes a bit sad to see someone trying to arrange the lives of others as a substitute for his or her own life.

## THE EXTROVERT

The behavior we have described is characteristic of extroverts or "outward" people. They are bright, cheerful, sociable, active—the executives and effective people who get routine things done in the world. They have strong feelings and express them readily. If they are with you they are strong for you; if against you they are bitter. It is not hard to tell where they stand on an issue. But their feelings are often only transitory. They do not usually hold grudges. They get over their antagonisms and their enthusiasms. They are not usually reflective, and can decide things readily when others waver. One can observe them early in life as the active, noisy, expressive infants and children.

The type we have described is closely related to the emotionally regressive one. It is a much more wholesome reaction as a rule than the former. We have seen that the mind and brain of man seems to have developed in order that he might live more fully, i.e., that he might adapt himself more effectively to his environment. The environment of nature and society, things and people, he tries to understand and control in order that he may live more successfully. Now, the extrovert turns to doing things in the physical or social world in the face of trouble. It is obvious that many of the activities of the extrovert, even if done merely as a refuge, are more valuable for himself and for society in general than are mere emotional explosions. We are thinking, feeling, and doing creatures, and we are not meant to let one of these functions crowd out the place of the others. A mother who, having lost her only child, devotes her time, thoughts, and money to the community life, in developing health and happiness in other children, is clearly acting more satisfactorily, both from the social and personal points of view, than the woman who retires passively into melancholic brooding and weeping. It should be borne in mind, however, that action that is socially praiseworthy may be personally inadvisable if the driving force is unconscious escape from personal conflicts. It may be the right thing from both points of view and even as a solution of conflict, but it should be followed only after deliberation and understanding of the conflict.

There is considerable normal extroverted activity in everyday life. If, however, this tendency to overactivity becomes excessive, then in times of great stress and strain, it is too readily adopted. It is wise to recognize our typical reactions to the small problems of life so that we may be able to meet successfully the greater ones.

As has been indicated, extroverted activity, if not carried to an extreme degree, may be a useful method of meeting mental dissatisfactions and conflicts. Temporarily, at least, the mind may be wholesomely diverted from a personal problem, which seems to be literally without an answer. Solace may be found in new channels of activity. Without doubt, not only individuals but society and civilization have been enriched and advanced by the energy and accomplishment which comes from the spur and lash of serious conflicts in our inner mental lives. It is not too much to say that in many fields of human endeavor—in art, painting, poetry, and music—the throes and sufferings of the soul have been transmuted into beautiful pictures, immortal words of song and prose, and glorious symphonies of sound. And science, so often thought of as coldly intellectual and, for that matter, even the seemingly mundane activities of commerce are often unquestionably stimulated by human purpose and energy, originally derived from attempts to escape from perplexing, personal mental conflicts.

For some years we have made a careful study of extroverted activity. Often enough it indicates nothing beyond the expression of normality and adjustment in an individual who belongs to the outgoing, social, or extroverted type. There are numerous instances, however, in which it is obviously a psychological mechanism employed by the mind to escape the anguish of serious mental crosspurposes.

## DANGERS OF EXTROVERTED ACTIVITY

Sometimes, extroverted activity is purposeful, useful, helpful, and constructive. Sometimes it is purposeless, useless, harmful, and destructive. There are individuals who turn feverishly from one thing to another. There are human beings who frantically pursue lines of activity for which they are obviously unfitted. Finally, not only in literature but also in actual life, there are examples of extroverted conduct which strike at the very foundations of society. The classical siren visits unhappiness and even death upon other men, because her love has been spurned and her honor betrayed by her first lover. In Eugene O'Neill's *The Strange Interlude,* Nina prostitutes herself and harms those whose life paths cross hers, since she cannot accept the untimely death of her lover Gordon.

Is there a way in which we may protect ourselves against the dangers of extroversion? May it be made personally and socially acceptable and constructive? May we avoid the snare of endlessly turning from one activity to another without satisfaction or purpose? May we escape the pitfall of engaging in pursuits for which we are not suited?

There is this to be said. When extroversion is utilized to escape from an intolerable conflict, then *the activity is effective and constructive in proportion to the degree of realization and understanding with which the individual has faced his conflict.* He will then be safeguarded against extreme overactivity, against an increase in personal dissatisfaction, against unwise spheres of action.

Sometimes the necessary knowledge may be gained by taking counsel with self. In more serious situations psychotherapeutic help may be needed. It may be added that there is the temptation to avoid a survey of the conflict. It need not and should not be endlessly reviewed, but some conscious appreciation of its nature and import constitutes the proper point of departure for extroverted activity.

A diagram (Fig. 15) may serve to put one or two aspects of the situation before the reader in graphic form.

Let the hexagon A represent an individual who has a serious personal conflict. Because he is of the extroverted type, he naturally turns to extroverted activity—a flight into extroversion to escape from his conflict. Let B, C, D, E, F, G, H, I, J represent a few of the many paths of endeavor which are available to human beings.

Some of these paths (occupations) are suitable for A.'s capacity and personality; others are not so suitable; a few are utterly impossible. A. could not possibly fit satisfactorily into them. For instance, he could never force himself into E, F, or H.

Now, if A. refuses to face his conflict in consciousness or, at best, takes a furtive and frightened look at it and then goes into action, he will run into difficulties.

His troubled mind takes the merest glance at the various paths spread out before him. They all seem about the same to him. He does not look farther. He cannot see at all that he will not fit into some of the paths. He simply plunges in—running away from trouble

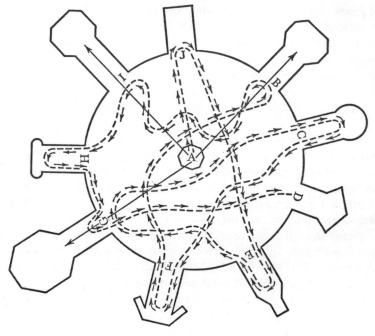

*Figure 15*

and into more trouble. He finds no relief and turns in another direction and still another and another. His probable course is illustrated by the arrows along the dotted line.

Suppose, however (either without or with help), A. faces his conflict openly and intelligently. This may not make the conflict any easier to bear, but, even if it does not, it opens the way for rational instead of illogical activity. Then he is much more likely to observe some selection in the type of activity, and there is much more likely to be relief and satisfaction for the individual. Such a course is represented by the straight lines.

## Chapter 16

# INTROVERSION, FANTASIES, AND DAYDREAMS

*In this chapter is pictured the* Introvert, *wielding his most powerful weapon,* Thought, *with which he fights the battles of his mental life. The strengths and the flaws of this weapon are discussed. Finally, there is considered the utility of a balanced personality.*

WE HAVE PICTURED TWO HYPOTHETICAL INDIVIDUALS SEEKING TO escape from their conflicts. The one dropped to the level of childhood behavior, that is, he regressed; the other ran away and attempted to cover his flight from himself and others by a tremendous outburst of activity. A third method of eluding difficulties is to think about them excessively or intellectualize them.

"Talk it over before you act," is a motto of the introverts. The "dyed-in-the-wool" introvert, however, will not talk it over with others but only with himself. "Think before you leap" is a common expression "Think twice before you do that." In these expressions, common sense indicates that emergencies are not always best solved by emotion and immediate action. Thought, it implies, not only often clarifies a situation but robs it of excessive emotional tension. The final result is usually more effective, and there are fewer occasions for regret.

Thought, then, de-energizes situations and conflicts. A situation that is tense and evokes emotional and instinctive reactions can often be rendered more or less harmless by thinking about it. As drugs and

*161*

sera counteract poisons in the body, so do ideas detoxicate us emotionally. Webster says that intoxication is a state of being emotionally wrought up. Thinking often helps us to become unwrought. It untangles emotional situations and renders them innocuous.

We may think of many simple examples. As we walk alone in a forest just as night is descending, a dark mass suddenly appears at the turn of the road and threatens and disputes our progress. "Man" or "wild animal" is the first impression. We are tense, and turn to flee or rush forward to fight. If, however, we can force ourselves to think and not act too hastily, it is discovered that the dark mass is only the large branch of a tree which has recently fallen. At once, the tension and the fear or anger are relieved. The ideas "man" and "animal" are harmless, since nothing has been found to correspond objectively with them.

There is a good illustration of this in *Open House in Flanders* by Baroness Ernest de la Grange.

This morning at dawn, running out with "Mino," I thought I saw a watching figure under the limes. It seemed dressed in grey, knapsack on back, a helmet on the head. It must be a spy, I thought, leaning against the trunk of one of the group of limes which form a graceful cluster around the house. I have kept the Reverend Father Andries with me in case we have to get our invalids down into the cellars, and I begged him to watch the man.

I went out with "Mino," then, and from some feeling, which was not pluck, called to her in German, hoping to soften the spy! As nothing moved, I approached, and saw, not without disgust, that my nerves had played me a trick. My "spy" was the huge knot of a big gnarled tree, and the point of the supposed helmet was a whetstone left there by one of the reapers.

And this reminds me that once, in my childhood, I shrieked for help, believing there was a thief under my bed. But it was only the old watch which my governess had hung at the head of the bed, and which had slipped down. I thought the ticking came from a watch in the pocket of a burglar! Another time I got a terrible fright from hearing the stealthy slipping of a silk petticoat from a chair to the floor. Anything or nothing will make the heart beat too fast when suffering, as we are now, from continual sleepless nights and overwrought nerves.*

* From *Open House in Flanders,* copyright, 1930, by Baroness Ernest de la Grange. Courtesy of Frederick A. Stokes Company, New York.

If two men begin to pass from discussion to heated and vehement argument, the check and calm consideration of one may avoid blows that would have caused chagrin and irreparable damage. In any game of skill—football, golf, basketball, tennis, when the sides happen to be evenly matched, nine times out of ten, the side that "keeps its head," i.e., thinks, will win. A great golf champion continually lost his matches until he learned to ignore the "gallery" and *think*. So it is in the game of life.

Think how much we should save ourselves, if instead of leaping to conclusions we should stop and deliberate. A hasty word may lead to chagrin, embarrassment, and even shame. A moment's thought would have provided a satisfactory explanation. Many regrets and much unhappiness would be avoided, if, instead of quick assumption followed by mean insinuation or sudden accusation, time would be taken more often for second thought.

The above uses of thinking are to be regarded as wholesome and normal. They preserve a balance among thinking, feeling, and doing. But there are other uses whose value becomes increasingly doubtful.

There are people who appear to think, not merely to ensure effective action, but apparently for the sake of delaying or avoiding action. They are the individuals who analyze situations, problems, and motives ad infinitum. This is the type of person who gets lost in details. They see too much pro and con. There is indecision and wavering. They become so entangled in problems that action rarely or never occurs. If attempts at action are made, they are often feeble and inadequate. Fundamentally, these people seem to lack the ability to face problems and make decisions. We all know those who cannot say "yes" or "no" to a fairly simple question. There are others who are given plans to execute but they come to naught. A man may try to write a book and become submerged in details, or see too many debatable points. To this group, too, belong the people who appear to prefer to talk rather than act.

Thinking, then, employed to check spontaneous and hasty action, and to clarify issues, is fulfilling its proper function. When, however, it is used to dodge issues and avoid making decisions that should be made, it is not only not performing its proper service, but it is untrue to its own *raison d'être*.

## THE INTROVERT

The person who tends to be a thinker rather than a doer is an *introvert*. Introversion means the turning in of the mind or self onto its own problems. The introvert gets his chief pleasures from within himself—the extrovert, from without. The kingdom of the mind and thought, or the external world, are their respective spheres. Thought is pale, nonvital, unreal, to the one. Action is irrelevant or valueless to the other. Introverts are inclined to be cold, apparently gloomy, unsociable, and rather inactive. Their feelings are seemingly not strong and they do not express them readily. They are not the executives who get things done, but the planners and theorists. They are inclined to be the visionaries.

Each of us is more predominantly one or the other of these types, but most of us have elements of both. It is good to know our tendencies with regard to introversion and extroversion so that when we find one side of our nature developing excessively, we may consciously compensate and direct ourselves. One type is not more desirable, admirable, or more useful than the other. The world needs both, like the conservatives and the progressives. The extroverts get things done; they are the executives, the men of the world, the sociable, and cheerful people. The introverts are those who supply innovations and plan for the future. The present belongs to the one, the future to the other. From the lack of sociability, and from their detachment, introverts see more clearly problems and solutions which never occur to the extroverts. The introverts are the dreamers and inventors. Many of the greatest discoveries have been made by them. Both types developed to the extreme are equally useless and harmful; the extrovert in senseless overactivity, and the introvert in aimless fantasy.

If thought becomes developed or exaggerated to the stage of continued fantasy, it is obviously harmful. Then thought is carried on with no reference to possible action and often with little regard to the demands of the physical or the social world. Thought becomes interesting in and for itself. It creates problems for its own amusement. Philosophy, for many, constitutes just such a game of words, concepts, and problems, of highly specialized and often of most limited significance. Philosophy and even fantasy are helpful if they are used for making us happier and more useful citizens of the universe. But when these worlds of thought and dream become the exclusive and supreme interest of the individual, it is unwholesome. We know, too well, the detachment of the dreamers, their lack of concern for the ordinary conventions of life. When such mental problems serve as distractions and alternatives to actual difficulties and conflicts of real life, it is harmful.

Daydreaming is a form of fantasy or thinking for its own sake. It is example of the all-powerfulness of thought. We may picture ourselves as the hero or heroine of a story and derive great pleasure from this. We may imagine that our ambitions are fulfilled; that we have the wealth we desire; that our home is like a palace; that our mother is the fairy godmother; that our lover is a prince; or that we ride in chariots of gold. Thought, like Aladdin's lamp, for these people can make things come true. It is used as magic, but like magic it is not real. Saul's sister in Donn Byrne's *Brother Saul* furnishes a good example of this daydreaming type of thinking.

—She was a dark, secretive girl, intensely Jewish, forever dreaming of bygone glories and plotting for triumphs to come. She was always reading of the Maccabees, and imagining herself one of the flame-like women who sent their menfolk to die defending the city walls, crying "Hear, O Israel, the Lord our God is One!" Or imagining herself as Judith, which was the daughter of Mirari, the son of Ox, who showed proudly the head of Holofernes, the chief captain of the army of Assur, crying "And the Lord hath smitten him by the hand of a woman"; or as Joel, who slew Sisera. Actually she could not bear the sight of blood, and the killing of birds taken in the fowlers' nets. The mention alone of it made her white and dizzy. But *in her mind* she was a *heroine* of the Jews.*

## DANGERS OF INTROVERSION AND THE IMPORTANCE OF BALANCE

Introversion, therefore, as a refuge and escape from conflicts has valuable uses and somewhat serious dangers. Its threat to mental peace is carried by the ever-present temptation to utilize it excessively. In a few words, if carried too far, *nothing is ever done*. The individual

* From *Brother Saul* by Donn Byrne. Courtesy of The Century Company, 1927.

stagnates. Civilization is the loser. Shakespeare's immortal poetry would have meant nothing if it had never escaped the confines of thought and been born onto paper. The most perfect bridge ever devised by the mind of man would have been utterly useless to the world, if its plan had perished with the brain of the engineer. The most altruistic conception would not have spared humanity one whit of suffering, if it had remained a prisoner of thought in the mind of the altruist. Suppose Louis Pasteur had carried, unspoken and unwritten to the grave, his thoughts about pathogenic bacteria and had never activated those thoughts into lifesaving sera?

There is a second danger which follows upon the heels of the first. Even though he may prefer it, still it is true, that the introvert cannot accept (within the sphere of sanity) his own complete inactivity without mental uneasiness and dissatisfaction. He is troubled by the accusing finger of his self-ideal and the disappointment of the herd (society). A very hazardous method of self and social justification is at hand. He may plunge into daydreaming where it *seems to him* that he is in action; that *he is* accomplishing; that his life is not abject failure but soul-satisfying success. It is a subtle poison. If used constantly, it leads to the nirvana of mental nothingness.

Daydreaming at occasional intervals is quite normal, and, as a matter of fact, it may enable us to work and accomplish. If the dream of success leads us to buckle down, work hard, and *compete* for the reward, it is beneficial. If it helps make dreams come true, it is beneficial. But if time on time is spent in daydreaming, unquestionably, we gradually become less and less able to tackle jobs and compete with others. For it is *much easier to imagine* things are so, *than to make* them so. The daydreaming tendency becomes tempting and fascinating like a drug. It becomes more satisfactory and pleasurable to disregard reality and live in the world of fancy. It is enervating and devitalizing but rather pleasantly so. The individual begins to weaken more and more against the buffets and knocks of life. He resents the raps of reality upon the gates of his dream castle. Unsociability develops. Interest in relatives, friends, and the usual things of life is lost. In the presence of his fellows he is uncomfortable and sensitive. With the widening of the breach between reality and unreality, casual and concrete happenings in the everyday world are misinterpreted. Now, we are not so far from the territory of mental

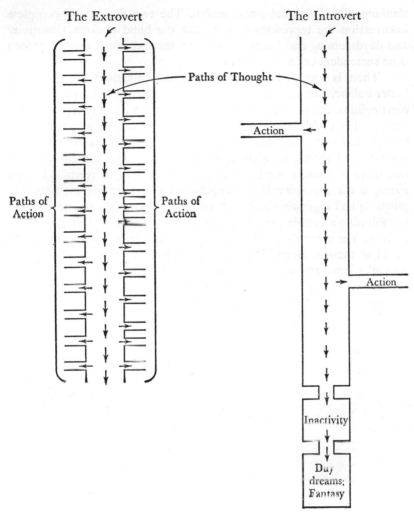

The Extrovert                    The Introvert

Paths of Thought

Action

Paths of
Action

Paths of
Action

Action

Inactivity

Day
dreams;
Fantasy

*Figure 16*

disease, and there may come a day when the gates of the real world
are finally closed and locked forever.

A simple diagram may be used to illustrate the contrasting life
paths of the extrovert and the introvert. The vertical paths represent

*thinking;* the horizontal ones, *action.* The two dangers of complete introversion are represented. They are the blind pockets (inactivity and daydreaming and fantasy) in which the individual may be placed if he surrenders entirely to fantasy (Fig. 16).

There is another lesson to be learned. We should all strive for a better balance between the extroverted and introverted aspects of our personalities. An extrovert cannot be made into an introvert and vice versa. All in all this is fortunate. Much valuable human material would be distorted and destroyed. On the other hand, both the extrovert and the introvert should take stock of each other. The former will find this more difficult, since he does not use thought so readily. In any event, if the inventory is reasonably calm and intelligent, both the outgoing and ingrowing man will be gainers. The one should succeed in inhibiting a certain percentage of useless and thoughtless and futile activity. The other should come to realize that man cannot live by the bread of thought alone. The one should learn to utilize, in some degree, the inner resources of thinking; the other, in some measure, to activate and socialize the self. They will understand each other better. Personally, they will be better adjusted and happier, and each will be able to reap greater profit from the intrinsic assets of his distinctive personality.

*Chapter 17*

# RATIONALIZATION—HOW
# WE DECEIVE OURSELVES

*A brief discussion of Rationalization, a psychological device, that prevents us from seeing ourselves as others see us.*

WE ARE STILL CONSIDERING METHODS OF AVOIDING THE FRICTION and mental dissatisfaction which arise from the existence of conflicts whose opposing elements are apparently irreconcilable. Our instincts, motivations, and driving forces, in general our complexes, are not always "high-minded" or idealistic. Frequently, they would meet not only the disapproval of our own self-ideal, but, also, the condemnation of others (the herd). "Know thyself" is an excellent admonition of mental hygiene, but the psychological mind tends to shrink from too complete and revealing self-knowledge. In addition, since man is gregarious, he will go to great lengths in order to win the approval or, at least, escape the blame of the herd. Another method of avoiding too disturbing recognition of somewhat humiliating personal motives is *rationalization*.

World War I popularized a very expressive word—camouflage. By taking advantage of the laws of perspective, battleships, transports, railheads, roads, gun emplacements, etc., were disguised, and, to the enemy, they appeared innocent and harmless. Rationalization is mental camouflage. It changes and bedecks or camouflages unworthy motivations, so that to others and even to ourselves, they appear satisfactory and even praiseworthy.

*169*

Deception is not an unusual phenomenon of everyday life. Someone asks us to dine. We say we cannot come because of illness or a previous engagement or what not. The real reason is we dislike the giver of the dinner. Or his dinners are dull and uninteresting. A boresome caller comes to the door. The butler is instructed to say, "Madam is not at home." Many such "white lies" are told to save the feelings of others—and to spare ourselves unpleasantness.

A more serious kind of deception is illustrated in this example. The committee is considering the appointment of Mrs. X. to manage the important bazaar of the season. Mrs. Y. remarks that Mrs. X. lives so far out in the country that she could not possibly do justice to the undertaking and in addition she, Mrs. X., is so interested in the art exhibit that she really would not have enough time to run the bazaar effectively. Mrs. Y. has no difficulty at all in thinking up all sorts of reasons, all of which may have a partial basis of truth. But she never breathes (and in fact does not fully realize and acknowledge) her real reasons, namely, that Mrs. X. is getting far too popular and, furthermore, she did not invite Mrs. Y. to her large dance a year ago. Another example: We work hard to elect someone to public office. As we frequently declare, we are so strongly for him because he possesses so many qualifications. We scarcely recognize, even privately, the real, dynamic factor in our partisanship—we are personally deeply indebted to the candidate. We wish to repay the obligation and more firmly entrench ourselves in his favor.

It is clear in the above instances that the real and complete guiding motives were not made known, because they were not admirable and would not have carried much weight in respectable society. Observe that the reasons given were all *socially acceptable*. We make ourselves appear to be better than we really are. We do not like to avow, much less display, our egotistical or baser sides. Therefore, our best foot is forward, and in a sense we put people off the track. In this way, then, hypocrisy has to pay its little homage to virtue. We seek to win social approval by apparently conforming to herd ideas as to what is right and wrong, although we do not wholeheartedly agree.

Now this process of socialization or moralization of our thoughts may go so far that in talking things over with ourselves, or in thinking, we may fail to recognize the actual source of our thoughts and tendencies. This attempt at *self-justification* before the bar of public opinion often merges into *self-deception*. Such self-deception is called *rationalization*. It is the habit of thinking which gives plausible reasons rather than actual ones for our thoughts and behavior.

When people so habitually assign respectable motives for their thought and conduct that they cannot recognize real and fundamental motives, the process has gone too far. Mental harmony or balance then rests on insecure foundations. The unwillingness to recognize the roots of unhappiness and conflict may result in self-deceptions that are quite as unsatisfactory as the original problems. All this, of course, should not be taken to imply that respectable motives may not often be fundamental ones.

The person who has elaborated the recounting of an incident to numerous people finally reaches a stage at which he is not sure of the true details of the original happening. In the same way secondary motives are elaborated and adorned until we are honestly unaware of primary factors. We think we are more altruistic or socially minded than we really are and fail to recognize the elemental drives.

## DEGREES OF RATIONALIZATION

There are all sorts and degrees of rationalization. Behold the man who periodically "swears off" smoking or drinking! Soon, he begins to smoke or drink again. As he says, a friend has given him a box of cigars and it would be ungrateful not to try them, or the men at the club are beginning to think he is too "high hat," or he cannot be the only one to refuse a drink, or one has to be a good fellow, or one has to drink with a customer. All the reasons are plausible reasons to be sure, but none of them gives any indication of the fact that the dominant motive is the desire to resume smoking or drinking.

When true motives are not recognized, we are likely to have rationalization. For example, the mountain climber who is afraid to scale a forbidding peak may be ashamed to acknowledge the fear. He says he is all played out physically and must postpone the ascent. Or the individual with overgrown self-assertion and superiority is unable to complete the task which he has undertaken with such high hopes. He stops abruptly and says the problem has turned out to be not worthwhile. The cynic uses such mechanisms. He treats difficulties as unreal or worthless and thus disposes of his problems. The basis of such action may often be found in some keen disappointment. In humor, difficulties are regarded as jokes and their bitterness is diluted or destroyed.

A miser excuses his sin on the ground that he must provide for his family. As a matter of fact they are more than provided for. A tyrannous foreman declares that, to get out the work, he must enforce rigid discipline. The real reason is an inordinate desire to lord it over others. The same factor may be at work in the home where there is a lord and master. The desire for cruelty and revenge may be masked by mouth-filling phrases of justice and patriotism.

A wife may nag a husband for his demeanor and attire, earnestly believing that these judgments rest on the basis of fact. In truth, she may be unconsciously protesting, because he is not cut after the pattern of her father, whose mold for her contains all that love should desire. Dissatisfaction with wives may have a similar basis. The wife falls too far short of the mother ideal. A man's "interest" in his work or in traveling may be merely a desire to get away from home.

It is apparent, therefore, to what cross-purposes we live if rationalization has come to the point of confusing the real issues of our lives. It is not a satisfactory or desirable method of handling conflicts. It is better to recognize the difficulties and plan our actions clearly and effectively. As has been said by someone, if it is not good to deceive others, still less is it good to deceive ourselves. Certain people, being so accustomed to giving ready-made replies with little regard to the facts, under emotional shocks that exceptionally arise, are unable to analyze situations and see them as they are. Their replies often are stereotyped, show little that is relevant, and offer less that is constructive. The first problem is to get such people to face the facts squarely. Not having been habituated to this for years, it requires considerable time and effort to overcome this unfortunate habit of thought. But the time and effort is worthwhile, and will be reflected in improved mental health.

## DANGERS OF RATIONALIZATION

Perhaps, we may think of two chief degrees of rationalization; mild and severe. In its milder manifestation as an occasional indulgence, it does not do any particular harm and may even help to oil the wheels of social usage. After all, no one is damaged, even if a man rationalizes his real reason for the resumption of smoking after "swearing off." Rationalizations of this kind are especially common a few days after the opening of each new year, when the resolutions begin to irk.

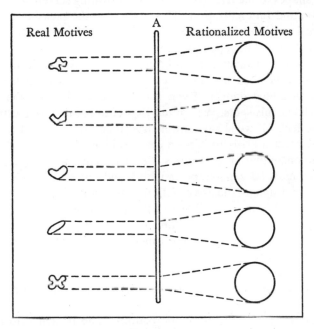

Figure 17

Again, even if a "philanthropist" does not recognize that the moving factor back of his munificent gift to the hospital for crippled children was a love for publicity, no one is much hurt. The crippled children are benefited just the same. While the device of rationalization is always questionable, yet no human being may hope wholly to escape its occasional exhibition.

Rationalization or self-deception becomes serious when it is constantly indulged in. Then, it becomes interwoven into every pattern of the fabric of mental life. Practice makes perfect. The reaction of self-deception may become so habitual that one may conceive of it as a transforming screen between the real person and his self-estimate. This screen changes the appearance of every motive into a form which pleases the individual and gains the approval of society (Fig. 17). Naturally, real motives remain unchanged.

Real motivations may be represented by the designs of odd and various shapes to the left. "A" is the transforming screen which is self-deception and rationalization. The circles are the pleasing forms into which real motives are seemingly transformed, for the satisfaction of the individual and the appeasement of the herd.

When rationalization is so firmly established, that it has become a daily and even an hourly practice, then, as has been mentioned, there is an added danger. Even should the need arise, the leopard cannot change his spots. We cannot expect to break a long-established habit suddenly. If we always rationalize, then, too, we shall rationalize when we meet a crisis in life—a real problem. Each one of us must expect to encounter at least one such crisis. Then we need to face the issue. We must be capable of weighing and contrasting the pros and cons for and against decisive action with some degree of frankness and honesty. We must be able to estimate with some truth the effect of such action upon ourselves and upon others. This we cannot do unless we have acquired at least a moderate amount of facility in the recognition of underlying and real motivations.

The time to break a habit is before it has become a habit. A bit of self-understanding is a valuable check against too complete rationalization.

It may be wise to insert one caution. The person who feels inferior is usually given to self-blame and self-depreciation. He is apt to rationalize in a reverse direction. He suspects and maligns his own motives, when they should not be suspected or maligned. Erroneously, he questions the personal worthiness of his every act. He, too, needs self-understanding, but not in the direction of rationalization.

*Chapter 18*

# SEGREGATION, OR A CERTAIN BLINDNESS TO OUR INCONSISTENCIES

*Wherein is discussed a somewhat hazardous psychological stratagem, with the object of preventing the mental right hand from knowing what the mental left hand is doing. It is called* Segregation.

REFERENCE TO THE FOLLOWING DIAGRAMS MAY PREPARE THE READER for a brief consideration of that method of evading conflicts which is called segregation or the development of logic-tight compartments. It is a curious psychological mechanism of not letting the mental right hand know what the mental left hand is doing. It is a simple and not uncommon method of avoiding difficulties.

The first diagram may represent the mind filled with complexes. They flow into the stream of consciousness and express themselves more or less harmoniously in our everyday life (Fig. 18).

But, as has been indicated, complexes are scarcely ever in complete agreement. In the second diagram the complexes which put forth opposing claims are indicated by paired light and heavy circles. The ensuing conflict is represented by a heavy line. If these conflicts (heavy lines) enter the stream of consciousness in this form they cannot be openly expressed, since they would do violence not only to the self-ideal but also to the code of the herd. An ideal solution (worked out at A) is to face the conflicts frankly in all their implications. This should result in sufficient modification of one or the other of the claims of the conflict, so that they may merge harmoni-

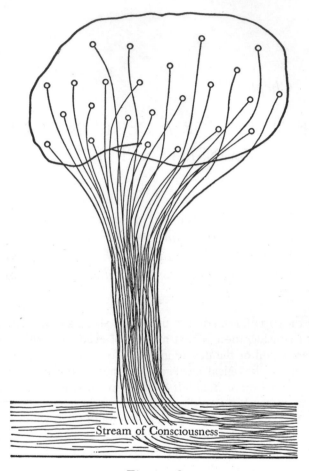

*Figure 18*

ously and be expressed in the stream of consciousness without too much disruption of the personality (Fig. 19).

Often there is not and cannot be an ideal solution. In that case some of the mechanisms already discussed (regression, extroversion, introversion, rationalization) and others, still to be considered, may be utilized in order to escape from the conflict. Let us assume they operate at A. As has been stated, some of them are useful; others are

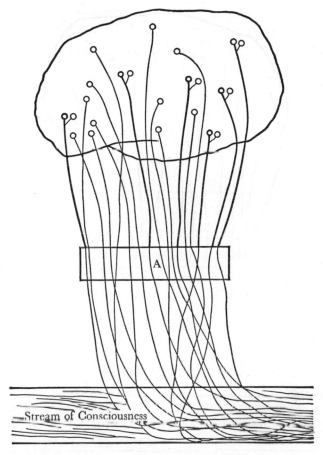

*Figure 19*

futile and even dangerous. None of them is ideal. The conflict (heavy line) is not solved completely but is modified enough (∿∿, ———, -----, ∿∿∿) so that the resultant behavior merges fairly well into the stream of consciousness. This is what the majority of us do with many of our conflicts (Fig. 20).

In the final diagram the method of *segregation* or the *logic-tight compartment* is represented. Conflicts are *not recognized*. They are ignored. They produce a type of conduct which is utterly inconsistent

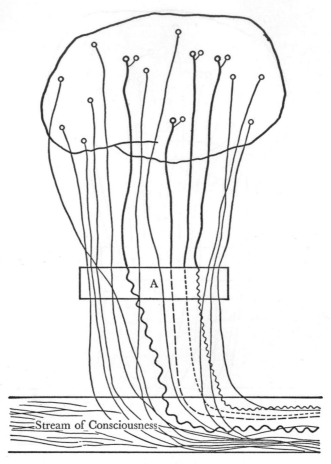

*Figure* 20

with the remainder of the personality. The individual does not recognize the inconsistency. Consciousness flows on in two separate streams, the one independent of and inconsistent with the other. In itself and to the observer, the resultant behavior is quite paradoxical—but not to the individual himself (Fig. 21).

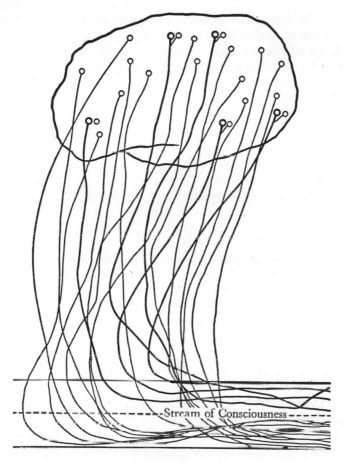

Figure 21

## SEGREGATION AND THE DEVELOPMENT
## OF LOGIC-TIGHT COMPARTMENTS

The fifth method of circumventing conflicts and permitting outlawed complexes to express themselves in consciousness is called *segregation* or the development of *logic-tight* compartments. It is a method somewhat more frequently resorted to by the extrovert. By understanding the mechanism and recognizing it, we may be able to pre-vent its excessive development in ourselves.

Logic-tight compartments involve the frequent or close occur-rence in the mind of thoughts and ideas, plans and tendencies, de-sires and drives that are inconsistent and contradictory. To the de-tached observer it is obvious that the ideas are mutually exclusive. In the presence of one kind of idea, it is reasonable to assume that the individual does not hold, at the same time, the opposite and con-tradictory. But this is exactly what happens in the logic-tight com-partment. For instance, there is the woman who is extremely active in the interests of the poor girls of the city. For them she plans wholesome living conditions and relaxations and diversions. For this purpose she contributes much time, money, and energy. On the other hand, she is personally a hard employer. She drives her own servants. She is exacting as to their work hours. Their living quarters are neither cheerful nor attractive. She gives them neither time nor opportunity for self-improvement. It is astounding that this lady's interest in poor working girls would not include her own servants. But it does not. To them, she is very inconsiderate.

A certain businessman was the leader of the community in a town in the Midwest. He was president of the board of trade, super-intendent of the Sunday school, and a generous contributor to the Boy Scouts. Yet he pressed a very close business deal, and several times ruthlessly ruined competitors. Religion may be love for fellow men on Sunday, but, in this instance, business was strictly business on the remaining six days of the week.

This is the motif of Ibsen's *Pillars of Society*—those who lead double lives or practice secret vices may use this double type of think-ing. The politician who runs his campaign with the slogan "a square deal for the working man" and, then, after he has secured the office, becomes involved in deals which ignore and even harm the worker, is thinking and dealing doubly.

There is an extreme example in the case of the Russian lady, who, inside a comfortable and warm theater, underwent the very throes of anguish at witnessing the imaginary sufferings of one of the actors, while, in the bitter cold outside the theater, her coachman, who had been ordered by her not to leave his exposed seat, slowly froze to death.

Barriers, apparently, may prevent one side of the personality from observing what the other side is doing. Instead of thinking them out and reconciling them or adjusting them consciously, we follow one line of conduct and then another without ever bothering about the inconsistencies. We develop a blindness to our contradictions which may be so patent to others that it becomes humorous— if it is not tragic. The extreme degree of this sort of personality is found in the classic *Dr. Jekyll and Mr. Hyde.*

This process of segregation or the development of logic- and emotion-tight compartments should now be clear. With the average person, the ideas and emotions a man has on Sunday carry over and influence his ideas, emotions, and conduct the rest of the week. There is a more or less harmonious personality with the "good" and "bad" sides exerting a mutual influence on one another. It is a commonplace that often we are different personalities to different people. But in most of us there is a give and take between our two selves. A sort of compromise is reached, which presents a more or less united and consistent front to our friends and associates. At least with the average person there is enough consistency and similarity of purpose, so that he can be counted on by his fellows. He is held to be reliable. His conduct within limits can be predicted by those who know him. This personal consistency and reliability is the essence of character.

With the man who constantly and markedly develops logic-tight compartments, it seems almost incomprehensible that he can be one and the same person. In fact, we often say, "so and so is two absolutely different persons." This type of mind, developed to the extreme, is probably what we find in the so-called psychopathic personalities. They live, many of them, as we do, on the same physical plane, for example, they may talk as we do and be as well educated and informed, but in questions of truth, decency, and morality they behave as people entirely beyond the pale, with ideas, emotions, and actions that seem incompatible and astounding. There is not the least consistency. They are a law unto themselves. Their conduct is highly capricious. They are unreliable, and their behavior cannot be anticipated.

The solution of difficulties by the development of logic-tight compartments is a sort of free and easy way of doing. The lively, carefree, unreflective extrovert can cheerfully adopt such processes.

In a sense he simply refuses to accept the conflicts and inconsistencies. With his pressure for activity and drive to be "up and doing" he solves the conflict by spreading the different and inconsistent tendencies out in time. His mind cannot work out a solution at a given moment, but, by following first one urge and then another in *sequence,* the conflict is resolved for him. Then, with his unreflective habit of mind and a convenient memory, no qualms remain.

We treated a patient, a typical extrovert who had developed a state of mild mental overactivity. Unfortunately, before proper advice could be secured, he had dissipated a large fortune. It was necessary to present the exact facts to him. Seemingly, he grasped them with perfect understanding. Yet, in five minutes, in cheerful and lively fashion, he broached a vacation plan involving the expenditure of thousands of dollars.

## DANGERS OF SEGREGATION

While it may be true that many human beings get through life by building logic-tight compartments, yet this scarcely constitutes constructive living, either for themselves or for others. An occasional lapse into segregation is the lot of everyone. This does not involve any threat to the balance of the personality. A bit of inconsistency, now and then, is not unattractive. It may help to leaven the loaf of daily living. But it is a far cry from this to constant and complete segregation and the endless building of logic-tight compartments. The personality which does this, is hopelessly contradictory and ineffective. Furthermore, it is impractical. The herd disapproves. If the conduct continues, pressure is brought to bear against the offender. The powerful punishment of ostracism is meted out to the culprit. In an extremity, society may even invoke its criminal code.

While segregation is not a cause of mental disease, yet it is classically exemplified in its $n$th degree in the most serious form of mental disease, namely, schizophrenia. Here, the patient may believe herself to be the "Queen of the World" and entitled to homage from all men, yet, she is seemingly content to remain in a mental hospital, eat ordinary food in the dining room with other patients, and, perhaps, each day perform a round of humble duties. In a milder form it is seen in hysterical conditions and in personality disorders.

*Chapter 19*

# REPRESSION—WHY AND WHAT WE FORGET

*On the advantages and disadvantages of "Forgetting."*

IN CHAPTER 18 WE SAW THAT CERTAIN PERSONALITIES PRESENT NO persistent, dominant purpose which unifies their thinking and acting. They are a bundle of obvious and sometimes astounding inconsistencies. They are full of cross-purposes that seem irreconcilable. These different purposes are divided or segregated into logic-tight compartments. They do not have the same influence on one another, as they do in the average, normal individual. Such a mind is like a department store in which the different departments are run on entirely distinctive plans without reference to the others or to unity. The policy of one may be to give good value in the hope of building up the business. The policy of the other may involve getting as much as possible of the purchaser's money irrespective of the value given. A department store with such lack of harmony would not be a success in the long run. Neither is the mind that is so split up. If a house divided against itself cannot stand, neither can a divided personality.

The introvert rarely adopts the segregation method. He is too reflective. He discerns the inconsistencies too keenly. The drive and pressure of activity, since they are not so strongly developed, do not carry him through and over the difficulties. Instead of using action to help him out, he uses his most ready tool, thought.

We all like to forget the unpleasant and painful experiences of life. There are two ways of forgetting, however, i.e., passive and active. The type of forgetting that is employed depends to a great extent on the nature of the objects, ideas, or experiences in question. Unimportant events and thoughts that have *little feeling* attached to them or with little or no significance or interest for us gradually disappear like the circles of water caused by a pebble thrown into a pool. We soon forget the details of dress on any usual morning, the food we ate for breakfast, or the state of the weather, unless it was most unusual. The common occurrences of life which have little more than a casual meaning for us die away in memory—they are sunk almost without a trace. Finally, it is difficult and even impossible to recall them at all. Almost, it would seem as though the memory could retain just so much, and the trivial and inconsequential drop out in order to make room for the important and purposeful. This is *passive* forgetting.

The things that are forgotten in the second method of forgetting (active) are matters to which a *strong* and, often, *disturbing feeling* is attached. We "forget" to pay a bill we think exorbitant. Physicians who receive unsigned checks may reflect that occasionally, at least, it may be an indication that the patient does not regard their services as worth the amount of the charge. We miss an appointment with someone we dislike. There is the story of the man who instructed his secretary to make a dental appointment for him, but added that it would be all right if she forgot to remind him of it. We lose an address that would have led to an unpleasant call or to the writing of a difficult letter. We forget to leave an agreeable companion in time to go to a boresome tea party. The young girl makes a date with another boy, forgetting that she already had one—but with a rather poor dancer. The child happily immersed in his play, forgets—and wets himself. The boy is cautioned to be home at four o'clock. He arrives at six. He has forgotten. He has been in swimming. The high-school girl forgets to stop at the store on the way home. She has been window shopping. And so on.

These examples have at least one factor in common. There was an advantage for the individual, even though it may only have been a temporary one, in the "forgetting." Furthermore, the factors which permitted and directed the forgetting were not clear-cut and conscious. If they had been, it would not have been a question of repression, but of pretense and even dishonesty. We simply find ourselves pursuing such lines of conduct and we may not realize that they are dictated by repressions, unless it is pointed out to us, or we read about it, or discover it in some way or other. We then appreciate that the "forgetting" has been subconsciously guided.

Such subconscious tendencies and thoughts, then, may be said to have a certain degree of independence. They lack the association and the connection with conscious elements that one finds in the well-knit, successful personality. This lack of unity and splitting up of tendencies means dissociation. Logic-tight compartments exhibit dissociation. But there the elements are conscious and are expressed directly. In active, purposeful (whether conscious or unconscious) forgetting, elements are dissociated, but the elements are not of equal clearness. The tendency that is submerged is said to be *repressed*. And repression is just a name to describe the phenomena we have been discussing. Segregation is dissociation at one level of the mind; repression is dissociation at different levels. The introvert, using thought (his most trusted weapon) in a conflict, wields it to drive the unpleasant and painful, disagreeable and embarrassing memories, ideas, emotions, and tendencies from the clear light of consciousness. This is classically illustrated in the complete forgetting that may be witnessed in some of the neuroses, notably hysteria, and which is termed amnesia. The amnesia removes from the patient the remembrance of a certain portion of his life, perhaps, hours, days, weeks, months, and even longer, and occasionally everything is wiped out, so that he no longer knows even his own name. It is precisely within the span of time covered by the amnesia that highly charged emotional events occurred. It was then that the soldier saw the head of his "buddy" carried off by a shell; the daughter saw the idolized mother die; the maiden witnessed the inconstancy of her lover; the husband beheld the infidelity of his wife.* By not recognizing overwhelming and devastating forces, by turning aside from them and repressing their intolerable content, we may attain a measure of peace of mind and avoid the conflict. The conflicts that, at times, may force upon us these drastic *methods of avoidance* are derived from the three elemental drives or complexes of man: ego, sex, and herd. In psychoanalytic terms is the conflict between aggression, hostility, sex, and the superego.

* These are actual instances from practice.

## Chapter 20

# DISSOCIATION AND THE DANGERS OF UNRECOGNIZED TENDENCIES

*In which are treated the hazards incident to Repressed and* Dissociated *material, and the difficulty pertaining to keeping such material buried, so that it will not intrude and disrupt the harmony of everyday life.*

THE SEPARATION OF IDEAS, EMOTIONS, AND TENDENCIES INTO DIFferent groups or complexes that have reached no working agreement among themselves (whether it is by segregation or repression) is called *dissociation*.

Let us consider further examples of dissociated elements and note their influence on mental life.

Whenever an emotional disturbance follows some trifling or insignificant incident, we may be sure that some complex is aroused. The man who makes a scene over slightly overdone eggs at breakfast is an example. This incident touches off his dissatisfaction with home life in general. The trifle is the spark to the fuse. The motive power for the explosion is a system of ideas and feelings which have been in the fringe of consciousness, that is, partly dissociated, and never fully acknowledged. And never facing them or bringing them into the light of clear and rational thought and discussion has merely added to their potency. In the same way a comparatively insignificant incident may stir up an emotional reaction which has been smoldering for years, and the final explosion may then persist as a full-blown nervous breakdown.

In instances where we feel that "there is more here than meets the eye," we are probably dealing with one of these separated and somewhat independent elements. If a person is particularly reticent about something that one naturally might expect him to discuss frankly, or about which he seems to be somewhat uncomfortable, we have a right to infer that some ideas are interfering with his speech and conduct. In other words, he has a sensitive mental spot. He may be perfectly unconscious of the elements, i.e., he may honestly not recognize the inhibiting or disquieting effects of certain ideas. Yet such ideas can be proved to exist and exert their influence. There is a machine called the galvanometer which registers electrically when we are sensitive to a certain idea, to which we do not realize we are sensitive. There is another experimental procedure which is used to explore these *independent* ideas and feelings. This is called the association-reaction experiment. By the type of answer and the time taken to reply to each of a given list of words, we can discover elements that are apparently active in a person's thought and behavior which he has not recognized. For instance, all ideas concerned with sex, indecency, marriage, and divorce might set off tremendous reactions by these methods in an individual whose thoughts, prima facie, one would have said were of the most puritanical kind and whose character was famed for its modesty. The latter might very well be so consciously, but such a reaction would show that unconsciously sex ideas were more active and much more influential than anyone supposed.

When people suddenly "lose their heads" in the midst of a casual conversation, then something deep and significant has been touched. Common sense has a way of tapping the unconscious and getting "a rise" out of us. It educates us. Sensitive spots are touched. "We hit the ceiling," that is, there is an emotional response out of all proportion to the casual, surface incident or remark. These little emotional explosions should lead us to become conscious of our sensitive tendencies and accordingly modify them. "Kidding" and even mild "hazing" may have such useful influences. The boy who always asks his playmates to walk home with him at night is finally teased by them and told that he is afraid of the dark. Then he realizes how much he has been afraid. He is ashamed of the fear and begins to make a better and more conscious adjustment to it. He makes up his mind that they won't be able to tease him about that again. Thus, social pressure has enabled him to overcome a handicapping tendency, which he had not fully realized he possessed. The "shell-shocked" soldier is often finally relieved of his disabilities, when he begins to understand why he was afraid. In the face of such understanding the disassociated fear became attached to the real reasons and was no longer able to express itself by all manner of unusual symptoms. Another example is the boy in his late teens whose behavior is absurdly romantic and sentimental. His hair must be parted in the exact center. His clothing must be meticulously correct. He would feel disgraced if caught doing chores for his mother. He is unmercifully teased, and finally makes a conscious survey of the situation and a better adaptation. So, too, no doubt, teasing may bring into the daylight of the mind, in both girls and boys, a recognition of being too closely tied to the apron strings of the mother and, thus, become a strong factor in determining emancipation and independence.

Opinions and beliefs which pass as rational, and which seem to the individual sincere convictions, may from time to time, on analysis, be demonstrated as springing from either the desire to be "solid with the crowd" or from fear of losing a cherished place in a certain social circle. Whims and fancies may have their origin in buried experiences and their emotional reactions. A wife may grow to dislike her husband not because of any great fault of his, though she may find many, but because he does not dress, behave, and think like her own father, who unconsciously has remained her ideal man. The lover may think he has picked his beloved solely because of her unexcelled virtues. It may be that the physiological sex drive has more to do with his choice than reason. Or, perhaps, many of her qualities are duplicates of those found in his own mother or favorite sister.

The radical, the "progressive," or the free thinker may only be showing a belated revolt against too strict early discipline. His father in the son's unconscious mind may be the symbol of all restraint and authority. He is rebelling not against society but against his father. Again, "feeling his oats" may be the unconscious protest of a young adult against rigid and uncompromising childhood training. One of us in youth knew a family in which there were two children, a boy and a girl. The father was dominating; exacted always immediate obedience; if crossed in the least way, he became an ugly brute and, finally, he was narrow-mindedly "moral," so that the girl was barred from that social interchange which is such a normal and necessary phase of sex development. Today the boy is a hopeless failure with dangerous radical tendencies, while the girl is the lowest type of prostitute.

So many repressions reveal themselves in various ways. There is nothing sordid or highly mysterious about these processes. They do not always need special methods for their discovery. They are common and frequent. But the point is that here are influences, tendencies, ideas, that are guiding our modes of thought and behavior of which we are not always conscious, which we do not recognize until we are informed of them. Wherever we meet bias, prejudice, and intuition, such dissociated influences come into play. With patients suffering from nervous breakdowns, one of the greatest problems is to get them to consider and face these so-called dissociated factors.

## DANGERS OF SEGREGATION, REPRESSIONS, AND DISSOCIATION

We are now in a better position to weigh properly the merits of and the objections to segregation with its logic-tight compartments, repression, and dissociative processes in general, as methods of relieving the conflict. Perhaps their most serious and practical drawback is that they fail to accomplish their purpose. Even if the individual is blind to the inconsistencies of his own life, segregation is soon recognized by the herd. Then, at least, if not before, he can no longer remain blissfully unaware of his paradoxical behavior and his weaknesses. Repression would be the most potent of all mental weapons, if forgetting was equivalent to effacing. Unfortunately, it is true in psychology as it is in physics that *something which has once existed, even though it is only a thought, can never apparently be wholly effaced.* It can never be wiped out as though it had never been, without the possibility of reappearance, either in its original or some other form. In this way, segregation, repression, and dissociation may be thought of as slumbering volcanoes, whose craters are at the very threshold of consciousness, and, whenever, as frequently happens, they are stirred into activity by some association of ideas, there is an eruption. Such eruptions may be indicated by great sensitivity, timidities, uneasiness, tension, overvehemence, "nervousness," unexplained silences, embarrassing irritability, etc. The person who has so many sensitive spots, which are always in danger of being "set off," can scarcely

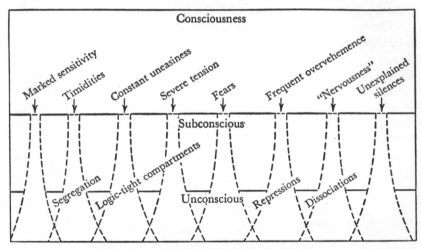

*Figure 22*

have a peaceful mind or an adjusted life. In addition to the minor explosions, there is the danger of severe eruptions or "nervous breakdowns."

The mind of a person who has many dissociations may be represented by a diagram (Fig. 22).

It is obvious that the advantages that accrue from dissociative processes are scarcely enough to compensate for the endless trouble in guarding against the appearance in consciousness of the segregated, repressed, and dissociated material. *The game is not worth the candle.*

*Chapter 21*

# THE CONVERSION OF MENTAL CONFLICTS INTO PHYSICAL SYMPTOMS: ANXIETY, NEURASTHENIA, HYSTERIA

*In this chapter very serious mental hazards are discussed. The mind, unable to face the conflict, in its extremity, utilizes the body, and presents the conflict to the world as physical illness or disability.*

WE NOW COME TO THE ACTUAL CAUSES OF NERVOUSNESS. MUCH THAT passes as nervousness and nervous exhaustion is due to the activity of partly or totally unrecognized inclinations, desires, and inhibitions.

The processes of dissociation and repression may be compared to the administrative difficulties that may arise in any organization, a crowd of boys, a student body, a club, or in society at large. The group votes in favor of a certain plan of action. Let us say that a majority of the boys want to hold meetings in Smith's garage. Or, a larger number of the student body want to meet "X" college in the annual football game. Most of the women in a club vote that the club as a whole go on record in support of the coalition candidate for mayor. Apparently, when the votes were counted, it seemed as if national sentiment were in favor of prohibition. And so on. Now, in each instance a significant and clever minority opposes the majority. The majority reads the minority out of the meeting. What happens? The minority does not, *ipso facto,* remain defeated. By all manner of unusual, irritating, and irrational ways, it hampers the working of the

majority. It may bully them, tantalize them, and try to wear them out.
It may attach the funds. It may take away the brains of the crowd, and
form a separate team or group which acts independently (dissociation). Thus, the energy and drive may be removed from the majority.
The latter may remain harassed, ineffective, and lacking the vitality
to accomplish anything without the push of the vigorous members
who have been lost. The Allies, to win World War II, needed a
coalition of interests; so does the human being. Merely throwing one
interest out of consciousness does not remove it from the field of activity. The activity of a subconscious or repressed complex may be
much more sinister and harmful than if it is met frankly in the full
light of consciousness, and a working arrangement established. This
repression of minority complexes from consciousness may, just as in
the political or social spheres, hamper and harass the working of the
majority forces in the conscious mind, so that it becomes distracted,
incapacitated, and exhausted.

Sleeplessness, night terrors, and somnambulism may be due to
disassociated desires. Dreams are thought to be fulfillments of strange
and bizarre wishes, which in our waking life we should condemn and
reject at once. Occasional dreams that contravene morality may be
dreamed even by a pillar of the church. And not only sex, but certain
ego desires, acquisition, selfish power, etc., may all appear in dream
life.

In our waking life, problems, whose sources are not at all clear to
us, may be taking toll of our emotions and producing nervousness.
Once the origin of the problem is clear, the solution may be surprisingly easy. Dissatisfaction, unhappiness, worry, and nervousness are
frequently due to detached, isolated, and hidden factors. The student
complains of lack of concentration and poor memory. His marks are
atrocious. To talk with him is to know that he has enough ability
to sail through his work with flying colors. He has not fully recognized
the strong physiological and psychological pull to marry an attractive
girl he met two months ago. Children with superior intellectual capacity are brought to our clinic because they cannot get on in school.
Their grades are far below their ability. Their difficulty is to be found
often in the vaguely understood but strong stirrings of puberty.

Many harmless mistakes of everyday life, such as slips of speech
and mistaken readings of words and the unusual and bizarre per-

formances seen in nervous breakdowns, all may be due to unrecognized, dissociated desires seeking some fulfillment in consciousness.

## ANXIETY AND NEURASTHENIA *

Neurasthenia, or so-called nervous exhaustion, is largely the fatigue resulting from mental cross-purposes. The cause is not actual fatigue and exhaustion of the nerves. It is fatigue and exhaustion as a result of excessive emotion. Being defeated by personal problems, whose origin and nature are almost totally misunderstood by the patients themselves, they naturally feel unable to tackle other problems that deal with the world outside themselves. Obtaining little help or sympathy from their friends, relatives, and even sometimes from doctors, they retire from the world of accomplishment as pathetic, defeated creatures. The physicians who unsuccessfully handle such cases usually dismiss the patient with the trite remark, "There is nothing wrong with you." Often such people can hold out as long as a parent acts as surrogate, arbiter, and helper in many of the important problems of life. But when this support vanishes through death or illness, the retirement becomes complete. All of us know those who all their lives have been shielded, protected, and in a sense spoiled. They break down under difficulties. They have not realized that they habitually were using infantile modes of reaction. Their parents always made decisions for them. As adults they are easily discouraged. They cannot stand pain. They protest readily. They are supersensitive and very conscious of bodily or somatic reflexes which the healthy organism does not know. They turn from the activities of daily living to a morbid interest in their own bodies. In the face of difficulty, the mind is turned inward. There is introspection into such perfectly normal sensations as the peristaltic (digestion waves) movements of the intestines, which are automatically disregarded in health. Such sensations become substitutes for unfaced problems. To be sure the close consideration of such sensations is unpleasant; they are elaborated into discomforts and pains, but, all in all, they are less unpleasant

---

* Neurasthenia is not here used in the limited psychoanalytic sense of sexual overstimulation and exhaustion, but fatigue as a result of chronic excessive emotion of any type with the associated physiological disturbances (cf. "combat fatigue").

than a survey of the conflict. The retailing of the bodily symptoms gains attention and sympathy. There are new and interesting treatments to be tried; an endless list of medicines; many fascinating specialists. These patients describe creaking in the joints, painful movements of their muscles, sensations of heart and stomach movements, feelings of oppression, and the like. The interesting thing is that, from describing these inexhaustible sensations in extreme terms of distress and at times almost of anguish, they can turn by magic to smiles and exuberance, if one discusses subjects that interest them—things even of trivial moment. One knows that no organic disease can yield even momentarily to such slight efforts of distraction. There is a childlike transport from the depths to the heights. This is a point that one can bear in mind and apply to himself without the help of doctors. If one finds that his complaints and symptoms always disappear when he goes to the movies, or plays cards, or goes out with friends, he may usually conclude that his trouble is a functional one, and that there are probably unrecognized factors which are driving to such reactions. The word "functional" here as elsewhere in writings on nervousness means "not organic." A functional nervous disorder refers to a disorder that is not caused by actual organic disease of the nervous system. Functional troubles, therefore, usually imply emotional and instinctive difficulties which are being met by inferior habits and inadequate mental mechanisms.

One of our patients was very neurasthenic. He had battled so long that he was physically tired. When he came to us, he had written out a long list of physical sensations with various organic implications appended. Actually there was a lifelong but unrecognized feeling of inferiority. There was the handicap of disproportion between desire and capacity. To keep ahead of this handicap, he threw himself violently into all sorts of endeavors—intellectual, educational, social, and religious. Finally, wearied by the one-sided struggle against an unknown *"something,"* he developed a long train of physical symptoms. He tried to do too much, accomplished still less, and was very dissatisfied with himself. Eventually, through a thorough consideration of his reactions to life problems as he had met them from school age to adulthood, it finally dawned on him *what* he had been trying to overcome and how useless a fight it was. With this realization, and with a clearer consciousness of his capacities and limitations, he rearranged his life, and the symptoms vanished.

Another man came to us, after a long series of genitourinary treatments and manipulations and with a remarkable list of prescriptions calling for various ductless gland preparations. He had taken them all very faithfully. The last specialist he saw told him to consult a neurologist. We have never heard a more exhaustive and detailed description of sensations referred to the genital zone. A few talks brought to light the fact that his wife was very strongly sexed and passionate and that he had a strong, unconscious fear that sooner or later he would fail to satisfy her sex needs. After understanding and explanations, the symptoms vanished.

Neurasthenia is a state reached after the patient has had a long battle with himself. It does not arise suddenly as scarlet fever or some of the nervous disorders do. It is of gradual development and, in a sense, creeps upon the victim. So often, only when it is full blown, is it recognized. The patient is wanting in vigor and attack, and feels helpless before his problems. He lacks punch and is more or less passive. The problems that occupy him are usually not the real ones but substitute ones, i.e., sensations from his own bodily organs.

How does this come about? It has been found that frightening, angering, or inflicting pain on animals cause definite physiological disturbances in them. We may think of a cat frightened by a fierce dog. All we see is the serpentine crouching of the cat, with hairs standing on end, and, if we are close enough, the dilated pupils. We hear the spitting and hissing. Within the cat's body, however, a great deal more is going on. The heart is working faster, the blood is flowing more rapidly, and the pressure of the blood is increased. The first of these factors pushes more blood into the muscles so that in case the animal has to fight or run, it will have an emergency supply of fuel. The second does the same thing and also assists ready and prompt disposal of waste products that are formed in this overactivity. The increased blood pressure not only helps to supply more effectively the muscles and various organs of the body with blood, but also sends more blood to the brain, where quick and ready decisions must be made. In addition to the above-mentioned factors, certain ductless glands of the body throw into the blood their secretions in increased amounts. The secretions of these glands are called hormones in the technical language of physiology. An example of this is adrenalin from the little adrenal glands lying on top of the kidneys. In fact, this substance in the blood will itself cause an increased heart rate, blood flow, and blood pressure. It is, therefore, an emergency safeguard or second line of defense for ensuring the accomplishment of these ends. Further, it has been shown that adrenalin in the blood stream will make the blood clot more readily, so that, if the animal is bitten, it will not bleed so profusely as it would if an unemotional or tranquil condition. Adrenalin also causes the liver to discharge more sugar into the blood, so that again the muscles may have an extra supply of food for their emergency work. The respirations are increased, and the purpose of this is obvious. The movements of the stomach and intestines cease, so that all the blood and energy of the animal may be mobilized for meeting a critical situation. Other glands, such as the thyroid, aid in this mobilization of bodily energy. Suffice it to say that some of these glands of internal secretion are necessary for the effective meetings of certain emergencies.

It may be objected that, after all, human beings are not cats and there are no "fierce dogs" in our world. But the objection is not valid. Human beings are affected by pain, fear, anger, and other emotions just as the cat is; sometimes we are subjected to the same physical frights, and the same reflexes described in the cat are initiated. Now and then, instead of quieting down after the fright is over, the reflexes remain. Hyperthyroidism, a condition in which the heart persistently beats very rapidly, the eyes become very prominent, the hands become shaky, and the patient feels continuously nervous and easily startled, may arise in this way. These patients have the appearance of frozen-fright, or graven fear, i.e., they have always the facial expression of fear, although they may not feel afraid. We recall two cases in which such states originated, one from the terrifying experience of a shipwreck and rescue at sea, and the other from a horrible automobile accident.

We once had a patient who was with her husband, a naval officer, stationed at Haiti during the uprising of the natives. One day while she was in the interior of the island, she walked into the living room and found a poisonous reptile coiled under the table. Later in the day she opened a closet and a tarantula started out toward her. That same evening there was a shooting affray in front of the house. Immediately, she stiffened into a state of "frozen fear." She was brought back to the United States and for six months was mute, did not eat, had to be fed through a tube, and, when placed upon her feet, she would collapse to the floor as though her knees were made of water.

It is true that most of the shocks we encounter in the present stage of civilization are not as physical, acute, or dramatic as the fright of the cat; but the emotions engendered in us are, if anything, the more devastating. Human beings stand a *single* mental shock relatively well, even if it is severe, as, for instance, the drowning of an only son. It is the series of shocks or a long-continued single emotional strain like worry or apprehension that finally breaks us. Such tiring and destructive emotional stress may be due to a prolonged struggle with difficulties and problems which we are not meeting in a straightforward manner. Long-drawn-out fear, anger, shame, resentment, or other intense emotion may produce an increased heart rate, the alterations in the activity of the gastrointestinal functions, just as fear did in the instance of the cat. If these reflexes become established, they tend to keep going even after the original situation has disappeared. They are like the toy that must go until the spring unwinds. Human beings, however, may be wound up as fast as they are unwound—that is, the situation remains. Thus, anxiety, states of intense fear, worry, agitation, and loss of control may dominate almost every waking hour.

Is it thinkable that such situations can arise in the midst of the culture and refinement and material ease and protection of modern life? Not only conceivable but exceedingly common! Here are a few taken at random from our practice. Think of the fear of the woman who has reason to believe that her husband is no longer in love with her and may, at any time, leave her for another, and this at an age when she is no longer able to shift for herself. Or the young girl who is carrying on secretly a questionable love affair. Or the worry of parents at the degradation of a son or daughter. Or the state of mind of the wife who is carrying on an illicit love relationship. Or the haunting fear of poverty. Or think of the man, getting on in years and with a large family to support, who lives in fear of being displaced by a newcomer in the business organization. These and many similar situations are anxiety producing. In this type of reaction the individual is still fighting and aggressive. His symptoms are part of his endeavor to overcome the difficulty. If the physiological state or the reflexes and sensations continue long after the inciting conditions exist, the patient may lose his aggressive attitude, and find his world consisting mainly of these residual sensations. He comes to the doctor complaining of palpitation, weakness, and dyspnea (shortness of breath); flushings and feelings of coldness; tingling sensations; lightness, heaviness, or gastrointestinal disturbances. He wants medicine to cure these symptoms. It should be clear that medicines can be only palliative if effective at all. The best remedies are understanding how these states have developed, making determined efforts for more satisfactory solutions and substituting new reflexes and fresh habits for old ones. The athlete, when he first starts training, often feels palpitation, dyspnea, distress, weakness, and even nausea and vomiting. (These are all frequent complaints in neurasthenia.) By training, practice of body and mind in new habits, he overcomes these disabilities. Nine-tenths of the people who are nervous and come to the doctor for complaints of the type we have discussed need *training,* not medicines. It must be emphasized, however, that when we say a person is nervous or is suffering from a nervous condition, or from a functional nervous disease, we by no means imply that the trouble is imaginative or nonexistent. Usually the troubles are only too real, and often more unpleasant than actual organic disease.

## HYSTERIA

In hysteria the origin is somewhat similar, but the mechanism and reactions are quite different. Instead of introspective occupation with sensations, fatigue, and anxiety states, total disabilities are developed. The neurasthenic complains that his eyes blur after reading a few minutes, and there is a mist or black spots; the hysteric cannot see at all. The neurasthenic complains that noises hurt his ears, for they are so loud and painful; the hysteric cannot hear at all. The neurasthenic hears the buzzing in the ears which anyone can hear (and in normal health automatically disregards) when it is quiet and which is due to the blood circulating in the auditory apparatus. The hysteric transfers his difficulties grossly onto a physical or physiological plane. The arms will not work—as in the case of the student nurse whose arms would not move when she was told to scrub the operating room floor stained with blood. The legs will not obey the conscious mind—as in the case of the soldier whose legs became paralyzed when the order to charge the enemy was given. Or there is deafness after listening to the cries and groans of the wounded.

Hysterical symptoms are much more clear-cut and definite than are those of the neurasthenic. The neurasthenic has indefinite feelings of tightness, choking, or oppression in the chest, with dyspnea and palpitation. Perhaps also he is uneasy or apprehensive. The hysteric simply faints, while the neurasthenic has all the feelings of a long-drawn-out process of suffocation. Whoever converts his difficulties wholeheartedly into physical disabilities is using the hysterical mode of reaction.

Spasms, tics, paralyses, anesthesias, vertiginous (dizzy) seizures, in which the patient falls over, are all typical of hysteria. The hysteric talks over his problems much more objectively than the neurasthenic. He treats the disability as a detached phenomenon absolutely outside his own control and responsibility. The neurasthenic is profuse in his talk, but he connects his symptoms more readily with subjective factors. The hysteric is much less conscious of his own personal problems. His is an extroverted attitude, while that of the neurasthenic is more introverted. On investigation, the problems that trouble the hysteric are again more clear-cut than those of the neurasthenic. The nurse develops a disability of her arms because unconsciously she does not want to do the menial work of scrubbing and revolts at the sight of blood. The soldier may not only shrink from killing, but there is a conflict between the instinct of self-preservation and the duty to charge and kill. The paralysis saves him from going forward.

On occasions, any of us may resort to mild hysterical mechanisms in our everyday life. The boy who develops a headache so that he cannot go to school; the girl who sheds tears to force her will on her companions; the businessman whose blustering gets service; the housewife whose ills win the sympathy that otherwise is not forthcoming—these are all homely illustrations of hysterical mechanisms.

You ask how we can detect whether a disability is hysterical or organic, or how we know dissociated ideas, emotions, and tendencies are concerned? In the first place, an arm that suffers from hysterical paralysis can be made to contract by electrically stimulating its nerve, while one that is paralyzed through organic disease of the nerve will not contract on electric stimulation, or the usual contractions are reversed. The person who has an hysterical inability to talk, technically called aphonia, can cough, while one whose laryngeal nerves are diseased cannot. The hysteric who is blind, for example, may not recognize a finger in the field of vision, but may develop convulsions on seeing and recognizing a match held in the same position. There are numerous ways of finding whether incapacity is functional or organic. Whenever we meet hysterical symptoms we should raise the following questions. What is the difficulty that is being solved in this temporary and unsatisfactory manner? How does the disability get us out of this difficulty?

If we can find the answers to these questions, we have gone a long way toward helping the patient. The soldiers who developed such symptoms were often helped when the real explanation was forthcoming. In fact, recovery often ensued by removing the patients from the field of action. It is generally believed that most of the soldiers who developed anxiety states and hysterias were those who never faced clearly the problem of fear and acknowledged it. They tried to place it outside their conscious mind—beyond their attention. They tried to believe they were not afraid. The complex was outlawed, but it would not down—just as so many minorities cannot be conquered by wholesale methods. Those who did recognize that they were afraid and acknowledged it and still carried on were much less prone to functional incapacities.

Occupational neuroses, so-called, belong to this class of phenomena. The person who cannot write any longer or finds it painful to write (really because he hates his job for one reason or another) can still play the piano or use the fingers in playing cards or eating (which are more or less enjoyable procedures). People who have been reduced in the social scale or who have been transferred from a friendly to a foreign, unfriendly, and difficult environment develop these difficulties easily. German and Jewish refugees are not infrequently in American hospital clinics with such symptoms. It is not unlike the boy who says he cannot carry the bucket of coal because he has not strength enough, whereas the real reason is he does not desire to, or he wants to protest against some fancied injustice. These refugees protest the injustice of fate by bodily symptoms.

From these instances, it is a step to compensation cases in the courts and the vagrancy that not uncommonly follows minor injuries. A person suffers a bus accident, is jostled and scared. He is upset nervously, i.e., the fright stops his digestion, speeds up his heart, and may produce in him vertigo and flushings. He is bruised and becomes acutely aware of his bodily reflexes. He feels that his back has been strained. He favors it whenever he can. But unused muscles tend to grow weak. Whenever, therefore, he does use his back muscles to lift anything, they naturally feel strained, weak, and often painful. For several days the back aches. Therefore, the back is again protected and the person becomes acutely conscious of his back muscles. A vicious circle is established and a morbid consciousness of back muscles develops. The company must pay for the disability. In a sense, then, the disability, which in time is not very great, becomes profitable. It pays to be sick. And so there are hundreds of people trying to force companies to continue to pay them more money because of their own bad habits of mind and their inability to train themselves into new ones. There are, of course, actual disabilities that should be paid for. When, however, a disability is utilized to trade on the sympathy of the public, it is an unwholesome extreme for the individual himself. All social agencies are familiar with those who have suffered accidental deformities and who make more money using these as their basis of appeal than they could make in legitimate work. It is clear that here we are in a region where the dividing line between malingering and honesty is very fine.

## ILLUSTRATION OF HYSTERICAL AND NEURASTHENIC MECHANISMS

Perhaps it may be worthwhile to reduce to a diagram at least one of the important psychological differences between hysteria and neurasthenia and the anxiety states (Fig. 23).

A and B may each be taken to represent an incident or emotional shock or trauma which actually occurred in consciousness. At A, let us say, a soldier, advancing in charge across a wheat field in France, in World War I, suddenly turns his eyes to the right, and at that instant he sees the head of his "buddy" torn from the body by a shell from the enemy. A few hours later he is carried into an ambulance dressing station, totally blind, although his eyes and all their physiological connections are quite intact. All that is to be found on the surface is that the soldier *cannot see nor can he remember*. He can recall charging across the wheat field and he remembers being carried

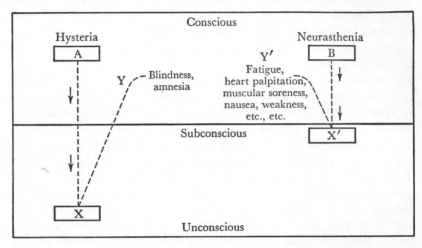

*Figure 23*

to the ambulance dressing station, but the intervening time, including the second when the head of his friend was blown off, is a complete blank.

Now turn to B. It too represents an actual happening. Let us assume that it symbolizes a scene or even a quarrel between husband and wife. The husband is accusing the wife of sexual indifference and frigidity. It is an oft-repeated scene. He has accused her many times before. But this time he is more angry, more vehement, and even somewhat threatening. The wife defends herself. In turn she is apologetic, tearful, angry. The husband leaves to go to his work. The wife feels tired, her heart palpitates. Her muscles are sore, she is nauseated and weak. She has felt this way before, but this time the physical sensations remain. More or less constantly, she continues to feel weary, sore, nauseated, and often, her heart palpitates. Other and more distressing sensations are added. She becomes interested in these sensations, complains about them, analyzes them, wonders what they signify. Does she have this or that disease? Is she about to have a stroke? In truth her body is sound enough organically. She has *neurasthenia*.

It is obvious that neither the hysteria nor the neurasthenia began as suddenly and dramatically as has been recited. Both were preceded by a long series of events—the details of the conflict. In the case of the soldier, there was the unconscious battle between the dominant instinct of self-preservation and the contrasting complex of self and soldierly ideals. Deprivation, fatigue, and the horrible incident on the battlefield merely determined the time of the occurrence of the hysteria. In the case of the wife, there had been many antecedent years of strain, worry, and anxiety. For a long time the mind had been a battleground of conflicting emotions—fear and repugnance at the very thought of the sex act against the strong desire to please her husband and retain his love. Inexpressibly wearied by endless emotional stress, various bodily sensations had appeared. At first they were intermittent and trivial; at last they became fixed and serious.

Psychologically, what has happened? In the instance of the soldier, one element of the conflict may be traced from the surface incident at A, to its hiding place X deep in the subconscious. At the same time of the incident A, the conflict was resolved—simply, expeditiously, and effectively—but pathologically. Self-preservation triumphed. The conflict was converted into two disabling and protecting symptoms Y, blindness and amnesia (loss of memory). Hysteria is a simple, naïve, childlike device. It is almost like the expedient of the little boy, who closes his eyes to keep away the bogy man.

Neurasthenia and anxiety states are much more complicated in their mechanism. The disturbing situation or conflict is not driven very deep into the subconscious. It is fairly close to the surface. In the diagram it is placed at X'. Furthermore, neurasthenia and pathological anxiety usually require a much longer period for their full development. During this preparatory phase, the mind is fatigued by the conflicting emotions, possibly the resistance of the body is lowered, and the emotional strain is expressed in the form of various physical sensations (fatigue, heart palpitation, muscular soreness, nausea, weakness, etc.) at Y'.

Although different in their mechanisms and appearances, hysteria and neurasthenia are basically the same in their objectives and purposes. They both seek to protect the individual. They aim to rescue him from what, for him, is an intolerable situation. And they strive to accomplish this protection and rescue without loss of approval of the self-ideal and the herd. Temporarily, hysteria succeeds completely; neurasthenia and anxiety neuroses, only partly. They are both pathological.

There is a moral. Society will scarcely permit the patient to retain his symptoms. Furthermore, the patient *consciously* strongly wishes to get well. Many complicated and more or less unpleasant and expensive procedures are required. The steps which led to the development of the conflict must be painfully retraced. Self-knowledge, which should have been obtained before the objective manifestations of the neurosis appeared, now must be purchased at a hard psychological price. *It is almost axiomatic that in the presence of clear, calm, honest, and conscious understanding of the conflict, a neurosis cannot occur.* Often, measures which modify the seriousness of the conflict become available. Even if the individual must face a more or less hopeless impasse, open recognition and understanding are still a valuable protection.

*Chapter 22*

# THE MENTAL USE OF SUBSTITUTES, THE TRANSFERENCE OF EMOTIONS, AND THE IMPORTANCE OF SYMBOLISM

*In which it is shown that disagreeable and painful experiences may be* Displaced *from consciousness. Even though they reappear in consciousness under the guise of apparently harmless* Substitutes, *nevertheless, there are left too many sensitive mental spots. The use and misuse of Symbolism are also discussed.*

WE ARE ABOUT TO CONSIDER AN EXTREMELY INTERESTING GROUP OF psychological mechanisms which may be utilized to escape the distasteful conflict. They are called *displacement, substitution,* and *symbolism.* The meaning in the physical sphere is clear. If a stone is dropped in a tumbler flush full of water, some of the water runs over (displaced by the stone); the stone takes the place (substitution) of the displaced water, and, finally, the stone represents (symbolizes) the water. An experiment is often performed in the laboratory on animals. If food is shown to a dog, saliva begins to flow, and the flow may be accurately measured. If simultaneously with the exhibition of the food, a bell is rung and this is repeated a number of times, then finally the mere ringing of the bell, without the food, serves to initiate the salivary flow. Colors and sounds may be similarly utilized. Animal psychologists have built up a large series of experimental observations on such phenomena.

## CONDITIONED PSYCHOLOGICAL REFLEXES

It is believed that much of our education proceeds along such lines. For example, after a sufficient amount of reading and teaching, when someone says 1815 we immediately think of Waterloo; when one mentions Anthony, we think of Cleopatra; or if one says "two" and "two," we think of "four." Learning and training are built on a similar pattern. The dog learns to obtain candy by raising his paw when his master holds out his hand containing candy. Finally, merely holding out his hand will cause the dog to present his paw. The horse learns to trot when the driver speaks and touches him with a whip. Finally, merely speaking to him causes the horse to quicken his pace. Washing hands before dinner brings approval and pleasantness from father and mother. Dirty hands bring frowns and perhaps punishment. The hands are washed—more or less frequently. It does not take long to develop such conditioned responses, as they are called. First a single object or stimulus is presented. It produces an idea or a response. Then another object or stimulus, which ordinarily would not invoke such a response, is exhibited simultaneously with the first.

Eventually the primary exciting object is omitted, but, on presentation of the second, the original response is performed. The second object or stimulus in time produces the same response as the first, that is, it displaces it.

The psychophysiological process may work either for our mental weal or woe. It is a common mechanism in some bizarre and apparently unexplained nervous reactions. A former soldier has a terrific fear of thistles. He cannot account for it. Analysis reveals that, during the war, he had experienced intense fear while lying under a thistle bush trying to hide from the enemy snipers. He had entirely "forgotten" the experience. Another soldier cannot ride in a trolley car. He "cannot stand" the unexplained feeling of dread which promptly appears. It was found that the trolley running along the wire sounded to him like the hissing of bullets. A gentleman disgraced himself at a social gathering by a violent attack of vomiting, while one of the guests was picking out a sailor's ditty on the piano. It developed that years before he was distressingly sick in his bunk on a coastwise steamer, while just below him a sailor was drumming out on an old piano the selfsame ditty. He had forgotten the incident. In other words, neutral objects like thistles, trolley cars, and ditties invoked unusual reactions—reactions they do not ordinarily elicit, just as the ringing of a bell does not usually start a flow of saliva in a dog.

Numerous illustrations of such *mesalliance of emotions, ideas, and objects* occur in everyday life. Jones "hates" liver. It is found that, as a youngster, he was on numerous occasions forced to eat it against his will, and often became emotionally upset and physically sick. A certain woman becomes nauseated when she sees a red rose. It relates to a previous decidedly unpleasant emotional experience in which a red rose figured prominently. Smith dislikes a certain tree. On reflection, he calls that switches from the same kind of tree were used to adjust him to the path of virtue in childhood. Whims and fancies often arise in such accidental circumstances. It is our experiences that mold antipathies and preferences for persons and objects and not the persons and objects themselves.

In our clinics there are patients whose chief symptom is that they have had untoward experiences and have made unfortunate connections between objects, ideas, and emotions. A woman has painful gums because of an ill-fitting plate. At the same time she is depressed, feels she has sinned, and is unworthy in the sight of God. The two experiences go on side by side for some time until, finally, the patient believes that the pain is a sign of her unworthiness or even a punishment for it. The whole emotional complex associated with unworthiness somehow gets so closely tied up with that of the pain that it envelops it into its own system of ideas.

A man has evil thoughts—thoughts which are not allowed free expression in respectable society. At about the same time he is experiencing the discomforts of a mild neuritis. Two sets of experiences are occurring which are totally unrelated causally. Finally, the organic sensations are taken as the symbol of the sinful thoughts, so that every time these sensations are felt, sinful thoughts and guilt are aroused, and the physical discomfort is accepted as just punishment for evil thinking. The only connection is the simultaneous appearance in consciousness—just as two automobiles may at the same time arrive at a crossroad, but have no other relationship. These examples show the danger of permitting an emotion to sway us so completely that all thought and action are warped. Furthermore, continuous introspection on bodily sensations is mentally unwholesome even if there is actually bodily illness, and all the more so if there is no organic disease.

A patient worries about his physical sensations. He becomes hypochondriacal. He seeks the doctor and demands medicine for odd and disturbing sensations in his reproductive organs. In the given instance, the odd sensations had at their roots an unsolved sex problem. Splendid and highly religious women may be literally tortured by connecting natural engorgment and sensations from their genital organs with immoral desires that they want to repress. We may say, therefore, that in these cases the stimulus or object has awakened a wrong and unfortunate idea or emotion. For mental health we must be careful not to make such connections, or if, having made them, to sever them promptly. Much obsessional thinking has its basis in the mechanism we have just described.

### SYMBOLISM

With the development of language, man learns to manipulate words in place of objects. If we wish to discuss something, we use a word to call the object to mind. Children go through a stage of development before they learn the use of language. They point to an object, or go and get it to show you, every time they want you to do something about it. A great deal of time and effort is lost in thus manipulating concrete objects. Words, with the development of language, enable us to deal with our world figuratively or in the mind's eye. By using words we can take a trip around the world with friends without ever leaving our living room, just as in a familiar children's game one follows with certain moves the paths of great steamers around the world. Words, then, are used as symbols of things, whether of ideas or objects.

Similarly, objects become the symbols or the substitutes for ideas, feelings, and tendencies. Thus, we express conceptions significantly and economically. It is a kind of mental shorthand.

The flag is a symbol for patriotism. In a Fourth of July speech the orator indifferently substitutes the words "the flag" for the word "patriotism." They mean the same to his auditors. Both words (one concrete and the other abstract) awaken in us feelings of warmth, pride, and gratitude; ideas of sacrifice, honor, and glory; and tendencies and impulses toward noble and praiseworthy actions. All this mass of mental impressions is made up of feelings we have experienced, perhaps under the influence of some stirring patriotic spectacle; memories of heroic deeds (like the suffering of the Puritans); and hopes and aspirations we have felt at one time or other. All this the words "the flag" or "patriotism" may arouse. The mere appearance of the flag itself—the "stars and stripes"—may awaken this in us. Thus we see what mental and physical economy symbols afford us. It has taken several sentences to indicate in a superficial way what we mean by "the flag" and "patriotism," and we have made scant reference to concrete experiences which must come to everyone's mind when these words are uttered or when we see our flag waving. Yet the words or objects touch off these innumerable meanings for us, as by magic. Symbolic objects or words thus are laden with tremendous meanings. They are charged with uncommon significance when they are used symbolically.

Objects of art often owe most of their value to their symbolic significance—the Arch of Triumph in Paris, the Washington Monument, the Statue of Liberty. All these objects have inestimable meaning for us through what they represent or "stand for." Rodin's statue representing Verdun can never be forgotten by one who has seen it. It represents insensate, fighting fury aroused by the most extreme degree of fear and despair. Attitudes in art stand as symbols for states of mind. Primitive written language used such symbolism. Even in the highly developed Chinese language of the present day, words are still represented by ideographs called "characters." In many of these the original symbolism is quite apparent. The character for "filial piety," for instance, can readily be seen to have been derived from the picture of a child at the feet of an old man. The ideograph for "peace" is a woman under a roof. That for "east" is a picture of the sun shining behind a tree. Two trees side by side represent "woods" or "forest." A picture representing a woman and a child side by side means "good." The older religions are all highly symbolic.

Our everyday work, play, and love life are replete with symbols. The check, intrinsically worthless, is accepted at monetary value. A child bestrides a broomstick and accepts it as a prancing steed. His father proudly displays a rather insignificant silver cup. It is a symbol of a golf victory. In poetry, the lover begs a handkerchief or tress of hair from his mistress. It symbolizes HER. Once (but long ago) a wedding ring symbolized bondage for the woman.

Attitudes and actions have a symbolic significance of which the actor is unaware. In this sense they may be said to be unconscious. The very "carriage" of a person is indicative of certain attitudes of mind. There is the broad-shouldered, deep-chested, heavy-muscled, vigorous approach of the self-assured extrovert. On the other hand, there is the concave-chested, poorly muscled, hesitant approach that betokens the diffident and insecure state of mind of the extreme introvert.

Our dress is symbolic of our mental state. There is the carefree, "mussed" state of clothes of the person whose position is assured. The same appearance may be indicative of an abstracted, other-worldly, impractical turn of mind. On the other hand, we have the attempt at correct form and style in the person who has not yet "arrived." This external perfection may be an unconscious effort to conceal the imperfection which is felt within. Speech and gestures in the same way may express, unconsciously, states of mind.

We may go beyond the spheres of gestures to those of habitual actions. Here, too, many little habits have symbolic significance of which we may not be aware. For example, excessive washing of the body may be merely a natural inclination to be clean. On the other hand, it may represent an effort to cleanse one's mind and wash away some moral uncleanness of which one is not clearly aware or does not wish to acknowledge.

Some people are given to the performance of little daily rituals, which in themselves are relatively harmless. Nevertheless, the repeated testing of gas cocks to be sure they are properly turned off, or the endless examination of doors and windows to see if they are securely locked may have symbolic or emotional significance of insecurity, fear, or guilt, of which we are totally unaware. Certain avoidances may be fraught with similar import. An intelligent, cultured gentleman avoided every reference to the number thirteen. He stayed in bed on the thirteenth day of each month. As he walked along he hopped each thirteenth step. Likewise, he hopped over the thirteenth step of the stairway which led to his lodgings. He counted the words in conversations, so as not to miss the thirteenth or its multiples. He would not walk along a certain street because of an advertising sign that contained thirteen letters. His life was made miserable. He could not tell why he was "forced" to act in this manner. An exhaustive investigation brought to light a repressed experience of boyhood life—sexual intercourse with an ignorant and very superstitious servant in his father's house. . . . A woman had an overwhelming fear of dirt and suffered because she thought she might cause disease in others through dirt. Analysis revealed that dirt symbolized venereal disease to which she had been exposed. . . . An old maid lovingly cares for cats, and, thus, symbolically discharges her maternal instinct.

We thus see that many useful and likewise many senseless acts derive much of their significance from substitution or symbolism. It is clearly not wrong to employ such mechanisms. They contribute not only to the economy, but to the fullness of life. But they have their excesses. The point is that it is important to know when such mechanisms are acting overtime and to call a check on them. Without romance and sentiment, which can often be best expressed symbolically, life is dull and uninteresting. But too much symbolism leads to misunderstanding and instability; and, in excess, to the bewilderment and perplexity that one finds in certain nervous conditions.

## THE DANGERS OF DISPLACEMENT, SUBSTITUTION, AND DISSOCIATION

Symbolism is such an important factor and has such real meaning in our everyday lives that it deserves further consideration. We may permit it to operate unconsciously for our woe, but also, in some sense, we may utilize it consciously for the furtherance of our mental weal. As has been mentioned, the first is illustrated by patients who finally are literally compelled to perform all kinds of senseless, ritualistic acts. Here is the woman who, unless she washes her hands thirty, forty, fifty, and even a hundred times a day, not only feels uncomfortable, but may actually suffer distressing agony of mind. Here is the man, in one of our cases, an important business executive, who would have distressingly restless and wearisome nights unless, before he retired, every article of clothing had been arranged with painstaking precision.

When such a state of affairs has been reached, then the individual is literally the slave of his symbols and they drive him without mercy. Release from such thralldom usually involves a slow and tedious search for the hidden meaning which the symbols mask and the painful breaking of deeply ingrained habits. How much easier and how much more sensible it is to check (either unaided or with professional help) the symbolic ritual before it has obtained such a mental strangle hold.

Probably all human beings make some sacrifices to strange gods. In all of us, even the most enlightened, there are left over a few odds and ends, an occasional grotesque remnant from archaic times. These come to the surface as superstitions. Unless excessive, they are practically normal and quite harmless. So the man who "touches wood" or refuses to walk under a ladder or cannot be induced to light a third cigarette from the same match may continue his mild superstitious practices without fear for his peace of mind.

Symbolism has its good uses. We may resort to it deliberately in the attempt to terminate an unpleasant emotional state. A man has had an irksome, irritating, and unsuccessful day at the office. He begins to feel "let down." But rather than allow himself to be gripped by an irritating-depressing mood, he forces himself to square his shoulders, whistle a cheery tune, and greet his wife and children affectionately. The squaring of the shoulders, the tune, and the pleasant greeting are symbolic of good humor. They are effective. Soon he is not only acting cheerful, but actually feels cheerful. Or a woman begins to feel "fed up" with household duties and the care of the children. Rather than let herself slump, she arranges a shopping expedition in pleasant company and buys a new hat. The change of scene and activity, the friendly gossip, and, perhaps, particularly the new hat are symbolic of the fact that life is not all harassing routine. She feels much better.

We are now in a position to understand and visualize the mechanism of displacement and substitution and the utilization of the symbol. Let us take the example of the woman who is made deathly sick with distressing nausea at the sight of a red rose. The facts of the situation are these: Many years before, she was betrayed and subsequently jilted by a lover. On the night of their last meeting she wore a red rose which he had given her. She never saw him again.

Now let us refer to the following diagram (Fig. 24).

The conscious union or wedding between A (the original idea or remembrance of the affair) and B (the unhappy emotions induced by the memory) has become too painful. The unconscious mind oblig-

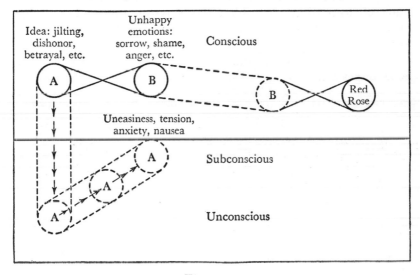

*Figure 24*

ingly secures a divorce. The original and painful idea is banished or repressed into the unconscious. The free emotion which remains is joined or wedded to a new idea, which, when it is devoid of its emotional implications, in itself is not unpleasant (red rose). But the second marriage is not successful. The unconscious mind works too hard at repressing the original idea (A). Yet A is always trying to push back into consciousness. And, whenever there is danger of its being remembered, as there is at the sight of a red rose, then there is nervous uneasiness, tension, anxiety, and the sensation of physical sickness and nausea.

From all this, there is defined a course of action for mental hygiene. Emotions must be somewhat desensitized. At sometime in life everyone of us is embarrassed, humiliated, frightened, shamed, and occasionally, perhaps, even disgraced. If our only concern is to forget or repress the disagreeable happening as quickly as possible, then we are in danger of retaining unattached emotions, which may be stirred into disquieting activity every time they come into contact with the object or thought which has become the symbol for the repressed idea. A moderate amount of thoughtful consideration of the whole affair, possibly a sensible effort to repair some of the damage to self, a willingness to accept the situation frankly and the intention to profit by the lesson the experience teaches, may all combine to avert the danger resulting from the retention of highly charged emotional fragments.

*Chapter 23*

# PROJECTION, OR FAULTFINDING AND SHIFTING THE BLAME

> *Wherein is discussed the psychological temptation of shifting blame which we should accept ourselves upon others or the conditions of life. All in all,* Projection *is a considerable hazard, and leads into rather dangerous mental waters.*

THERE ARE TWO VERY COMMON WAYS OF LOOKING AT THINGS, WHICH temporarily make us feel better. They have to do chiefly with our ability to get around deficiencies and weaknesses or, in other words, circumvent conflicts. These habits of thought help us to avoid a certain amount of mental discomfort and pain, but peace and comfort are often purchased at a questionable price. We live in false security. There is peace only because we do not see clearly. It is as if we were wearing smoked glasses for the first time, and could see only the gorgeous shapes of the clouds in a threatening sky. Without the glasses, we should readily recognize the ominous color and nature of the clouds and could seek safety before the storm breaks. As it is, recognition may come only when the storm is upon us. So, too, if we do not see the origin and implications of our thoughts, we may find that a storm has been developing without our being aware of it. Perhaps our thoughts have concealed things from us rather than made them clear.

We may avoid recognizing our deficiencies and faults by attributing them to others or to the nature of things. This is called *projection*.

In this way, we may deny our weaknesses or responsibilities. Conversely, we may claim as our own, qualities which actually belong to others. The latter is the mechanism of *identification*. Let us consider projection first.

Smith makes an atrociously bad shot at billiards. His friends laugh. He is humiliated. Promptly and very positively he asserts that his cue is badly balanced. The pitcher throws the ball just below the shoulders, where he knows the batter is weak. "Strike three and out!" calls the umpire. "Too high—that's a ball!" angrily shouts the batter as he throws his bat to the ground. His teammates reproach the fullback for a poor kick at the critical stage of the football game. He replies, "The ball was slippery" or "I have a loose cleat on my shoe." A woman drops a crochet stitch. Someone has distracted her. The salad dressing is not right. The oil is at fault. The biscuits do not rise. The baking powder is of a poor quality. A business deal goes wrong. The associates and assistants are stupid. In an automobile collision, it is always the other driver who is at fault. And so examples of the projection mechanism may be endlessly multiplied.

We all use projection, rightly or wrongly, nearly every day of our lives. It is the universal complaint that the tools are bad when we make a mistake. We thus "pass the buck" in the slang of the day. That is the common factor in all the examples we have cited. When we have made errors or something has gone wrong through our own incapacity or poor judgment, we relieve ourselves of responsibility and attribute the failure to something outside of ourselves. This *objectifying of personal difficulties is the essence of projection*. Through it we purchase temporary satisfaction and relief from humiliation, weakness, and self-criticism. By it we avoid the recognition of our own personal shortcomings. Such recognition is always unpleasant and embarrassing, if not painful, and by the projection mechanism we escape such feelings. In the face of conflicts, projection is useful (?). At least, there is the temptation to employ it. Socially blameworthy desires, incompatible with our own higher natures, may be readily discounted or attributed to others. The chronic alcoholic may avoid facing his own infidelity (or perchance his sexual impotence) by charging his wife with actions of which she is wholly innocent. The spinster may escape recognition of her own sex longings by condemning the "bold" tendencies of her nieces. Traditionally, the man blames the woman. Projection shields us from the pain of self-criticism and reproach. It is easier to rebuke others or to damn inanimate things than it is to accept the source of trouble as in ourselves.

It is not implied that every time we blame others or things it is necessarily ourselves who are at fault. The facts may justify our attitude. But the individual who habitually overuses projection is readily recognized by his fellows, and his assertions are apt to be discounted. His statements are not accepted at par and are taken with a very large grain of salt. The projection attitude of mind is not consciously unfair—again it is a question of complexes deceiving and misleading thought.

Whenever we find intense prejudice, intolerance, excessive criticism, and cynicism, we are likely to find projection. We are prone to see in others our own unexplored tendencies. Some people who are overconcerned about the morals of the rising generation are fighting, no doubt, some of their own projected inclinations. They may have certain natural desires which for them have remained unfulfilled. They see others fulfilling that which they have unconsciously desired. The struggle *within* has determined their interest in things *without*. And by fighting the "devils" of their own personalities in others, they do so with great peace of mind and frequently with considerable social sanction. The herd or society helps them and fortifies them in this process when it is advantageous to society, while in other matters where society is less obviously concerned, the individuals are often left as lone combatants with the herd against them.

Intolerance, too, may in a sense protect us from the tendency to deviate too far from accepted standards in this or that direction. It may fortify us against our doubting tendencies. Usually there is then an interesting psychological backwash. The person who almost succumbs to the temptation to break the rules of an organization or club often becomes the severest critic of someone who has actually broken the rule. The boy who resists a strong desire to set aside the fraternity rule against lending the fraternity pin to members of the fair sex often advocates excessive penalties for the culprit who has really lent his pin. The man who just manages to "break into" an exclusive club is apt to be meticulously careful about the admission of other candidates. The politician who is read out of his party for some bit of insurgency will have as his bitterest foe the one who was tempted to do what he did.

Excessive criticism in great or small affairs will usually be found to have an extra-rational basis. Expatiation on the mismanagement and incapacities of others often has its foundation in our own unconscious limitations along the same line. We see these things in others because unconsciously we feel them in ourselves. The clever man does not waste time in empty criticism; he is up and busy, doing constructive, creative things. The critics are rarely the creators—they often are disappointed creators. The art critic, whether in painting, sculpture, or music, so often is criticizing his own weaknesses (projection), and praising not nearly so frequently the achievements for which he has longed. The theorists who have failed to make a success in business are often the "experts" who tell just how it should be done.

Inordinate criticism often leads to cynicism. Nothing is regarded as of permanent and essential value. In people with this type of mind, there may be found sources of great personal dissatisfaction which remain unrecognized. This sense of dissatisfaction and valuelessness is transferred from the personal to the objective level, and nothing in the world is held to be useful or constructive. We often see this reaction in the man whose life has been a tremendous disappointment to him. The whole world, then, he sees through these glasses of personal disappointment. Nothing is worthwhile. All is vanity. His criticism of the world is one long dirge of personal dissatisfaction. What he has formerly loved, he now hates; and the hate seems to have its origin not in himself but in the very nature of the external world. In reality, the hate arises from blocked love in himself. Tennyson says, "Dark is the world to thee; thyself art the reason why—" Universal criticism adds a certain luster of cleverness and uniqueness to a personality. It may have a social value, too, in the wholesome criticism which its grain of truth possesses. Personally, also, it may sustain an individual who has an excessive feeling of superiority and who could not stand the realization of failure.

The above discussion should enable us to understand the development of projection. We see things, all things, in a distorted way. Previous experience colors every perception. When this personal contribution to perception becomes excessive we are using projection.

When the world becomes too much imbued with our own emotions, ideas, and tendencies, it takes on a peculiar, personal hue. We speak of the world as being colored by our feelings. That is projection. The wind in its rage may represent despair, or in its soughing, peace and contentment. Thus we may see in nature only our own feelings. We may describe the cat as a gentle creature, the symbol of contentment, or as a villain in pursuit of his prey—according as our moods and feelings dictate.

Feelings and emotions literally alter and create the world in which we live. Someone performed the experiment of sounding a tuning fork and asking an assembly of people what they heard. There were all sorts of replies: an organ, a whistle, a horn, a human voice. All these notions were closely related, no doubt, to the past experiences of the individuals concerned. Obviously the source of the sound could not have been all these different things. It was only so in imagination.

In Poe's famous story, the guttural cries of rage of the murderous baboon were variously interpreted by listeners as German, French, Italian, Russian, etc. Judges and lawyers know that scarcely ever will witnesses report in the same way a very simple happening which they have observed even at close range.

We can readily see how different and how erroneous our inferences may be even in reference to more or less unemotional material. Where feeling and emotion are concerned, our mental conclusions are much more doubtful and much farther afield. Common sense has crystallized this observation into the expression that the wish is father to the thought. The creak of a board in the old house may be taken to be the footstep of a lover, or the approach of a burglar, according as our minds are filled with thoughts and feelings of love or fear. The same sound by others may be interpreted as the walking of spooks, ghosts, spirits, or other supernatural beings. Who has not felt at some time or other the actual presence of some danger that later turned out to be illusory? A man wagered one hundred pounds that he could remain all night in a famous haunted house in Sussex. Armed with a loaded revolver, he went to bed in the ghost chamber and soon fell asleep. At two o'clock in the morning he was awakened by a faint scratching sound coming from the foot of the bed. He looked in that direction and by the pale cold light of the moon he saw a white, ghastly hand trembling to and fro. It was horrible. He was aghast with terror. Frantically seizing his revolver, he aimed, pulled the trigger, and blew off *his own big toe.*

The child may see in the shadows on the wall pleasant things like babies' faces, if he is happy, contented, and not nurtured on gruesome things. On the other hand, if he has been frightened and scared into being good, these same shadows may represent the evil one, or the bogy man trying to get him.

Just as the external world may be colored and distorted by our feelings, so, likewise, may the internal world of our bodies be grossly distorted. Somewhat similar to substitution but with a slightly different mechanism, sensations from the heart or stomach or flushing of the skin, in certain attitudes of mind, may represent sinful thoughts and feelings.

Much more complicated misinterpretations may arise. A very sensitive person may develop so-called ideas of reference. Such a girl is riding in a bus. Suddenly she discovers a hole in her stocking. She begins to twist herself into various positions to hide the hole. But she is sure some of the passengers have seen the hole and are looking at her. See, they are whispering. Now they are smiling and even laughing. She squirms and blushes and is thoroughly miserable.

Holes in stockings and many other worse things are common everyday occurrences. The passengers were not looking at the hole nor were they whispering or smiling about her, but only about their own affairs. She feels absolutely sure that she has interpreted correctly what she has seen. Thus may the interpretation of the objective world be distorted by our feelings.

Sometimes spinsters and very shy girls may be oversensitive to male glances. They, who have not learned to recognize the sexual significance of perfectly normal sensations and feelings, may unconsciously sexually color their world.

Any male attention is taken to indicate a proposal. Or, ordinary male behavior may be interpreted as improper. Such notions may be due to repressed and unrecognized or faintly identified complexes. Therefore, it is important to have at least some awareness of fundamental feelings and tendencies, even if they are not always highly respectable.

Another example. A boy has stolen another boy's pencil. For

the guilty boy, every glance of the teacher seems to have special significance. She seems to eye him with suspicion. She may even walk down the aisle near the boy. He feels she is watching him. She may ask someone to lend her a pencil. Her whole procedure may have no reference to the boy who stole the pencil. Yet he feels it because of his feelings of guilt. These color his world and the actions of the teacher toward him. The wind may suddenly blow and bang a door so that he jumps, believing this a reminder on the part of God that He knows what he has done. And he may be impelled to return the pencil.

An individual at one time in his life may have been guilty of a moral lapse. Gradually he becomes extremely sensitive about it. Soon he is convinced that everyone knows about his sin. The most casual behavior of others is to him unmistakable reference to his guilt. Normal sensations in heart, stomach, or limbs are interpreted as just punishment. The patient's whole world is circumscribed by the feelings of sensitiveness and guilt. The boundaries between subjective (self) and objective (environment) are lost. To argue is useless. It is emotion and not intellect which is affecting judgment so strongly. We are now within the territory of actual mental disease, where not only ideas of reference but hallucinations (hearing of voices, etc.) and delusions of various kinds, particularly delusions of persecution, operate.

Projection is an important molder of many of our social and philosophical points of view. The brilliant and inspiring leader may project and propagate his own point of view with such vigor that a given society will accept and adopt his attitudes. The person who feels beauty, kindness, and goodness sees this in the world and projects this into the very heart of things. On the other hand, the person who is filled with bitterness, resentment, and hate projects this onto the center of the universe and sees only the struggle of wills, competition, and the fight for survival as did Nietzsche. The one type of projection is called "good" because it promotes constructive, enjoyable, social living. The other is called "bad" because it interferes with social cooperation and cohesiveness, by emphasizing the disruptive forces at work in human nature. Theologically one set of forces is of God and the other is of the Devil. Projection, starting from a very personalized basis, may call attention to important needs of society.

For example, a person who has suffered from poverty in childhood or economic injustice as an adult may see (projection) these forces at work everywhere in society, and write about them with such intensity and emphasis that (although his point of view is limited and exaggerated) he rouses the public to certain genuine evils that exist and helps in effecting a correction of these evils. Thus projection may help to bring about social changes of great value. As for the individual, projection enables him to externalize his troubles and often escape the pinch of humiliation and self-reproach. Here, of course, its use is very questionable.

Whether our view of life remains dark or bright depends very much on our own personal experience and problems. Those to whom life has been generous and abundant develop an optimistic and conservative philosophy which finds expression in the verse:

> The world is so full of a number of things
> I'm sure we should all be as happy as kings.

The individual possessing these sentiments proclaims them as a sort of right and obligation for all, because *his* world is so full of things that make *him* happy. It is easy for him to join Pippa's song that all is right with the world, or to concur with the ideas expressed in the following quotation:

> Then take your fortune as it comes
> Whatever God may give,
> And through the day
> Your heart will say
> 'Tis luck enough to live.

This philosophy is good enough for the "haves" but rarely helpful to the "have-nots." It is the philosophy of exuberant affluence. It does not help those "in the clutch of circumstance" or those who have felt the "bludgeonings of chance." The sinned against, the sorrowful, and the beaten may develop a bitter, cynical pessimism. Neither of these philosophies paints a true and complete picture of the world and human life. Both are distorted and too highly colored by fortuitous circumstances of personal experience.

Here, as in so many things, it is a question of proportion and balance. We have pointed out some unfortunate consequences of too much projection. Carried to excess it may lead to a mental breakdown. This mental mechanism, however, may be of use to man. It may be protective in more senses than one. It may have some wholesome effect in blinding us to our own shortcomings, so that we tackle things and make efforts and, at times, accomplish things that a proper appreciation of our limitations would prevent us from attempting. In this way it may ward off the almost paralyzing blows of cold, hard facts.

Occasionally, projection may be individually constructive. The young man who feels ill treated by his boss, instead of realizing he has not measured up, may inwardly accuse his employer of unfair treatment. He then adopts an "I'll show him" attitude, buckles down, and overcomes limitations. The attitude he unconsciously really wanted his employer to show was a modified coddling or protective attitude, an infantile reaction. This was a hang-over from childhood ways of adaptation. Projection here, then, serves a useful purpose *if* the person reacts favorably. It is clear, of course, that if the individual were not of a vigorous, combative turn of mind he would react to his projected fancies in a very inadequate way. He might sulk or react emotionally with irritations and modified tantrums. He might even lose all ambition and quit, a defeated individual.

## DANGERS OF PROJECTION

All in all, it may be written that projection is more likely to multiply difficulties than it is to solve them. On the surface it is altogether too simple. We escape recognition of our own faults and defects by blaming others. We soften disappointment and failure by attributing it to others or to the conditions of life. What could be easier? And perhaps that is the chief objection to projection. It is altogether too simple and too easy.

It is a mental habit which feeds on itself. When we have experienced the surcease it gives, then we readily use it again and again. Soon, we are not only employing it as a defense against the trivial irritations of life, but resorting to it in serious problems. Like a narcotic drug, more and more is required to produce the desired effect. Gradually it determines moods and emotional reactions, so that the outlook on life becomes hopelessly distorted. Where at first it gave satisfaction, it now results in unhappiness. If it does not produce mental disease, it is nevertheless true that in several forms of mental disease

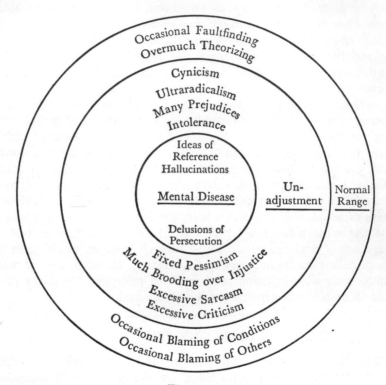

*Figure 25*

the symptoms are elaborately developed for the apparent purpose of escaping self-recognition and self-blame.

Perhaps we may picture the results of various degrees of the projection mechanism (Fig. 25).

It was said that projection feeds upon itself. It does. It must be used at more frequent intervals and in larger amounts if it is to continue effective. Furthermore, society or the herd begins to penetrate the personal disguise and to criticize the individual. In turn, he may take refuge in more generalized projections—overmuch theorizing, pessimism, cynicism, radicalism. These for a time may pass current as "intellectual" and gain a few plaudits. Sooner or later, more often than not, society discovers the fallacies, with their insecure foundations. In the long run, the individual is apt to lay himself open to the very fate which he sought to evade, the censure of others.

Projection is rarely constructive. Persistent, long-continued effort and striving are discounted, since there is too readily at hand an available explanation for cessation of the struggle or reversal. It is too much like going into battle, carrying a previously prepared excuse for defeat.

## Chapter 24

# IDENTIFICATION AND IDEALIZATION

*In this chapter is discussed* Identification, *a psychological mechanism which enters into the life of every human being, from almost the cradle to the grave. Identification is potent mental medicine, and must be used sparingly. In excessive doses it is a subtle and dangerous poison.*

BY PERMITTING US TO IGNORE OR DISOWN OUR WEAKNESS (conflicts), projection gives us the feeling of security and strength. It is more comfortable to turn our mental backs on our own faults and condemn them in others. In the related psychological mechanism, *identification,* we identify ourselves as closely as possible with people and institutions that represent for us ideal qualities. Such qualities embody our strongest aspirations. We admire them. We wish to possess them. Both projection and identification constitute psychological magic, employed by the mind to bring peace, harmony, and happiness into life. Projection, by a sort of mental sleight of hand, blinds us to the unpleasant real in ourselves by fixing our attention on its presence in others. Identification by another kind of magic "pieces out" or supplements the real with the ideal. Sometimes, it may even wipe out entirely an unsatisfactory real and replace it by a soul-satisfying ideal. We are more familiar with identification, and, all in all, it is considered a more "respectable" process than projection. People admire and praise it. On the whole it is individually and socially useful. The man who avails himself of projection is apt to become pessimistic,

cynical, and sarcastic. The optimist is more likely to employ identification.

Identification has the same objective as projection. It seeks to
lift us over the hurdles of difficulties and conflicts. Our feelings of
inadequacy and inferiority urge us to borrow strength from our conception of the ideal. Usually the urge is an unconscious one. Often,
not until it is pointed out, do we realize that identification is being
used to bolster up our weaknesses, or perhaps to gloss over deficiencies. The extrovert, with his surface carefree attitude, is a bit
more likely to employ identification. He skips over problems with as
much assurance as though they did not exist. Identification comes so
spontaneously that it seems almost like a simple, instinctive process—
merely the unfolding of a native tendency of the human mind, unrelated to anything like difficulties or disharmonies. The need for
identification arises when there is an unconscious lack of something
which leaves life very incomplete.

Identification must have been recognized many, many years ago.
Aesop wrote a fable about a fly perched on the wheel of a furiously
racing chariot. The fly surveyed the enveloping clouds of dense dust
and remarked: "Lo, see what a dust *I am raising.*" Common, everyday examples of identification are observed when we read a book that
literally enthralls us with interest or see a play which holds us spell-
bound. Our minds are so gripped and held, because, unconsciously,
one of the characters in the book or one of the actors on the stage
depicts the yearned-for self-ideal.

## IDEALIZATION

The most usual form of identification is *idealization.* It is met in every
stage and phase of life. The young child not only idealizes but even
idolizes his parents. In them, he instinctively feels, there rests the
Alpha and Omega of all wisdom and authority. Intuitively, he assumes
that his parents possess the knowledge and the power to succor him
in every contingency of life. The father and the mother are the repos-
itories of the last word an any subject. "Listen in" on a dispute between children. Sooner or later, one will hear this statement, "My
father said so and I guess he knows." Or "My mother said so." It
made no difference at all that Bobby Smith's father happened to be

a world-wide authority on a given subject. *Our own* parents knew best. We could not be dislodged from our stand by the opinion of others. We were secure in the fortress of our parents' beliefs and opinions. The insecurity, uncertainty, and disquietude of the child are relieved and supplemented by the more positive and stable qualities of the parent. The judgment of the father and mother can be pronounced with absolute confidence and their convictions asserted, as if they belonged to the child. Thus, he is rendered impregnable. With the unconscious voice of genius Shakespeare wrote:

> The voice of parents is the voice of God's
> For to their children they are heaven's lieutenants

The responsibility of the parent is great and obvious, and, yet, it is rarely completely realized. Too often, the tragic problems of childhood are taken very light-mindedly. Later in life, unnecessary difficulties are produced. Children will defend to the last ditch that great citadel of parental authority and security, but there must come a time when the citadel begins to totter.

It is with great difficulty that children give up this sense of security they find in their parents and begin to think for themselves. The emancipation comes at varying ages with different children. Some never experience it. For others the experience comes prematurely or in the wrong way. It is a serious matter if self-reliance is never attained, but it is equally serious if children are suddenly thrown upon their own resources through the betrayal of their faith in their parents. Therefore, it is important to answer a child's questions truthfully. It is normal and natural for him to reach out for the knowledge which is a prerequisite to independence. He may be feeling his way and need help. If children ask where babies come from, they receive a variety of replies directed by the wisdom or sometimes the folly of the parent. Now if a number of children argue with vehemence the doctor's bag theory versus the stork theory, some of the children may finally realize to their horror that their parents have been untruthful. And their castle falls. That which they had considered impregnable has been found to be miserably weak. Some children never recover from the sudden and dramatic realization of unreliability and insecurity and they never feel the same toward their parents. The latter, instead of trying to emancipate their children gradually and rationally, have unwittingly pushed them out. The trust of a child is a beautiful and complete thing, but, once shattered, the result is an almost ineradicable resentment and distrust.

It is important for parents to keep faith with their children, not only by telling them the truth, but also by helping them to achieve gradually a larger and larger measure of independence. Some parents are never willing that their children should be emancipated. They hang onto them eternally. They make decisions for them—what they shall do, what they shall wear, where they shall go, what they shall study, what career they shall follow, whom they shall marry, and even what the grandchildren's names shall be! A play, *The Silver Cord,* develops this theme. The mother could not bring herself to sever the mother-son bond. The result was such ruin and wreckage for two sons that it could be predicted that one of them would end his days in a mental hospital.

Much of such interest which masquerades as love is in reality misguided selfishness. Parents unconsciously desire to extend their own spheres of influence and keep alive their own personalities. They are usually perfectly sincere, for they are unaware of what they are really doing. But sincerity and ignorance can scarcely excuse the unwise course they follow. If the children do not learn to emancipate themselves as youngsters, they must learn it later in life. Like any established habit, the older a person grows the more difficult is it to change. Deaths, marriage, and careers force emancipation ultimately. And all doctors know how disastrous may be such forced and delayed emancipations. In fact, a considerable portion of people who are nervous develop states of anxiety, indecision, and incapacity, when, after a too guarded life, the course of events throws them on their own. These people are like captainless or rudderless ships. They are buffeted hither and yon by the winds of chance until they are blown into some haven of authority which will make the process of emancipation a more gradual one. A teacher, a priest, a physician, or a friend may supply this authority and security.

Mother and father ideals are frequently determinative influences in love life. Analysis shows that often there is an attempt to refind the mother or father pattern in wife or husband. Sometimes the same attitudes and even physical characteristics are unconsciously sought.

A man whose mother is dignified, matronly, and serious may be inclined in this direction, when he comes to select his mate. Furthermore, he may be disdainful of the informal, jolly, and carefree type. If questioned, he would assert positively that his judgment is purely intellectual and rational; he does not recognize that the mother-love ideal is directing him and that it is primarily emotional.

There is danger of failure in marriage if either husband or wife demand in the mate too great conformity to the parent ideal. They find that they have not married the person they thought they had. They have married an ideal. Then comes the period of disillusionment. This is the rock on which so many marriages are shattered. Processes of identification may even lead people to avoid marriage while their parents are alive. A man, for example, may be unconsciously afraid he will not find the security in the loved one that he finds in his mother, though this thought may never formulate itself in his mind. Or he may fear that his new attachment will cause his mother to withdraw her interest and protection. It is needless to point out how harmful are such attitudes.

Even though there is a pull to continue the parent-child relationship to the very end of life, it is obvious that the identification is bound to be modified. In some instances, nurses stand as surrogates for the parents. The child transfers the parent attitude to the nurse. Adult reactions toward the opposite sex and toward life in general—loves and hates, morality, guilt, religion—a whole range of tendencies and desires—have been determined in many cases by attitudes which have become habitual and which were fostered early in childhood by nurses or governesses. The questions of identification, security, and emancipation are most important in a child's early and intimate contacts.

We meet the same problem in school life. The teacher appears on the scene. She is supposed to broaden the experience of the child and impart knowledge that the home cannot give. But information is only one part of that broadening process—a fact which is so often forgotten.

The teacher therefore enters as a source of authority number three. The first was the father and mother. The second was the nurse or governess. Now the teacher becomes a citadel of security and protection. She is regarded as a stronghold of wisdom. A highly ideal relationship often becomes established, and too much identification here is fraught with the same dangers that exist in the home. The child argues that the teacher said so and so, and feels secure from all assaults, until he learns that there are equally eminent teachers who differ.

This process does not cease with maturity. We have seen men and women working for doctor's degrees in philosophy who, because of their devotion to a favorite professor, have uncritically adopted his philosophy in toto. Herein they found security. Too often it is only after they leave the precincts of academic walks that young people realize that the opinions of favorite professors are not necessarily true. It is a cruel awakening. The loss of support and the realization of it may leave a state of persistent apprehension and a feeling of utter inadequacy which may handicap the individual for years. Institutions of learning should stimulate a spirit of reasonable independence and self-reliance instead of the reverse. This is every whit as important as imparting mere information, and probably more so. Knowledge will not find any motive force for application and activity in a broken, inadequate personality.

In play life, identification is ever active. On the athletic field the youthful hero reigns supreme. He is almost worshiped. One is put on the social school map, if the football star is his friend. Adolescence is the age of the most profuse flowering of hero worship. What American boy or girl was not thrilled at the thought of the heroic stand of MacArthur and his men at Corregidor? At adolescence and later, more general types of ideals are formed. Frequently they are patterned on characters found in literature and more particularly in fiction. They shine for us in the light of romance. The longings we have in our hearts are realized in our heroes and heroines. The vague stirrings that are obscurely felt in ourselves are expressed in them. All that we might be and wish ourselves to be, we find ready-made here. From this standpoint movies or television programs have unlimited possibilities for good or ill. For there, almost in flesh and blood, the most amazing feats are enacted. The regular theater affords similar opportunities. The danger, of course, is that we may derive satisfaction merely in contemplation and fantasy rather than in actually trying to realize worthwhile ideals.

Identification in the form of hero worship does not stop with the school and athletic field, nor with the movies, the drama, and literature. The hero-worshiper in all of us influences life from almost the cradle to the grave.

We can see the inestimable good in these tendencies of the human mind. We tend to imitate those we admire. Trying to duplicate perfection helps to improve self. We have both a personal and social stimulus for self-perfection. The harm, of course, comes when such idealization becomes so exaggerated that the deficiencies of our heroes, their "clay feet," are condoned, overlooked, strike our blind spots, or, worse still, are imitated.

There is much identification in the ordinary associations of life. In a sense, our friends are our heroes. Running through friendship is a vein of admiration for their qualities and attainments. Unconsciously, too, we wish to develop similar capacity and performance. Friends may stimulate character formation. They provide security and guidance.

In a larger sense, we may say with Ulysses—"I am part of all that I have met." In a considerable measure, standards and principles of conduct are governed by friends, colleagues, and social groups. Their conscience becomes our conscience. We strive to win approval and avoid condemnation. In other words, we conform, and one of the stimuli to conformation is identification. In school, business, and social life we imitate the popular, the successful, the approved. Law and medicine have their traditions, and the contravention of certain precepts and rules precludes real success. In Galsworthy's *Loyalties,* the lawyer withdraws from a case which the conscience of the law cannot countenance. The oath of Hippocrates has set a high standard for the practice of medicine which has been maintained for centuries. The apprentice and guild system was founded on strict rules of organization and practice.

Laws, whether written or unwritten, make for stability and organization. Without them life would offer less opportunity for the individual. This makes for conservatism in all lines of conduct. We should never forget that conservatism has a great survival value. Conservative principles were once innovations and were only arrived at through costly experience. Therefore, it is not the part of wisdom hastily to overthrow that which has often been dearly bought. Conservatism is the "herd instinct" expressing itself in and through the individual. Through conservatism the individual purchases security by identification with the group. An overdevelopment of this tendency, however, is false to the very origin of conservatism, for the principles we now look on as conservative once were new. Fundamentally, conservatism is not, or should not be, opposed to all that is new.

Conservatism emphasizes social tendencies, while radicalism emphasizes individualistic tendencies. Both radical and conservative, however, are fighting for security. The one is usually fighting for the security he does not have and the other for the security he already possesses. They both, in extreme cases, use the projection mechanism to attribute their own "devilish" motives to the other group. The great personality is the one which combines both conservative and radical tendencies in a happy proportion. With conservative tendencies he will combine discriminating radicalism and venture the new when it seems reasonable. If intelligently radically minded, he will give reasonable consideration to the experience of others, rather than doggedly adopt his own inspirations and dreams as the only principles of conduct.

In religion we find the mental processes of identification and projection very prominent. Those who believe in the devil project upon him all the evil tendencies which they can possibly imagine. And it is natural to emphasize the tendencies which they find, in themselves, especially difficult to curb. This is the reason that the base urgings of the devil apparently take different forms for different people.

On the other hand, we think of all the nobler promptings of our natures as coming from God. That which we find of supreme value for our personal and social life, we find in God. He supplements and sustains the inadequacies and frailties of our human natures. Alone we are lost and worthless. But by identification, we find in God the Perfect, while we are imperfect. We glorify His perfection. All that we hope to be we find in God. He is our refuge in times of stress, trouble, and tribulation. As our problems differ, so do the ideals we find in God differ. At one time we think of Him as the Creator. At another, He is the Law Giver and Lord of Justice. At times He is the God of Battles. At others, He is the Lover of Mercy and the God of Love. As our ideals and needs differ, so do we emphasize the various attributes and qualities of God. At all events, however conceived, whether as the Savior of society or as the Protector of an individual life, God represents that which is supreme

for the interests and needs of man. The best and noblest are found
in the attributes of the Godhead. We thus see that in the conception
of God the process of idealization or identification is raised to its
greatest heights.

In all walks of life, then, in all the ages of man, identification
finds a prominent place. It includes hero worship, standards of conduct to be imitated, and aspirations to be fulfilled. Wherever there
are courses to be followed that seem to have an overpersonal justification, wherever we have loyalties involved, there one discovers
identifications in the form of idealization.

We should be dull and drab without identification. It adds zest
to life. And this is the fine thing about it. We are stimulated to strain,
to reach high in order to supersede ourselves. Energies are called
out and qualities and capacities are developed that otherwise would
go unpracticed. It enables us to make the most of whatever talents
we have. Self-development, therefore, is greatly favored by identification. It is the antagonist of desuetude.

Identification performs another function. When energy flags,
when attainment seems impossible, when we are apparently defeated,
identification steps in to support us. It is an anodyne to discouragement. Ideals keep us going when otherwise we should give up the
ship. They carry us through the difficult and rough places of life.
Dull routine is sometimes alone sustained by them. They support
us when the energies of life are at the ebb. When buffetings bear us
down and weary the soul, ideals may carry us through.

## DANGERS OF IDENTIFICATION

If allowed to overflow the bounds of proper proportion, identification
has unfortunate and deleterious results. The criterion must be useful
action. If identification merely leads to idealization and fantasy formation, then it is harmful. The formulation of vague ideals may become so complicated and spun out that all the available time is con-
sumed and one looks in vain for practical results. This is the life
path which leads away from reality and adjustment. If this path is
followed too exclusively, there is, finally, the arrival at the point
where daydreams are preferred to concrete life problems. Ideals and
daydreams then degenerate to the lowest level. Identification on these

terms is as harmful, as illegitimate, and as ineffective in meeting the duties and difficulties of life, as is addiction to an opiate.

One inevitable result of overdeveloped identification is the confusion of the ideal and the real. We have all met the individual who cannot see the real because of the thick screen of his ideals. He is blinded by ideals. This type of idealist is the dreamer and the visionary, the poor executive and organizer, and, occasionally, the dangerous fanatic. Pursued to its ultimate conclusion, unchecked identification may lead to such absolute confusion of fact and fiction that we eventually have the delusion. Then we are only a short step from the magnates and millionaires, the kings and emperors, the redeemers and the gods—of the mental hospital. Clear thinking in the small things of life is an excellent preventive against departures into unreality.

It may be worthwhile briefly to review the situation from the perspective of mental hygiene. Identification possesses more potentialities for good than projection and

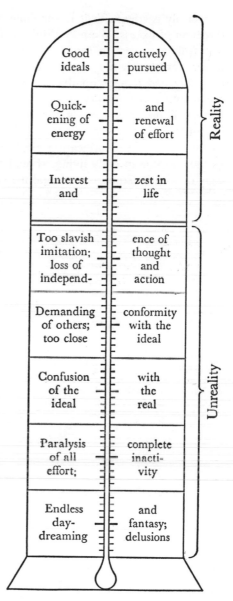

*Figure 26*

conversely carries with it fewer dangers. Its chief dangers are in the direction of excess. We may think of it as a flourishing plant yielding fine fruit at a certain range of temperature; below this range, it is either sterile or it may even produce poisonous fruit. The markings of safety and danger on the scale of this hypothetical thermometer are reality and unreality. In other words, if idealization is to be effective, it needs constantly the check of the real. It must be kept within the limits of the actual and the concrete. It is not too difficult to take our own identification-idealization temperature. The results, as they appear in daily living, should furnish a fair index of the efficacy of identification as a mental mechanism (Fig. 26).

*Chapter 25*

# THE INFERIORITY COMPLEX
# AND SELF-EXPRESSION

A *discussion of the* Sense of Inferiority. *An exceedingly common and understandable complex, which may make or mar our mental lives.*

WHILE IT IS TRUE THAT ALL THE CONFLICTS THAT BESET HUMAN beings may be reduced to the elemental drives that arise from the respective claims of the three great complexes, ego, sex, and herd, yet for the individual there are infinite variations. Given even similar conditions, there are still marked differences. Mary Jones may be facing a conflict in her love life because she is in love with the husband of her friend, and hundreds of miles away Anna Smith may be meeting an exactly similar situation. Nevertheless, since these two women are separate and distinct personalities, the details, the nature, and the outcome of their struggles may bear no resemblance to each other. It is obviously impossible to describe all the conflicts which may try our souls. There is, however, one conflict that may be traced to a complex that is so common and so often makes or mars human lives that it merits separate consideration. We refer to that so-called inferiority complex or the sense of inferiority.

## THE SENSE OF INFERIORITY

A sense of inferiority is an idea or set of ideas, strongly bound together emotionally, that makes us feel inferior or less than our fellow men. We may be clearly aware of our personal belittlement; we may recognize it faintly, or we may be totally unconscious of it, although it obviously expresses itself in our everyday behavior.

Disappointment, failure, defeat, infirmity are the seeds of the inferiority complex. We hate to be neglected; to remain unloved; to be relegated to a lowly position. We desire to succeed; to master difficulties; to feel strong. Success is usually rewarded by a feeling of security; failure made worse by the agony of insecurity. The basis of inferiority may be physical, environmental and mental, or a combination of the two.

## PHYSICAL INFERIORITY

The intense sensitiveness that torments the individual who feels inferior frequently is determined by physical factors. One of our little patients had had an attack of infantile paralysis, which left him a bit weak in one leg and made him limp. After convalescence, he attempted to re-enter the play activities of his playmates. At first, they were considerate of his handicap and inability to "keep up" in games, but soon, with the almost brutal frankness of childhood, they became impatient. He saw he was not wanted. One or two of the boys even called him "limpy." His house of cards crashed to the ground. Unwanted and miserable, he retired into himself. The yearning for a "place in the sun" would not be stilled. He began to steal money from his mother's pocketbook. With this money he took his former playmates to the movies, bought them soda and candy. For a short time at least, he could buy the right to be with other boys on equal terms. Fortunately, the situation had not gone so far but that it could be retrieved.

A serious physical cause of inferiority in boys is a real or fancied undevelopment of the sex organs. We are now dealing with a man of thirty-five, whose attitude toward life in all its relations—his marriage, his business, his social life—is one of hopeless discouragement and failure. When he was a boy in school, someone thoughtlessly made a remark about his sex organs, which were a trifle undersized. He began to avoid undressing before the other boys. Next, he invented all sorts of excuses to stay away from the gym and athletic field. Then, he assumed an interest in the violin, so that his athletic and social derelictions could be, at least partly, explained. He became less and less inclined to associate with others; his physical health was poor; he grew peculiar and asocial in his attitudes and beliefs. Later in life, marriage to a charming and understanding woman failed to lift him from the depths of his inferiority. Any physical defect, even an insignificant one, may have far-reaching results, and it is important to establish wholesome and rational compensatory activities as soon as possible.

We know a young woman who has splendid qualities, physically and mentally. She is quite tall but beautifully proportioned. On the basis of her size, she is simply overwhelmed by inferiority. With an extremely well-developed, informed, and cultured mind, nevertheless, she is socially awkward, because her inferiority and self-consciousness will not permit her to give utterance to her thoughts. Unusually endowed in two directions, she has twice turned her back on her accomplishments, when a little more effort might have very well meant not only a personal, but also a public success. She is well born and wealthy, but in her mind these natural and acquired advantages do not outweigh the fact that she is "as tall as a man." In this connection it is interesting to note that small men are often sensitive about their size and go about with a chip on the shoulder, daring the world to "knock it off."

Examples could be endlessly multiplied. Suffice it to say, any deviation from the average, either in appearance or in physical function, may in a given case undermine the morale to the point of inferiority.

## ENVIRONMENTAL AND
## MENTAL INFERIORITY

Environmental and consequently mental causes for inferiority are legion. A child is receiving poor marks in school and stands low in the class. He becomes discouraged. Instead of giving him understanding and help, his parents scold him. He tries harder, but the specter of failure and the lack of emotional support is always before him—a frightening specter. Naturally, he fails even worse. Now all his confidence is gone: "I am no good—I can't do it." Headache, crying spells, and then finally a nervous breakdown are at hand. It is the only escape from a sense of inferiority that he must meet alone and unaided.

The child of average ability who has brilliant parents starts life under considerable disadvantage. A noted psychiatrist remarked that he was sorry for the boy or girl whose father or mother had made Phi Beta Kappa. It is even worse when brothers and sisters are superior students or athletically and socially favored above the average. If the mediocre one is at all sensitive, such a situation, unless very intelligently handled, has in it the potentiality of disaster. The child is very likely to develop the idea that he does not "belong"; that it is not worthwhile to try to strengthen the few capacities which he does possess. Why try? He can never hope to do as well in school as Jane; to make the football team as Bill has; to be able to talk to girls as Jack does. Too often, capabilities which are not so striking but solid enough, as, for instance, aptitude along mechanical lines, are forever lost and a sense of inferiority permitted to ruin life.

Many children become inferior-minded because of home conditions. Quarreling between parents, separation, divorce, alcoholism; in short, anything of which the child feels ashamed, or which humiliates him in the eyes of his companions, are potent factors. One of the most pathetic stories we ever listened to came pouring out from the very soul of a boy of nine, who was going home from boarding school for the Christmas holiday. For weeks he had listened to his school friends excitedly tell of the good times they were going to have with their families in their own homes. And he was going to spend ten days with his mother in her fashionable apartment and ten days with his father in a large and ornate hotel!

We frequently encounter inferiority feelings in the children of foreign families. Take an orthodox Jewish family transplanted from Russia. The children are educated in our schools, assimilate our ideas of life and success. The parents are too old to change. The daughter of the family meets at a dance and becomes interested in a young man who is studying law. She is a bright girl and dresses attractively in the latest American fashion. The young man responds to her attractions. It seems inevitable that he should meet her family. Then the girl thinks of her humble home. Her father is an itinerant merchant of the pushcart class. Her mother adheres to the orthodox dress. The house is poorly furnished and in a dirty section of the city. The neighbors are far too neighborly. The girl cannot face the issue. She is ashamed of her parents, their manners, their surroundings, and is afraid to bring her sweetheart home. She breaks off relations with him; loses interest; refuses to go out anywhere; stays at home and sulks. Untold suffering results from such supposed inferiority. Clear thinking would show her that her family is really a superior one compared with those that have been left behind in the old country. It was only their greater initiative and foresight that enabled them to uproot themselves and start in life anew where there were more opportunities. And then, too, clear thinking would show her that manners of eating and sleeping are not the only criteria of true nobility of living.

Sometimes, inferiority is literally thrust upon one of the innocent actors in a drama of life. A man at the age of forty is only beginning to recover from the devastating effect of a sense of inferiority. At the age of twenty-two, his well-connected, socially, and commercially prominent family secured for him in one of the family-owned enterprises a position at a salary of $25,000.00 a year. He was not expected to know the work. In fact, it was not anticipated that he would work much, anyhow. But he happened to be a conscientious young man. Without much help, he tried to earn the money which his high-sounding position called for. He would have been illy prepared for even a much less important job. He felt that he was sailing under very false colors. He began to hate himself, his work, his family, and everyone who had had anything to do with the personally painful predicament in which he had been placed. His inferiority overflowed into every relation of his life. Socially he was inadequate and awkward. He believed that everyone recognized his deficiencies at once; he was overwhelmed by his real and imaginary shortcomings, and finally became little short of a recluse. Suicide was seriously planned. Then, fortunately, he resigned from the firm, sought an occupation within the range of his capabilities, and is now well on the way to a better and happier life.

A charming woman, with unusual personality assets, is sensitive and goes out of her way to find fault with herself. In any awkward situation, always, she accepts the blame. She has accomplished a great deal in life and against considerable odds, but in her mind these things are insignificant. Her many splendid actions are sifted through the screen of inferiority and, then, to her they appear trivial and inconsequential. The answer is this; in her childhood, an unwise mother constantly pointed out to her the supposedly superior charms and endowments of an older sister. Thus was conditioned lifelong inferiority.

A young widow was almost swamped by inferiority feelings. Yet she had beauty, grace, charm, intelligence, and a kind and generous disposition. Her married life was a series of personal sacrifices. Her husband unfortunately lacked the heterosexual instinct, and his whole life was lived on the basis of keeping a too disturbing realization of his plight from the portals of consciousness. She did not understand fully, but realized vaguely that something was missing; that he was more like a child and less like a husband in their marital association. She submerged her own sex desires; in fact, they never came clearly into consciousness. She devoted herself to her husband, ever seeking to protect him from something that she herself did not entirely comprehend. The self-appointed task was well done. Her husband was happy. She, too, found the happiness of service, but at the cost of her own ego striving. It was almost pathetic that, from time to time, she felt she "must talk," as she said, "about herself." It was a recital of the little happenings of her daily life—what she did, what she bought, the people she saw. Psychologically, it was more than a bare recital; it was a plea to be saved from the extinction of self by a constantly growing and ever-threatening sense of inferiority. Fortunately, better understanding was attained and she began to realize herself as an individual.

## COMPENSATION

Once a strong sense of inferiority, whatever the cause may be, has become a part of the personality, then the battle is on. Whether it is recognized or not by the individual, it inevitably produces cravings, yearnings, desires, and strivings for relief. It cannot remain in status quo. Either the person will beat it down and rise above it or else the inferiority will destroy him. Efforts to outdistance, to allay, or to overcome inferiority may be termed compensations.

A common compensation is the development of apparent superiority. At first glance people with a breezy, blustering, cocksure manner seem to radiate the very essence of self-assurance. Often, on closer acquaintance, it is not too difficult to penetrate the armor of surface confidence and reveal the shell of inadequacy and inferiority. Frequently their lives have been conspicuous failures or, at best, mediocre. There is little in the record to justify superiority. They could sell their opinions for a very small price. Yet, their statements are very dogmatic. With an air of absolute accuracy and finality, they will inform you of the stocks which are about to go up; the size of the future wheat crop; the name of the team which will win the pennant; who is going to be the next President; the kind of hat one ought to buy. They talk readily of industrial conditions in New England, and as glibly about the effect of single tax on New Zealand. Their range of information is too wide and too dogmatic to be solid. They are experts—pseudo experts. Their manner is in strong contrast with the modesty and reserve which usually characterizes the real expert. The superior attitude is so often a surface compensation for underlying inadequacy.

Naturally not everyone who behaves in a dogmatic and superior fashion is compensating for inferiority. Many have accomplished much. The extrovert likes to occupy the center of the stage. Analysis, however, discloses that often the roots of the seemingly fair and strong tree of assurance are inadequate and inferior. Our first tendency is to condemn superior behavior as insincere. It is well to remember that such conduct may be built up unconsciously. Fortified by such attitudes, individuals are able to get on more satisfactorily. If they had not been able to react to their difficulties and handicaps in this way, they probably would have been completely crushed and defeated.

Perhaps, the most usual way of compensating for weakness and insecurity is through the magic wand of fantasy. It is utilized in every epoch of life. The play life of children, especially their secret play, is largely fantasy. Imagination is golden and boundless. A thought or two and the scrubby dirty little girl of the slums is transformed into a golden-haired princess and the sordid tenement room into a glittering castle. Fairy stories allow the child whose life is meager and cramped to live in a wonderful world, where one may be blessed by a fairy godmother, frightened by ogres and giants, loved by the handsome prince, or gain the favor of the beautiful daughter of the powerful king. Above all, one lives happily ever after. Adults, too, indulge in daydreams. The bachelor may find in literary flirtations the outlet for his unsatisfied desires. The shopkeeper may dream of founding a great commercial dynasty and compensate for the restrictions of his two-by-four store. Religion, philosophy, art, and literature afford standardized compensatory mechanisms by which society attempts to resolve conflicts and restore security. They are institutions providing ready and tried formulas for meeting the major conflicts of life.

Compensations may create fictitious goals for the person who has a strong inferiority complex. The desire for superiority and perfection may soften inferiority. The man who is mediocre may set his standards very high—too high. Then he may freely criticize others because they cannot reach his goal, but his own exalted standards save him from too penetrating criticism. The goal is so high that failure to come within striking distance of it may be readily excused. This is close to rationalization. We purchase our own respectability or security by a questionable process of thinking. Again, along similar lines, the person who feels inferior may take up an occupation related to one in which he has failed. Thus, the man who has not succeeded in one of the professions may compensate by teaching students of that profession. He may not be able to do it himself, but he can tell others how it ought to be done. Vocations may be pursued, not from inherent interest in the subject, but as a compensation for inferiorities. The work disguises the real problem. The woman who feels inferior, first toward her father and later in life toward her husband, may become an extreme and fanatical advocate of women's rights. A man who feels at sea in the company of women and is worsted in every contact with them may become a misogynist or woman hater. In this way he may acquire a reputation as a connoisseur of the fair sex and he cultivates this reputation as a compensation for his original inferiority. People who are reticent and aloof are often esteemed as clever and canny. In this category may be placed a few solemn and owl-eyed directors of corporations. The aloofness may be merely the result of diffidence, insecurity, and even a bit of stupidity. Yet, such a person ultimately learns to bank on the impression which he has created, and uses it in business and in social life. It is a compensation.

Another form of compensation deserves mention. It may be called the specialist attitude. For instance, Jimmy is doing fairly well at school. In his studies and in athletics he is just about average. But he wants to be a star. He wants to shine. He feels keenly his inability to rise above the average and inwardly is nagged by discontent. Suddenly he reaches a solution. He develops an unusual or out-of-the-way interest. It may be astronomy, philosophy, Egyptology, or even the saxophone. Generally it is in some abstract sphere, ordinarily far removed from the interests of a boy of Jimmy's age. He reads voraciously. Time is taken from regular studies and his marks fall to a lower level. His "special study" requires so much time that he skips athletics whenever he can. Even social contacts are avoided. He absents himself from the meetings of his club and makes excuses for not attending parties. All this is done, ostensibly and, perhaps, consciously on the basis of an "absorbing interest," let us say in astronomy. The compelling motive, however, is escape from the unpleasant facts of undistinguished competition with his fellows in the classroom and on the athletic field. The specialist attitude has *not* developed on the basis of particular liking and special ability for an unusual subject. It is merely a compensation for inferiority. There are instances where there is rare ability, but they are very infrequent. Jimmy finds that average capacity in an unusual field brings distinction. His parents are flattered. Perhaps, they have begotten a genius. Jimmy has won the recognition he desires. It is won too easily and at too great a loss. For one thing the school lessons have not been learned. At first Jimmy poses. Then he may actually develop an asocial attitude. He prefers to be alone. He is not being prepared for life, and it may be predicted that he will meet it in a very inadequate manner. The path to unhappiness and disaster has been opened. Such reactions are not limited to childhood. In adult life they follow the same paradigm.

Compensation may be obtained by traveling the "path of opposites." If we are presented with a list of words, and, after each one is called out, asked to write down the first word that comes to mind, we shall have an illustration of the tendency toward opposites. "Light" will probably call out "dark"; "long"—"short"; "day"—"night." It almost seems to be a psychological law. If our love is blocked, it may change to hatred. The child whose will is opposed may scream and pummel and scratch its mother. But soon the situation changes and affection is lavished as never before. This is over-compensation. The lover finds his attentions repulsed and becomes bitter. But the way is opened for reconciliation and he swings back with renewed and even stronger protestations of affection. He over-compensates for his bitterness. The politician is read out of the party by the leader. He becomes bitter in his denunciations. But when truce is declared and the pipe of peace is smoked, his expressions of sentiment and tender regard for the leader are often excessive and ludicrous.

This tendency to swing to extremes is found throughout life. It may account for sudden and dramatic changes. The libertine becomes converted, and instead of taking his religion normally, he overdoes it. He becomes meticulously overconscientious about insignificant details of daily living. The Quaker or Unitarian may swing from simplicity to ritualism. The member of the authoritative church may reverse to rationalism or ethical culture. An unfortunate medical experience may add a recruit to Christian Science and vice versa. A man who has been exceedingly free in his social relationships before marriage may become puritanical in his after-marriage associations and rather overzealous concerning the social relations of his wife and daughters. The father whose childhood was hemmed in by too may restraints may give his children unwise freedom. Boys and girls who have led restricted lives in small towns overcrowd New York and Hollywood. The man who has lived his life in the busy marts of trade of a large city retires to a farm. The explanation of overdone behavior of this sort is often dissatisfaction, insecurity, and inferiority. The overreaction or exaggerated response may carry a person along temporarily, but it is usually unsatisfactory in the long run. Adequate analysis of a situation will often reveal less extreme and more satisfactory courses of action and endeavor.

So far, we have emphasized the negative sides of inferiority and compensation. If we recognize the pitfalls, we may avoid them. There are positive aspects of inferiority which are constructive.

The inferiority complex has been called the "golden complex," and a book has been written on the *Glory of the Imperfect*. As a matter of fact, it would be a sorry world without this sense of the imperfect, without this knowledge of our limitations. As Browning says, it is the "spark that disturbs our clod." It keeps us striving to reach beyond our poor selves. It prevents us from reclining in smug satisfaction with what we have and what we are. It is the very breath of inspiration and progress.

> Poor vaunt of life indeed,
> Were man but formed to feed
> On joy, to solely seek and find a feast—

The very lack of success and perfection keeps us in the fight, struggling, and enables us to make more of ourselves. "Gifts should prove their use" said Rabbi Ben Ezra, but often they would remain unproved were it not for the spur and lash of inferiority. It enables us to rise upon our dead selves. We are given strength to "welcome each rebuff that turns earth's smoothness rough, each sting that bids nor sit nor stand but go." This is the philosophy of the inferiority complex, and it enables us to transmute it into pure gold.

The sense of inferiority has great social value. It makes our friends livable. It makes them human. Those who have an overgrown feeling of superiority lack imagination and sympathy. They lack attractive qualities, capacity for friendship, and, socially, are more or less impossible. The sense of inferiority, therefore, far from being a handicap is for many a boon and a blessing. It is true that if it goes too far, it is damaging and crippling, and then it must be dealt with in a frank and understanding manner. Inferiority is a more or less relative matter and, although we may be somewhat inadequate in some fields, nevertheless, we are almost sure to find compensations in certain real excellences in other directions.

There are wise and unwise compensations. The latter are usually inadequate, because they do not come from a fair, square, and open facing of the problem. When the inferiority is brought into the clear light of consciousness, then the compensations are apt to be legitimate and helpful for a happy and useful life. When we are discouraged and feel that we have been cruelly buffeted by fate, it is good compensation to try to remember our relative blessings and fortune. Such compensation is surely more beneficial, personally and socially, than a cynical, rebellious, and anarchistic attitude. As has been mentioned, there are available well-tried and efficacious compensations in religion, philosophy, literature, and art. Thoughtful, mature, and conscious deliberation over various occupational opportunities may result in perfect compensation.

Bodily inferiorities may find many compensations. The boy whose one leg is shortened because of infantile paralysis, may perfect himself at tennis until he becomes championship caliber. The stammering Demosthenes became, through perseverance, the greatest orator of antiquity. The man who is blind cannot become a great painter or sculptor, but he may by extraordinary application become a superior organist. A Helen Keller may compensate for the loss of sight and hearing by remarkable development of tactile and intellectual co-ordinating capacity. The person who is not scientific-minded may become an expert linguist. The man who is not artistic may have uncommon latent executive ability. The woman who is not attractive to men may become a leader in social movements. So in every walk of life, there are resources which do not involve the setting up of fictitious goals, adoption of specialist attitudes, the swing along the path of opposites, unwisely selected activities, overcompensation, cessation of effort and fantasy. There are legitimate, wholesome, and necessary compensations that add to the satisfaction and meaning of life.

## RÉSUMÉ

The presence of a sense of inferiority involves for the individual two mutually dependent problems. He is in possession of a characteristic which, if wisely handled, may be made to produce attractive dividends of success, adjustment, and happiness. Conversely, if unwisely managed, inferiority may result in failure, maladjustment to life, and much unhappiness. The first step is the recognition of the existence of inferiority feelings. One cannot fight a battle unless there is at least some understanding of the nature of the enemy. At best, there would be quixotic attacks upon harmless windmills.

Sometimes the inferiority cannot be discovered without psychotherapeutic help, but very often it is close enough to consciousness, so that it falls within the range of the searchlight of awareness. It is not always necessary to find the exact starting point of the inferiority, although it is valuable to discover it. Frank, honest appreciation of the inward state of affairs is often sufficient to pave the way for an intelligent, well-ordered attack upon the difficulty.

The criterion of this attack is the effect on our conduct. There are excellent compensations, but, also there are efforts at extrication from the inferiority which are far from sensible and may even be dangerous (Fig. 27).

| | |
|---|---|
| Conscious utilization of available compensations—religion, philosophy, literature, art | |
| Selection of satisfying and useful fields of occupational endeavor | |
| Stimulation of ambition expressed in concrete effort | **Wise Compensations** |
| Attractiveness of personality if the inferiority is not excessive | |
| An effort to appreciate the relative advantages of our position in life | |
| Overcompensation; decided superiority reactions | |
| Too highly placed goals beyond possibility of attainment | |
| Specialized attitudes involving neglect of the highly important and necessary routine of life | |
| Occupation selected on a personal basis without regard to innate fitness and limitations | **Unwise Compensations** |
| "Path of opposites"; sudden and wide swings in conduct reactions | |
| Cessation of effort; paralysis of activity | |
| Excessive daydreaming and fantasy; unreality | |

*Figure 27*

*Chapter 26*

# SUBLIMATION, OR SOCIALIZING
# OUR INSTINCTS

*In which is discussed* Sublimation, *a psychological mechanism that is not a mental hazard. In sublimation no element is ignored—neither the original nor the social nature of man. Both are weighed, and a compromise is effected rationally and on a conscious plane. The energies deriving from the original, primitive desires of man, are diverted from their unobtainable goals into new, constructive, and satisfying forms of activity. Through sublimation we may hope to find the way out of the maze of our conflicts, and attain that mental "peace that passeth all understanding."*

WE HAVE BEEN FOLLOWING THE HAZARDS AND MENTAL FORTUNES of hypothetical individuals who are brought face to face with conflicts. But the situations which have been described are not hypothetical, and the methods utilized in order to escape from them are not imaginary. It is our everyday life with its joys and sorrows, its opportunities and its risks.

Again, let us recapitulate. Complexes are the lot of every human being. Whenever there are complexes, there must inevitably be at least occasional conflicts. The parent complexes, ego, sex, and herd, from which all other complexes are derived, cannot always be expressed in complete harmony. In the face of conflict, action of some kind is demanded. There may be advance or retreat; an open battle in consciousness or a screened skirmish in the "no man's land" (subconscious and unconscious) of the mind; there may be hopeless defeat or glorious victory. Usually there is compromise.

What factors determine the particular campaign of the individual when he fights the battles of his conflicts? When an animal is attacked, it defends itself with its natural weapons. The tiger uses his teeth and claws; the opossum feigns death. So, too, when he meets mental hazards, the human being employs the natural resources of his personality. The extrovert goes into great activity; the introvert resorts to his most powerful defense, thought. This is the first factor.

The second condition is determined by the innate seriousness of the conflict. This again is decided by the make-up of the individual. We know a wealthy and fine lady from New England, who, at the age of seventy-eight, is faced by an enormous conflict, because her physicians feel she should eat her breakfast in bed. To her it seems almost immoral. For most of us, such a dictum would scarcely produce a conflict. Generally speaking, the conflict is the more serious in proportion to the importance and strength of the opposing complexes.

A third factor is the verdict of society. Most individuals cannot survive the adverse judgment of the herd. In this connection it must be remembered that the pronouncements of the herd are variable not only in point of time but, also, geographically. The codes and conventions of 1400 A.D. or even 1830 were not those of the year 1950. Consider the long and checkered history which has finally culminated in the modern institution of marriage. Or more simple, behold the gradual shrinkage of women's clothing. Furthermore, the social usages of the South Sea Islands are not those of New York and the latter are distinctly different from those of continental Europe. Finally, there are circles within circles. The individual usually seeks to win the approval of the circle within which he lives. It might be added that from time to time bold spirits defy the herd. Columbus dared calumny, persecution, imprisonment, and public disgrace— and sailed across uncharted seas to discover a new world. Always will there be pioneers—and martyrs.

## SUBLIMATION

We have now almost concluded the story of the various methods which the human mind utilizes in order to escape the frank facing of the conflicts or mental hazards which result from the warring of our complexes. At some time in our lives and to some extent we all use one or the other of these methods. Nevertheless, they are all crutches that enable us to walk mentally. Some of them are well-constructed and sturdy crutches, quite serviceable and useful. Others are uncertain and unreliable. A few are sure to smash. And they are all crutches. There is one way of walking without crutches—walking mentally upright. It is called *sublimation*.

According to the dictionary, to sublimate means to refine or to purify. Psychologically, it may be taken to signify the utilization of instincts, desires, and tendencies in approved ways—ways approved by self and by the herd. It is really a process of education of instincts, desires, and tendencies, so that they will work according to acceptable and accepted standards. In sublimation there is a refinement of the crude, a raising to higher personal and social levels. The problems of sublimation arise from the fact that man has instincts and desires, which represent conflicting tendencies. They align themselves, essentially along personal and social lines.

Instincts and the resultant desires and tendencies not only prompt but demand unrestricted execution of action. Nevertheless, only the exceptional individual reaches the summit of his intellectual and emotional desires. Circumstances interpose between cup and lip, and the majority must accept substitution and compromise. In affairs of the mind as in the affairs of the heart, trivial or serious in import, it is often true that human wishes are thwarted, or, at best, only partially satisfied. Stormy weather postpones a long-anticipated holiday; ill health makes it impossible to consummate the businessman's long-cherished dream of consolidation, expansion, and leadership; death steps in, and, by taking an only son, blasts the hope of a powerful captain of industry concerning the foundation of a great commercial dynasty; a woman who was clearly intended to be a wife and mother either lacks the opportunity to marry, or, if married, is for some reason prevented from bearing children. One might go on indefinitely and recite a lengthy list of the adversities and buffetings which are the portion of every human being.

The desire to accomplish any objective represents energy. When we are turned aside from our goal, this energy does not vanish. If anything, it becomes all the stronger because it has been temporarily denied an outlet. Ordinarily, if we fall short in the accomplishment of a primary wish, unconsciously or even consciously, we seek a substitute which will satisfy, at least partly, our inner striving. Half a loaf is better than no bread. Thus, instead of the promised outdoor holiday, the rainy day may be pleasantly passed before the library fire; for the sick businessman golf may be the outlet; the captain of industry may adopt a child to replace his son; the childless couple may do the same; and the woman with a strong maternal instinct who has been denied marriage may make many orphan children happy by her vicarious interest in their welfare. The potential energy which was to be utilized to gain the heart's desire is diverted into other channels and employed to secure the secondary object. In a very broad sense, such diversion of energy from an unobtainable desire into new pathways, leading to constructive and satisfying attainment, may be termed sublimation.

Sublimation is not necessarily and entirely restricted to the domain of the unconscious mind. In other words, it is not impossible to look disappointment in the face, and (to write somewhat paradoxically) make the better of it. It is probable that when there is absolutely no willingness or attempt to follow such a course, then deep repression follows. The initial striving, which is now offensive because it has not led to its object, is buried in the unknown or unconscious mental life, and it is thought that here it may condition bizarre and unhealthy mechanism with strange and unhygienic end products. For instance, it has been said that the young man who has been betrayed in his love may, by refusing to make truce with his disappointment, become a pessimistic hater of women and a recluse from their society. Unjust or cruel treatment during childhood is regrettable and sad and may degenerate the victim into a radical enemy of society. Whether or not the psychology of sublimation is accepted, it is undeniably true that inability or refusal to meet failure, disappointment, and denial in an open frank way is productive of much nervous and even mental disability and unhappiness. How much better it is to school ourselves to accept rebuffs, not necessarily cheerfully, but, at least, consciously. By taking stock of the situation, a fresher and more promising outlook may be unfolded.

The social environment presents obstacles which prevent us from always taking, literally and figuratively, what we may want. In a sense laws are restrictions of our personal liberty. So are the customs and traditions of the various social groups to which we belong. They are often called taboos. When a person has transgressed a social regulation he is said to have sinned against society. So are we restricted. The traffic officer representing the law forbids four people, arriving at the intersection of two streets, from speeding through as fast as they may desire. The young man cannot just physically appropriate the lady of his choice as did the cave man. No matter how hungry, it is not good manners to place too much food in one's mouth. Thus, we are hemmed in by customs and laws.

Another group of restrictions come from within. They may be referred to as inhibitions. They are ideas and feelings, that oppose, check, and modify courses of action. By resorting to an immoral stratagem, "just within the law," a businessman could drive a competitor into bankruptcy. He cannot bring himself to do it. The forces that restrain and prevent are inhibitions. Long before psychologists spoke of inhibitions, the restraining influence of that still small voice called conscience was recognized. Inhibitions may have wholesome or baneful influences. Feelings of diffidence, shame, and guilt may inhibit a normal amount of social intercourse. A feeling of inadequacy may inhibit one from tackling a job which could have been successfully accomplished.

Conflicts may issue in several ways. Cruder, baser, and more elemental tendencies may win the upper hand. This is more or less unsatisfactory, since the conflict itself is determined by the presence of uplifting social tendencies. There may be an attempt to neglect or ignore entirely, the "original nature of man." We have noted the harmful consequences in the shape of dissociated and substitute activities that may arise from repression. A state cannot survive if it ignores either the capitalist, the middle class, or the laborer. Neither can man survive happily if he pretends that instinctive and fundamental tendencies are not a part of his make-up. Frequently, there is satisfactory compromise or sublimation. This is rational, helpful, and constructive.

In sublimation no element is ignored—neither the original nor the social nature of man. Both are weighed and a compromise effected rationally and on a conscious plane. The energies deriving from the original, primitive desires of man are diverted from their unobtainable goals into new, constructive, and satisfying forms of activity. Education, whether in the home, the school, or the church (and we might add in life itself) is in great part instruction in sublimation.

## SOCIAL SUBLIMATION

Sublimation should also be considered from the point of view of distribution of our mental energies. We are endowed with an almost infinite number of interests and desires which represent capacity for accomplishment. These are potentialities. In a sense, therefore, they really represent energy. To distinguish this kind of potential energy from that which is found in the physical world, the Latin word *libido* is proposed. If we think of it as the latent or potential energy of our desires and wishes, instincts and emotions, ideas and complexes, then we have a satisfactory notion of libido.

Just as in the material world a given amount of energy may be obtained from an engine, so in the domain of the mind, there is a limit to the available energy. A certain amount of gasoline represents energy or power. It may be used for driving an automobile from which packages are delivered, day in and day out. It may, however, be utilized to take the car and its occupants to new places, where there is healthful recreation and stimulating and inspiring society. If all the gasoline is used for the first purpose, then there will be none left for the second. Now, similarly in mental life, our instincts or desires, our ideas and capacity for thought, represent energy. We might use most of our energy in satisfying elemental or primary desires, for instance in obtaining the sustenance of life. This would leave little time or energy to follow other interests, playing, studying, or enjoying social intercourse. When a Robinson Crusoe is shipwrecked on an island, or we are lost in the woods and are forced to make camp, the first thoughts must be food, water, and shelter. And the first two are the more important. We must eat and drink to survive, but we can manage for a time without shelter. So we search for a spring, hunt, fish, and look for edible food. This would consume the greater part of our energies. The remaining energy would be applied toward constructing a shelter. With low-grade savages, the greater portion of energy is diverted into the satisfaction of these elemental needs.

As we get caught up with food and shelter we may direct our energies into other channels. We might relax and smoke, dream of what we are going to do in the weeks to come, or swap stories and anecdotes with our companions. So relieved from the pressure of driving needs, we are able to spend some energy in planning, daydreaming, and social intercourse.

If we should have to remain a long time and had collected a sufficient store of food, then, no doubt, we would try to make our shelter more comfortable, convenient, and attractive. We might even decorate it. Likewise, do semisavages and primitive people. Decoration and primitive forms of art make their appearance as soon as elemental needs have been provided.

Just as in camp, we might celebrate establishment and safety by extra food and entertainment, so did festivals and rites and ceremonials enter into the lives of primitive people. Thanksgiving for the harvest or joy at the return of spring soon led to ceremonies and rituals with great religious significance. At the peak of the gold rush or in the early days of establishing a homestead in the virgin forests, such as is described in *Maria Chapdelaine* or in Hamsun's *Growth of the Soil,* there was little time for sex or the procreation of children. When life grows less rugged and strenuous, these things appear and new rituals and festivities are founded.

With food, shelter, and children adequately provided for, then there is the opportunity for more varied and extensive social relationship, with neighboring camps, families or tribes, as the case may be. When leisure appears, we have energy to spare that may be used in improving ourselves and our condition by well-thought-out plans. Then we no longer need live from hand to mouth. Then is the birth of science, philosophy, art, and civilization.

The energy available for different aspects of our nature depends very much on the degree of civilization in which we are living. From this point of view, sublimation is a question of the distribution of our energies along certain channels. In sublimation, energy that might be used exclusively in carrying out primitive impulses is directed wholly or in part into more socially useful activities. But even with the leisure afforded by a secured civilization, it is possible to expend our energies in primitive ways. Gourmandizing, disguised by the finesse and frippery of subtle and expensive cuisines; sex, whose excesses may be rationalized under elaborate formulas of modernity and artistic temperament; primal and ugly acquisitiveness, which may be masked by the concept, "big business"—all these modish cloaks fail to conceal the fact that a rather unnecessary amount of energy is being diverted into primitive channels. Furthermore, the energy is not being applied to the constructive side of these activities, but to the sensual side. Primitive man may spend most of his time in obtaining food, raiment, shelter, and sex satisfaction, but in the main, for him, these efforts are constructive and wholesome. In a complicated civilization with available leisure, the disciplinary and constructive aspect of primitive striving is absent, when energies are allowed to flow excessively into elemental impulses.

Civilization permits time for cooperation and for the development of science, which are the rocks upon which modern society rests. The diversion of excess or leisure energy from these broad activities to the more elemental and egocentric ones strikes at the very foundations of society and is subversive of the best interests of the individual. With the present organization of society, an adequate amount of sociability, activities in the interests of society, and a certain degree of deference to the herd opinion are not only signs of, but guarantors of, mental health. The individual who is not reacting reasonably well to his fellow man and the social environment is under a serious handicap for his own personal development and mental health. Thus, broadly speaking, sublimation as a socializing process is interwoven into the fabric of our everyday lives.

Sublimation has always existed. Not only is it important in nervous breakdowns, but it is constantly applicable in our daily lives. The advice to count ten before speaking when angry is a piece of practical common sense given in the interests of sublimation. It is said that Goethe consciously tried to convert his joys and sorrows into poems, in order to set his mind at rest. This is sublimation.

Dining-room manners are sublimations of the primitive hunger impulse. We use knives, forks, and spoons instead of tearing and clawing at our food. The sex instinct is similarly sublimated by the customs and refinements of society. Many men and women who desire children, but who are denied them by nature or society, find satisfaction in serving on boards of children's homes, hospitals, and the like, or in organizing camps for boys and girls. Painting and sculpture may be outlets for balked primitive instincts, and then they are particularly apt to produce remarkable works of art which have enduring social value.

Salesmanship can raise a strong combative instinct into a socially useful occupation. Science develops an apparently fruitless curiosity into great accomplishments. Engineering directs the seemingly meaningless tendency of the child to construct things into lasting social uses. A love which is not satisfied on the personal level may be fulfilled in the warmth of religious devotion. Or it may be requited in the practical devotions of social service.

Inability to make these deferences to the social groups in which one belongs is fraught with potential danger. Life is a practical business, and one must be ready and willing to make compromises and adjustments between the lower and higher or more social self. Those who cannot effect these adjustments by way of sublimations often become unhappy and are prone to nervous troubles. Education, morality, and religion are organized aids to forward sublimations. But the influence of family and friends is the first and most powerful socializing and sublimating agency, without which one lives at a great handicap. Mental hygiene teaches that socialization is necessary, not only for the development and preservation of society, but also for the individual himself.

## CONCLUSION

It may be taken as axiomatic that every one of us will frequently meet the necessity for sublimation, not only in the great crises, but constantly every day in the trivialities of life. It is worth repeating that, fortunately for us and for society, many of our desires must be denied fulfillment. Each of us, therefore, is left with a considerable amount of energy on hand, which must be distributed. It cannot be made to disappear. It must be utilized—wisely or unwisely. In one sense life is like a stream whose outlet is partially dammed (Fig. 28).

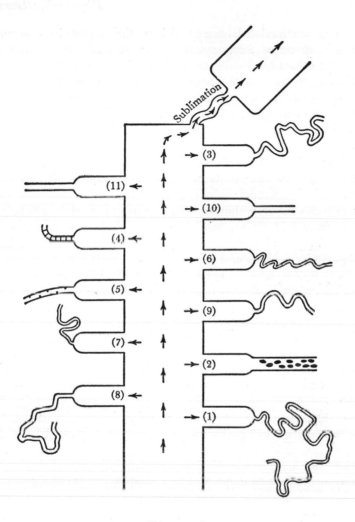

*Figure 28*

(1) Conversion of conflicts into bodily symptoms; hysteria, neurasthenia, anxiety states; (2) repression; (3) segregation and logic-tight compartments; (4) dissociation; (5) displacement, substitution, and symbolism; (6) rationalization; (7) projection; (8) regression; (9) extroversion; (10) identification; (11) inferiority.

The accumulated energy drives the water into secondary channels. Some of these channels take care of the overflow satisfactorily; others have dangerous turns and obstacles; a few are not navigable streams. At the point of departure from the main stream they all seem broad and inviting. But often their character soon changes, and navigation becomes extremely difficult, hazardous, and even impossible. These channels and their advantages and disadvantages have been discussed in Part III. There is one channel which in reality is more than a channel. It is really a continuation of the principal stream. At its beginning it looks difficult and unsatisfactory. This channel is called sublimation. Sublimation utilizes the energies of both thinking and feeling as vital in all behavior. As we have said earlier, behavior which would rest on a purely intellectual foundation would be pallid and ineffectual. Feelings add energy and glow to life. They vitalize ideas and make possible their realization. The intellect needs to be activated and energized by the emotions. Ideas need the driving force of emotions to become realities.

Because the emotions constitute such powerful driving forces both for good and evil, they must be guided into outlets which afford release and satisfaction to the individual and which find acceptance and utilization by the group. Sublimation does not just mean denial. It means finding satisfaction in the use of one's energies in such a way that the needs of others are fulfilled. We cannot live unto ourselves. Sublimation is not the death of feeling and the denial of individuality, but the quickening of both. If the navigator enters this channel boldly and outwits its initial difficulties, he will find that it widens, and he will be able to sail down this stream of life with satisfaction and achievement both for himself and others. Success does not mean absence of difficulties and continuous achievement. Failure does not preclude success. Disappointment, pain, frustration, failure, and suffering are of the very texture of life. It is what we do with these things that counts. Do we learn from them? Do they challenge us to renewed efforts? Do they stimulate our wits and ingenuity? Do they breed courage and determination, so that others can count on us and know that the majority of times we will try our best and give all we have to the effort? Success does not always come in succeeding. The achieving and satisfying life does not imply that we should be afraid of pain and suffering, or joy and fun, or that we should avoid them. The attitude of a patient who used to think it was a sin to enjoy himself has no place in a healthy life. Fear, hate, anger, and love have their function in human adjustment. It is the use to which we put these things that is the important thing. Sublimation is the satisfying, constructive, and socially contributing guidance of these energies. We must not be afraid of our emotions, of ourselves. We must learn to know ourselves and accept ourselves and our emotions in order to build, grow, and develop. Ideals, broad integrating purposes, constructive personal and social living are forged out of disappointment, frustration, and suffering—that is, out of the great emotions of fear (insecurity), anger (discontent), and love (the desire for personal and social security). Discontent with things as they are and insecurity can stimulate aggressive behavior (anger) which can be subdued and organized and directed toward constructive, satisfying, and social living—objects we can learn to love, whether persons, relationships, activities, or great social movements.

The "peace that passeth all understanding" will be found through the realization that the resilience and infinite variation of the emotions, constructively guided by our mind and ideals, can be used to vivify and beautify life and to achieve our potentialities of creative living. May we find the way out of the maze of our conflicts and direct the shape of our lives into this stream of creative living.

# Appendixes I-III

# I. QUESTIONS ON THE
## INDIVIDUAL CHAPTERS

*Chapter 1.* QUESTIONS PSYCHOLOGY HELPS TO ANSWER

1. What is human psychology? What sort of questions does it help to answer?
2. What kinds of discussion upset us? Why?
3. What are some of the problems suggested by psychology?
4. What is the value of thinking psychologically?

*Chapter 2.* THE INTIMATE RELATION OF BODY AND MIND

1. What is the difference between the body and the mind?
2. What do we mean by saying that the mind is spiritual? What do we mean by the spirit of a school? An athletic team? A man?
3. How can the body influence the mind?
4. What are some specific physical diseases and conditions that affect the mind?
5. What is the effect of peace of mind on the body? The effect of fright?
6. What is the effect of a pleasant environment on the body? On the mind?
7. What happens when the mind is not occupied with concrete problems? Does an idle mind affect the body? What is the effect of "all work and no play"?
8. Which emotions have beneficial effects on the mind? Give examples.
9. What is the effect of fear and anxiety on the body? How is this brought about?
10. What are some of the causes of fatigue?
11. What is the effect of excessive anxiety on the body?

12.  Explain how a gastrointestinal neurosis may be developed.

13.  What are some of the effects of physical overwork? Of mental overwork? Of social isolation? Of a feeling of inferiority?

14.  What is the effect of anger, hate, shame, distress, envy, etc.? Of surprise? Uncertainty? What feelings affect the body favorably and which ones affect it unfavorably?

*Chapter 3.*  NERVOUSNESS IS NOT A DISEASE OF THE NERVES

1.  What is the distinction between the concepts of "nerves" and "nervousness?"

2.  Are nerves the cause of nervousness? How do we know?

3.  What are the symptoms when the nerves are damaged?

4.  Does nervousness result from injury to a nerve? From an accident? From drugs?

5.  What four kinds of "nervousness" are sometimes spoken of? Explain each.

6.  What must we consider in order to understand our various feelings?

7.  Why is talking helpful in treating nervousness?

8.  What kind of knowledge is it important for a patient with nervousness to acquire?

*Chapter 4.*  ELEMENTARY PSYCHOLOGICAL CONCEPTS

1.  Can you give a definition of the mind?

2.  Why is it important to have a knowledge of psychological concepts?

3.  What are some of the things that occur to us when we think of the mind?

4.  How does the behaviorist school view the mind? What does psychology mean to them?

5.  What is introspection? How does it differ from observation? Why is introspection necessary in the treatment of nervousness?

6.  What is an inhibition?

7.  What is a stimulus? A response?

8.  Compare the nervous system to a telephone exchange.

9.  What are sensations? Perceptions? Thought? Imagination?

10.  What is the difference between logical thinking and fantasy?

11. What is a reflex? Describe some.
12. What is a sympathetic reflex?
13. What is an affect? What is a mood?
14. What three aspects of mental life have psychologists emphasized?
15. What is meant by an emotional difficulty with "bodily reverberation"? Why is it important to understand this?
16. What is the importance of emotions? How does a person ruled by emotion differ from a person governed by intellect?
17. How should a person's conduct be organized?
18. Discuss the ways in which the word "habit" may be used.
19. What is the difference between normal and nervous people in regard to habits?
20. What is the difference between habits and reflexes?
21. What is meant by "instinct"? Explain McDougall's definition and his list of instincts.
22. Name the four fields into which the activities of a well-balanced personality should be divided.

*Chapter 5.* ACTION AS THE GOAL OF MENTAL PROCESSES
1. What is the normal end or purpose of nervous system functions?
2. Of what use are sensations?
3. When does emotion become unwholesome and sterile? What did William James say in this connection?
4. What useful purpose is served by memory, thought, and imagination?
5. What is the problem involved in neurasthenia? In psychasthenia?
6. Explain "blocking."
7. How does a sojourn in a sanitarium help or hinder a patient?
8. In discussing the distribution of activity, explain the diagram of the meridians of mental activity.
9. What kind of persons live in each of these meridians and what must they learn?
10. How do types of activity affect people's happiness? Discuss the difference between routine and administrative work.

*Chapter 6.* THE DEGREES OF AWARENESS: THE CONSCIOUS, THE
             SUBCONSCIOUS AND THE UNCONSCIOUS

1. What is the meaning of unconscious? Subconscious?
2. What is symbolism?
3. What is the Freudian concept of the censor?
4. What does psychotherapy attempt to do in exploring the various aspects of a personality? How does psychoanalysis do this?
5. What service does an analyst render the patient and what knowledge must he have?
6. What is "transference"? "Resistance"?
7. Explain the diagram of the conscious, subconscious, and unconscious.
8. What are some of the frequent distractions that interfere with work?
9. What effect do illness, worry, unhappiness have upon work life?
10. Why does analysis consider subconscious or unconscious feelings and ideas, and discuss the environment and past history of a person who is nervous?
11. What is the purpose of analysis?

*Chapter 7.* THE COMPLEX, OR THE EMOTIONAL WEB OF IDEAS.
             LOGICAL VERSUS EMOTIONAL THINKING

1. What is a complex? Illustrate what is meant by this.
2. What does rational thinking do? What does nonrational thinking mean?
3. When are complexes good and when bad?
4. What are the three great complexes?
5. Explain how the instincts and emotions are grouped into the various complexes.

*Chapter 8.* THE MAJOR STRUGGLES BETWEEN THE HERD, THE EGO,
             AND THE SEX COMPLEXES

1. What is mental conflict? In what realm of consciousness does it take place?
2. Why is it important for us to learn the motives for our actions?

3. How does conflict affect efficiency and happiness?
4. How do the claims of the ego and of sex conflict?
5. To what are the major conflicts of life due?
6. How does the "herd instinct" conflict with other desires?
7. Give examples of conflicts between duty and desire.
8. What is the first thing to do when conflict causes trouble?

*Chapter 9.* PERSONALITY DEVELOPMENT

1. How has personality been defined? How do most of us regard our childhood and the experience of growing up? Would we be glad to relive our childhoods? How do anatomy and physiology enter into personality?

2. How is the newborn baby like a newborn animal? How does he differ? What happens if one does not succeed in severing the emotional ties of childhood?

3. What seems to be the most important part of his body to the infant? Why? What is this phase of development called? What is the result of his living in the present?

4. What is a further value of the taking of nourishment? What emotional force dominates the child's life? What is it called?

5. How otherwise does the mouth contribute to the child's pleasure and how is this pleasure expressed in adult life?

6. During the oral period, what must the child have in order to develop a healthy personality? What results from frustration at this time?

7. Contrast the child who has been deprived in this regard with one who has had the satisfaction of the breast.

8. When does the child become interested in excretory activities and products and what is this stage in his development called?

9. What is demanded of the child in toilet training? Why does he have to give up his pleasure in the excretory function?

10. Why does the toilet-training period have psychological importance? With what feelings do anal and urethral processes become fused?

11. What do we mean when we say a child is sadistic? Why is the parental attitude toward excretory functions so important?

12. What may be the reason for and the result of constipation?

13.  How many conflicting trends develop in the child's personality and what is necessary in this regard for sound personality growth?

14.  What is ambivalence? What is its importance in personality development?

15.  What change takes place at approximately the third year of life? In what area does the child now become interested? How does he procure pleasure? What is meant when it is said that moderate masturbation at this phase is a necessary and natural occurrence?

16.  In what ways and with whom does the little boy compete for his mother's affection? To what conclusion does he come?

17.  How does the little boy explain the fact that the little girl does not have a penis? What is the significance of injury, accidents, operations, disciplinary threats in this connection? How may certain religious ideas bear upon this situation? To what conclusion does he come in regard to himself?

18.  How does the little girl react to the knowledge that she lacks a penis? Upon whom does she blame this lack and why is she now drawn to her father?

19.  If the girl does not relinquish her desire for a penis and her erotic attachment to her father, what effect does this unresolved conflict have on her later life? In this respect, what does Freud think about the formation of neuroses?

20.  Describe the latency period.

21.  What is the superego and how is it formed?

22.  What are the attitudes and behavior between the sexes during the latency period?

23.  How does the adolescent stage differ from the other stages of development and what important decisions must be made at this time?

24.  What problems give the adolescent the most concern? With what do these impulses come into conflict and what must the child do to avoid guilt and anxiety?

25.  What is the result of masturbation at this time?

26.  How do mothers add to the girl's difficulty in adjusting to menstruation? How do many boys regard nocturnal emissions?

27.  What does the severity of adolescent conflict depend on? What attitudes on the part of parents aid in the process of development?

28. What is the relation between the early emotional relationships and the child's adjustment to adult life?

29. What is mature parental love and how is it expressed? When is it crippling to emotional progress?

30. What effect does early deprivation in love have on the adult and how will he react?

31. How would you define and distinguish passive and rejective love?

32. What significance has this chapter to child-parent relationships?

33. What significance has this chapter on the dynamics of marriage?

*Chapter 10.* THE SUPEREGO: ITS FORMATION AND IMPORTANCE IN HEALTH AND DISEASE

1. What concepts of Freud's have been of outstanding importance in the field of medical psychology and how has psychoanalytic investigation helped?

2. How has psychological thinking been expanded by Freud?

3. From what viewpoint has psychoanalysis approached the study of a personality? What are the three different systems that Freud described?

4. Describe the id as Freud conceived it.

5. What is the function of the ego?

6. What is the function of the superego and of what does it consist?

7. Why do we say that the young child is dominated by the id? What does this mean?

8. In what areas are the rudiments of the superego first discerned?

9. During the conflicts of toilet training, how does the mother image influence the child?

10. What is identification? From what does the superego draw its main force? Why is the superego called the internalized parent?

11. What are some of the words we use to note that we have offended our superego? What is guilt?

12. What place does the mature and healthy ego take in regard to the id and the superego?

13. What is sublimation?

14. What happens if the ego is weak and lacks integrative power?

15. How does repression work?

16. If the conscience is inordinately strong, give an example of what happens to sexual drives, for instance.

17. When is it considered that the greatest impetus to superego formation occurs? What forms the hard core of the superego?

18. By what period has the fear of parental punishment been transformed into fear of conscience?

19. Why do we obey the dictates of our consciences? What feeling does it give us? What feelings do we have if the superego is defied?

20. How long is the process of superego development? With what persons does the child identify later in his development?

21. What is meant by saying that the child's personality traits in later life may be a fulfillment of what he fantasied his parent to be?

22. When the conscience is lax and inadequate to what may it be reacting? What else may harsh training lead to?

23. Why do some children who are treated leniently by parents develop large amounts of guilt?

24. Under what conditions does the superego become a positive and constructive force?

25. Where do guilt feelings originate?

26. In the parent-child relationship, wrongdoing, parental disapproval, insecurity, followed by parental punishment, reconciliation, and forgiveness form the recurrent cycle. After the formation of the superego what takes place?

27. What is masochism and how does it come about? What are its common manifestations?

28. Describe the relationship between guilt and hostility and how it is shown in depressed states.

29. Under what conditions is the autocracy of the superego temporarily overthrown?

30. Give an example of a mechanism by which conscience can be bought off with suffering.

31. Give the reason for the rituals and ceremonials erected by the obsessive-compulsive patient.

32. In what other psychopathological state does the superego play a part? How?

33. How does the unconscious sense of guilt and need for punishment act in the case of some criminals?

34. What is the result when his conscience reacts to keep a guilt-laden individual from enjoying happiness or success?

35. When can the individual's personality be considered to be well integrated?

36. How is the superego related to religious practices?

37. What is the relation between psychoanalysis and religion?

38. What is education?

39. What is the importance of family relationships?

40. What is the significance of parent-child relationships?

41. What is training and its importance?

42. What are some of the chief characteristics and functions of society? Civilization? Are these desirable?

43. Discuss the psychological aspects of some different types of economic, religious, social, and political systems.

*Chapter 11.* EMOTION—ITS NATURE.

1. What is emotion? What would a person be like if he entirely lacked emotion?

2. In what ways is anger an asset? Illustrate.

3. Does fear serve any useful purpose?

4. When a stimulus to anger occurs can a person avoid becoming angry?

5. In what ways are emotional responses similar to reflexes and how do they differ from reflexes?

6. Is being afraid the same thing as being a coward? Why?

7. If inappropriate sexual feelings are aroused and cannot be stifled, does that imply that they must be strong?

8. If feelings have to be recognized and accepted, does a person have to become a helpless victim of these feelings? What choices are possible?

9. How may emotions be camouflaged and misunderstood by the person experiencing them?

10. What may be the physical effects if emotional energy does not find an adequate outlet?

*Chapter 12.* ANGER

1. Define anger.
2. What are some of the words which denote the existence of anger?
3. Illustrate how frustration causes anger.
4. Can a person be frustrated by someone he loves?
5. If the person responsible for the frustration means no harm, will anger be aroused?
6. What is meant by the statement that a person may be frustrated by the laws of nature?
7. How can a person frustrate himself?
8. Give examples of harm as a stimulus to anger.
9. In what ways may a person feel his survival is threatened?
10. Illustrate how a threat to survival often causes anger in the adolescent.
11. Explain individual differences in susceptibility to frustration. How is this related to what a person considers important in life?
12. Explain the stimulus-response aspect of anger.
13. How does it happen that shame and guilt are often concomitants of anger?
14. Does a person sometimes fail to recognize the fact that he is angry? Why?
15. In what ways may anger cause physical disease?
16. Show how anger may accumulate. Why is this dangerous? Illustrate.
17. How can anger provoked by harm be discharged? What difficulties does this present?
18. How can anger arising from frustration be dealt with?
19. Is "getting even" a satisfactory method of dealing with anger aroused by the domination of another person? Why?
20. How does understanding of the factors in a situation affect the degree of anger felt?
21. How does uncontrolled anger act as a boomerang?
22. When anger is directed against the self, in what ways is this evidenced?
23. Describe how conscience may become relentlessly punitive.

24. Illustrate how self-inflicted injury may be aimed at someone else.

25. What is the most frequent motive for suicide?

26. Has anger survival value?

27. Discuss effective and ineffective methods of dealing with anger.

*Chapter 13.* FEAR

1. What is fear?

2. What words are used to indicate the presence of fear?

3. What are the chief causes of fear?

4. In what ways are the causes of anger and fear similar! How do they differ?

5. Name some of the most common fears.

6. What danger arouses the greatest amount of fear in people?

7. In what ways is domination imposed by one person on another?

8. How can a multiplicity of wise suggestions produce in another a fear-ridden personality?

9. What characterizes a feeling of inadequacy?

10. What is anxiety? How is it related to a person's own impulses?

11. Can a person be afraid of his conscience? What may be the relation of anxiety and unreasonably rigid standards or perfectionist principles?

12. Give an illustration of how a person may fear his own aggressive impulses.

13. May anxiety be related to sexual impulses? How?

14. Give a number of examples which will show the difference between fear and cowardice.

15. Can a person avoid being afraid?

16. Can he avoid appearing afraid?

17. Can he avoid acting afraid?

18. How is "shell shock" related to the confusion between fear and cowardice?

19. Why is it important to admit the existence of fear?

*Chapter 14.* REGRESSION OR EXAGGERATED EMOTION

1. Enumerate the ways of meeting conflicts.
2. What does "regression" mean?
3. Under what circumstances is regression apt to occur? Why is such a reaction ineffective?
4. Give examples of such actions.
5. How can such reactions be discouraged?

*Chapter 15.* THE EXTROVERT AND HIS PURSUIT OF ACTIVITY

1. How does a person act when we say he has recourse to extroversion?
2. How are diversions an example of extroversion? Give other examples.
3. Describe an extrovert.
4. How may this type be related to regression?
5. When is extroverted activity normal?
6. What are the dangers of extroversion? Give examples.
7. How may one learn to escape such dangers?

*Chapter 16.* INTROVERSION, FANTASIES, AND DAYDREAMS

1. What is typical of the introvert's behavior in contrast to the extrovert's? Give examples.
2. How does the introvert's type of thinking lead to indecision?
3. When is thinking good and when is it harmful?
4. Contrast introverts and extroverts showing how both are needed and useful.
5. Why is continued fantasy harmful? When is daydreaming helpful?
6. How can excessive daydreaming lead to nervous breakdowns?
7. What can the introvert and extrovert learn from each other?

*Chapter 17.* RATIONALIZATION—HOW WE DECEIVE OURSELVES

1. What is rationalization and how does it come about?
2. Give examples of rationalization.
3. When does rationalization become serious?
4. What are its dangers? What can we use as a check upon it?

*Chapter 18.* SEGREGATION, OR A CERTAIN BLINDNESS TO OUR IN-
CONSISTENCIES

1. What is meant by logic-tight compartments?
2. Give examples of the kind of action that this leads to.
3. What is meant by a psychopathic personality?
4. Why is the extrovert apt to make use of segregation in dealing with his conflicts?
5. What are the dangers and disadvantages of this method of avoiding conflicts?
6. Describe how one type of mental disorder illustrates segregation.

*Chapter 19.* REPRESSION—WHY AND WHAT WE FORGET

1. What two ways of forgetting are there? Upon what does each depend?
2. Give examples of active forgetting.
3. What is the name given to avoidance of conflicts by this method?
4. Which type of mind practices it? Is the introvert or extrovert more likely to use repression?
5. What is the difference between segregation and repression?
6. Describe amnesia and its relation to repression.

*Chapter 20.* DISSOCIATION AND THE DANGERS OF UNRECOGNIZED
TENDENCIES

1. What is dissociation? Give examples.
2. How does the galvanometer show the unconscious emotional coloring of certain ideas?
3. Explain the association-reaction experiment and its value.
4. Why is it better to understand our fears rather than repress them?
5. What may be the cause of the rebellious attitude of the radical? Of the resistance to change of the conservative?
6. Why are segregation, repression, dissociation, fundamentally unsuccessful methods of relieving conflicts?
7. Why do repressed ideas and emotions break out or erupt? What are the symptoms?

*Chapter 21.* THE CONVERSION OF MENTAL CONFLICTS INTO PHYSICAL
SYMPTOMS: ANXIETY, NEURASTHENIA, HYSTERIA

1. Explain the comparison between administrative difficulties in social organizations and the processes of repression and dissociation in the individual.

2. What may be the cause of physical exhaustion?

3. How can a person tell whether his fatigue is due to unconscious conflict?

4. What may be the cause of sleeplessness? Of lack of concentration? Of poor memory?

5. What is neurasthenia?

6. Are the physical symptoms of the neurasthenic real or just imaginary?

7. How is the term "functional" used in connection with the symptoms of neurosis?

8. Explain the relation of the many physical symptoms of a neurasthenic patient and his feeling of inferiority. How were these physical symptoms overcome?

9. Explain the statement: Sensations become substitutes for unfaced problems.

10. Describe the physiological disturbances caused by intense emotional situations, for example, a cat frightened by a dog.

11. Enumerate other feelings which may have the same effect as fear.

12. Mention some situations that can produce anxiety.

13. What is meant by "frozen fear"? What are its manifestations?

14. Of what symptoms does the neurasthenic usually complain? What is the remedy?

15. How does the hysterical person differ from the neurasthenic? Contrast them in respect to symptoms and reactions.

16. Give some examples of hysterical mechanisms.

17. How can we tell whether a disability is hysterical or organic?

18. Do hysterical disabilities serve a purpose for the individual? How?

19. What are occupational neuroses? Why do they belong to this class of phenomena?

20. In what way are hysteria and neurasthenia similar?
21. What helps to prevent the development of a neurosis?
22. How may the patient get well?

*Chapter 22.* THE MENTAL USE OF SUBSTITUTES, THE TRANSFERENCE OF EMOTIONS, AND THE IMPORTANCE OF SYMBOLISM

1. What is displacement?
2. What experiments have been made by animal psychologists along this line? How does this apply to human education?
3. How does analysis help the patient to understand unexplained reactions? Give examples.
4. Explain how organic sensations sometimes come to be taken as the symbols of sinful thoughts.
5. What does symbolism mean?
6. What is the psychological function of symbols? How do they economize thought?
7. Give examples of objects used symbolically.
8. Explain how the posture and bearing of a person or his dress may be symbolic of his mental state.
9. Give examples of daily habits that may have symbolic significance.
10. When is symbolism useful and suitable and when harmful? Explain its use in ritualistic acts.

*Chapter 23.* PROJECTION, OR FAULTFINDING AND SHIFTING THE BLAME

1. Why is it important to see clearly the origin and implications of our thoughts?
2. What is projection? What do we gain by this method of avoiding conflicts?
3. How do persons of critical, cynical, or intolerant natures use projection?
4. How does excessive criticism lead to cynicism?
5. What do we mean when we say the world is colored by our feelings? Why may we call that "projection"?
6. How do feelings and emotions alter the world for us?
7. How may the same sound or sight be interpreted by different personalities?

8. Explain how great sensitiveness gives us mistaken notions. Give examples.

9. How may an understanding of projection help us overcome distorted thinking?

10. Describe the different views of life as seen by the "haves" and the "have-nots."

11. In what way is projection valuable and protective?

12. Why, in spite of its value in some cases, is projection a dangerous mechanism?

*Chapter 24.*   IDENTIFICATION AND IDEALIZATION

1. What is identification?

2. Contrast identification and projection.

3. What feelings cause us to employ identification? Why does the extrovert more often overuse it?

4. What is the most common form of identification?

5. Explain the value of idealization in the life of the child.

6. What responsibility does this put upon parents?

7. Distinguish between parental love and selfishness in dealing with children's problems.

8. What are the dangers for children who remain dependent?

9. What danger to marriage is occasioned by too great emotional attachment to the parent ideal?

10. In what other relationships does the process of identification occur? What are the dangers in each case?

11. What are the dangers to the student of too much identification? What is the responsibility of instructors in this regard?

12. Discuss identification and hero worship in adolescence— its value and its danger.

13. What is the similarity between conservatism and radicalism and what is the difference?

14. How is the process of identification used in religion in reference to the Devil and to God?

15. How is self-development favored by identification? How do ideals help? How can ideals be unwholesomely used?

16. How may identification be harmful?

17. What is a delusion and what type of thinking leads to it?

18. How can it be prevented?

**Chapter 25.** THE INFERIORITY COMPLEX AND SELF-EXPRESSION

1. What is an inferiority complex?
2. With what physical and mental handicaps and in what kind of environmental situations may it originate? Give examples.
3. How does the mind seek compensation for an inferiority feeling? Give examples.
4. What is one common compensation we develop? How does this help?
5. Mention another way of compensating.
6. Give examples of how the mind creates fictitious goals for those with inferiority complexes.
7. What is the "specialist" attitude? What is the danger in it?
8. What is meant by traveling the "path of opposites"?
9. What are the positive aspects of an inferiority complex?
10. Why has it been called the "golden" complex?
11. What is its social value?
12. Why are some compensations wise and others unwise?
13. How may bodily inferiorities find compensation?
14. What is the first step in the management of such a complex?

**Chapter 26.** SUBLIMATION, OR SOCIALIZING OUR INSTINCTS

1. What factors determine which methods are used in fighting conflicts?
2. What does "sublimate" mean? Literally? Psychologically?
3. How does our social environment affect us?
4. What is an inhibition? How is it connected with conscience?
5. How is a conflict resolved through sublimation?
6. How is the word "libido" used?
7. Compare mental energy with the energy in the physical world.
8. What are the various channels through which we express energy?
9. What makes the difference between the way the savage expends his energy and civilized man?
10. Give examples of the common uses we make of sublimation.
11. What does mental hygiene teach about sublimation?

## II. QUESTIONS AN INDIVIDUAL
## WITH PERSONALITY DIFFICULTIES
## OR NERVOUSNESS SHOULD
## ENDEAVOR TO ANSWER

A. PHYSICAL EQUIPMENT

1. How is your physical *health?* Comparatively speaking, has it been a handicap or an asset in your life? If it has been a handicap is that because of bad luck over which you had no control, or because of lack of knowledge of hygiene and of how to attain and maintain good health? Has it been due to procrastination or lack of "will power" to fulfill the requirements of good health?

2. How much *energy* have you? Less than average so you have to budget it carefully in order to get things done, or are you a human dynamo so that the problem is to find enough things to do to get rid of your energy?

3. How much *muscular strength* have you? Has lack of it handicapped you for doing things you would have liked to do? Has lack of muscular development been a cause of lowered self-confidence? Was it important during school years? Is it important now? Are you slow in movement compared with others? How is your dexterity? Has it helped or handicapped you?

4. How about your *personal appearance,* including features, figure, physical attractiveness, clothes? Is it an asset or a liability? Do you care about it or consider the matter unimportant? Do you make an intelligent effort to make the most of what nature has given you?

5. How intelligent are you? Apart from the influence of education or experience, are you naturally smarter than average? Are you a genius intellectually? How do you compare with college professors, lawyers, college students, high-school students, the average man you meet? How do you compare with your father, mother, siblings, hus-

282

band or wife? Do you pretend that you are more intelligent than you are—to other people, to yourself? Have people appreciated your abilities?

B. FEELINGS AND INSTINCTS

1. Do you have strong feelings, strong instincts, strong emotions, strong likes and dislikes? Are you calm and phlegmatic or high-strung and tense and excitable? Are you enthusiastic? Are you moody? Do your feelings change rapidly and unaccountably?

2. Do you habitually hide your feelings or show them? Are you an open kind of a person or do you keep things to yourself? If you keep things to yourself, why do you do so? Is it consideration for others or fear of others' disapproval, ridicule, or lack of understanding? Do you ever try to hide your feelings from yourself? Do you accept the presence of your feelings or ignore them? Do you deny them?

3. Do you control your feelings or do they control you? Is it hard or easy for you to control your feelings? Could you let your feelings go if you wanted to? Do you always try to control your feelings or just sometimes? Do you fight your feelings? Do you ever win? Do you think a person should hide his feelings or show them? At what age did you begin to learn how to control your feelings? What made you learn? Who taught you?

4. Do you know what role fear plays in your life? Can you always recognize it when it occurs? Are you ashamed of being afraid? Has fear been an asset or liability in your life? Or hasn't it affected you one way or another as far as you know? Were you brought up to believe that fear and cowardice were the same thing? When did you learn the difference? (If you still have not learned this go back and read this book again.) Have you ever failed to do something you wanted to do because you were afraid to try? Do other people usually know it when you are afraid? How do you handle fear when it comes? Does it affect you physically? Weakness? Trembling? Tension? Palpitations? Indigestion? Do you ignore it, hide it, suppress it, accept it, tell others about it? Do you do things in spite of it or because of it? (I'll prove to you I am not afraid to climb that tree!) Do you call fear by other names such as shyness, self-consciousness, tiredness, tenseness, being upset? What are the main things you are afraid of? Sickness? Pain? Death? Failure? Losing love? Losing self-control?

Losing face? Losing self-respect? Are you afraid of ridicule? Sarcasm? Of being ignored? Of being conspicuous? Of being laughed at? Of being left out of things? Of being pushed around? Of being humiliated? Of being imposed upon? Of being bossed? Of failing to do your duty? Of not getting married? Of not getting advanced in your work? Of "life's passing you by"? If you keep asking yourself what you are afraid of, what answers come?

5. Do you have a temper? Do you lose your temper? Do other people know when you are angry? Do you always know when you are angry? What synonyms do you use for being angry? Cross? Irked? Sick? Hurt? Tired? Upset? Fed up? Indifferent? Loss of interest? How does anger affect you physically? Tremble? Heart beat hard? Indigestion? Diarrhea? Headache? Weakness? Does your temper come quickly or does it take a lot to make you mad? Does it disappear promptly or does it stick with you? Do you bear resentment or harbor grudges? Have you ever hit anything or anybody, or thrown anything in temper? When was the last time? Have you ever felt like doing these things? When did you learn to control your temper? How did you learn? Who taught you? Does temper ever make you do and say things you are sorry for afterward? Has temper been an asset for you or a handicap? Would you amount to more if you had more of a temper? Do you ever not get mad when it would probably be a good idea if you did? Is anybody afraid of your temper? Is anybody afraid of your moods? How often do you get mad? Once a year? Once a week? Several times a day? Do other people ever make you mad to serve their own purposes? What are the causes of your temper? What are the main things that make you mad? What things in life have you been dissatisfied with? With what are you dissatisfied now? Do you get mad mainly at other people? Or at inanimate objects? Or at ideas, such as injustice and ignorance? Or at yourself? What person in your life have you been mad at most frequently? Are you more apt to become angry at someone you love or someone you don't love? Do you get mad when people step all over you? When they try to impose on you and push you around? When you can't have your own way? When people try to boss you? When people ask you too many questions? When you are left out of things? When you are made the center of things? When you are beaten in a game? When your wife or your child doesn't do what you want them to? Or when

your husband doesn't do what you want him to? Or when your mother doesn't do what you want her to? Or the President? Do you become annoyed when people do not do what they should for their own good? When your son deliberately goes out on a wet day without his rubbers? Do you get angry when people insult you, laugh at you, ridicule you, say things behind your back? Don't give you credit for good intentions, don't appreciate what you have done for them? What do you do about your anger? Do you try to avoid getting angry? Do you fight it? Try to suppress it? Ignore it? Pretend it isn't there? Do you take it out on other people? On things? Do you know how to get rid of it? Are you ashamed of it? Do you tell other people about it? Do you try to walk it off? Do you divert it into the "I'll show them" attitude?

6. Are you a warm, loving kind of person or cold and aloof? Are you affectionate? Demonstrative? Do you like demonstrations of affection? Do you show love or hide it? Is the feeling of love a strong one in you? Would you rather love or be loved? Do you need to be loved or can you get along without it? Do you try consciously to get people to love you? Can you love a person who doesn't love you? Is being loved more important to you than your work? Your duty? Your pride? Can you decide whom you shall love and whom you shan't love? Do you tend more towards protective love, dominating, or submissive love? Can you have sexual feelings which are distinct from feelings of love? Are sexual feelings something you try to avoid, to accept, or seek? Are you ashamed of sex feelings? Are you ashamed of not having sex feelings? At what age did sex feelings first occur in you? Did you recognize them for what they were? In what ways have sex feelings influenced your behavior and the way you spend your time?

C. CONSCIENCE, IDEALS, STANDARDS, PRINCIPLES, GOALS, CODES

1. Do you have a strong conscience? Are you conscientious? How strong is your sense of duty? In making decisions do you usually consider what is the right thing to do and what you ought to do? Do you have definite principles? Definite ideas of right and wrong? Definite standards of behavior? Do you have a code of behavior? A set of rules for yourself? Is guilt a strong feeling in you? About what things have you felt guilty? Have you felt guilty about not having done things you felt you should? Have you impulses about which

you feel guilty? A frequent feeling? Are you a perfectionist? How important is it for you to do your duty? If you had to choose between love and duty which would you choose? Between life and duty? Between your wife's happiness and duty? Do you usually do your duty? Follow your code? Live up to your principles? How do we feel when impulses are blocked? What things block impulses? Are you exacting with yourself? Do you expect other people to live up to your principles? Do you become angry if they do not? Are you tolerant? Do you try to impose your standards on your children? Could you be friends with a person who thought it all right to be promiscuous or all right to get out of paying bills? Have you ever been selfish in doing your duty at the expense of other people's feelings? Has anybody ever wished that you did not have such a strong sense of duty? Has your sense of duty brought happiness or unhappiness to your family? Why do you do your duty? Do you like yourself? Are you satisfied with yourself? Are you discontented with yourself? Why?

    2.   Where did you get your principles? Your code of behavior? How old were you when you formed your set of principles? Have you revised them since? At what age did you get your concept of right and wrong? Who taught you right from wrong? What person has been most important in the formation of your principles? Your code of behavior? Father? Mother? Teacher? Friend? Character in fiction? Have you formed your own set of principles or taken over that of your parents more or less intact? Is your code of behavior different from that of other people? Would life be easier for you if everybody had your code? Is your code conducive to survival in the competition for existence? Do you have a broad enlightened code or one that some people would consider narrow and selfish? Is living up to your code and standards an end in itself or merely to serve some other purpose? What is that purpose? What is your purpose in living? Are your own personal rules harsher or more liberal than the rules of society? Does your code ever conflict with laws of nature as far as feelings and emotions are concerned? Is it difficult for you to work with people who have a different code than yours? Does your code ever make you unhappy? Does your code ever hurt others? Have you ever changed your principles? Why? Are you conscientious? Hyperconscientious? Are you religious? Antireligious? What does religion mean to you? What place does it occupy in your life?

D. SELF (EGO) AND WILL

1. Do you habitually seek, accept, or avoid responsibility? What devices do you use to avoid it? Do you blame other people? Blame your tools? Blame duty (I'm sorry if I got you into trouble but it was my duty to tell the truth) or (Don't blame me, I HAD to do it!)? Do you disclaim responsibility on the basis of ignorance? (I'm sorry I stepped on your toes but how was I to know your foot would be in the way?) Do you ever feel responsible for things when actually you have no responsibility, or at least other people think you have not? What price have you paid during your lifetime for avoiding responsibility? Why do you not seek more responsibility? Are you ambitious? Do you make decisions easily? Do you usually ask advice? Do you usually take advice? Do you ever ask advice in order to avoid responsibility? Do you like to decide things for yourself or have them decided for you? Are you dependent on anybody for advice? Are you a dependent kind of person? Are you conspicuously independent?

2. Were you obedient or disobedient as a child? Are you antagonistic to authority? Are you a submissive person? Are you hypersensitive to being bossed? Can you be stubborn? Are you easy, difficult, or impossible to impose upon? Are you often imposed upon? Do you often feel imposed upon? Can you be talked into doing things you do not want to do? Is it difficult for you to say "no"? How is your sales resistance? Are you good at sticking up for your rights? Can anyone force you to do something you do not want to do? Do you do many things you do not want to do? Is it important for you to get your own way? Is it easy or difficult for you to give orders or direct other people's activity? Do you usually think up the things you do or fall in with the plans of others? How much initiative and enterprise have you? Are you an aggressive person? Do you usually think of the reasons in favor of doing things or the reasons against doing things? How important is procrastination in your life? Are you an executive? Do you like to organize things? Do you like to direct people? Are you impatient with yourself? Others? Circumstances? Time? Is it easier for you to do things yourself or ask others? Can you delegate work? Are you fussy about details? Neatness? Orderliness? Are you meticulous? Are you hyperconscientious?

3.   Are you self-confident or do you lack self-confidence? Do you have an inferiority complex? How is your self-esteem? Are you sensitive? Are your feelings easily hurt? What are your sensitive spots? For example, what are the main things a person could say to you that would hurt your feelings? When your feelings are hurt, do you tend to withdraw into yourself or fight back? How do you react to criticism? To kidding? To being scolded or bawled out? Do you respond better to encouragement or to threats? How do you react to compliments? Do you seek compliments or avoid them? Do you boast? Do you belittle yourself? Why? Are you critical of yourself, of others, of social codes? What are the main things in your life that have lowered your self-esteem? Self-respect? Self-confidence? What are the main things that have raised your self-esteem? What devices do you use to avoid having your feelings hurt? What are your main sources of increasing your self-esteem? Self-respect? Love? Attention? Sense of accomplishment? Sense of having done your duty? Power? Being independent? Belittling others? What person in your life has done most toward raising your self-confidence? What person has had most effect in lowering your self-confidence, your self-esteem? When you are with people, do you try mainly to raise their self-esteem or to maintain your own? Do you spend much time trying to explain or justify yourself to others? Do you prefer to talk about yourself and your problems, or get others to talk of themselves, their problems, and their ideas on things?

## III.  GENERAL  QUESTIONS

1.  What  is  health?  What  is  normal?  What  keeps  us  going?
What  makes  us  do  things?  What  forces  or  reasons  drive  or  lead  us
to  do  things?
2.  What  kind  of  a  person  am  I?  What  interests  have  I?  What
temperament  have  I?  What  interests  have  I  developed  consciously?
What  sort  of  training  have  I  had  for  life?  What  tasks  have  I  fulfilled?
What  tasks  have  I  failed  at?  What  are  my  ambitions?  What  have  I
expected  of  myself?  How  have  I  succeeded?  How  have  I  failed?  What
do  I  hope  for?
3.  What  are  my  interests?  Sources  of  happiness?  What  things
give  me  my  chief  support  in  life?  My  chief  sources  of  satisfaction?
Physical  activity?  Intellectual  activity?  Work—vocation?  Social  work?
Philanthropic  work?  Social  relations?  Artistic  activities?  Mechanical
things?  Making  things?  Hobbies?  Social  life?  Diversions?  Amusement?
Traveling?  Directing  others?  Executive  activities?  Power?  Domination?  Aggressiveness?  Working  for  others?  Carrying  out  others'  ideas
and  directions?  Independence?  Being  a  rebel?  Dependence?  Money?
Security?  Ambition?  Social  respect?  Being  in  the  limelight?  Living
for  others?  Living  on  others?  Living  for  self?  Living  for  family?  Self-
respect?  Duty?  Religion?  What  things  are  important  to  me  in  life?
What  are  the  most  important  things?
4.  What  questions  ought  I  to  ask  myself?  What  don't  I  know
about  myself?  What  questions  do  I  not  want  anyone  to  ask  me?  What
questions  do  I  not  want  to  ask  myself?
5.  What  sort  of  behavior  do  people  like?  What  do  I  do  that
other  people  like?  What  do  I  do  that  people  dislike?  What  makes
people  like  us?  What  makes  people  dislike  us?  What  things  bring
people  together?  Facilitate  social  contacts?  What  things  interfere
with  social  contacts?  The  development  of  friendship?  Why  do  people

*289*

make suggestions? Why do people talk to one another? Is it always
or usually for the sake of conveying information? Or seeking for
the truth? William James said words were used to cover up our
thoughts. What did he mean by this?

6. What is happiness? What is the difference between pleasure,
happiness, contentedness, security? Can a person be contented and
unhappy? Have I ever been?

7. What is success? What are my goals? What goals do I
have about which other people know? What goals do I have which
other people do not know? What goals or drives does my life show
or dramatize, like a leitmotif? What is my pattern of life? Does my
life or activity demonstrate any goals or desires of which I have been
unconscious? Goals which others have recognized or may recognize,
of which I have not been aware? Which I hate to recognize or acknowledge?

8. What makes us strong? What makes us weak? What makes
things go right? What makes things go wrong? What has made us
successful? What has made us fail? What makes us doubt? What
makes us indecisive? What makes us feel things? What makes us
fatigued? What tires us? What bores us? What makes us lose interest?
What makes us lack feeling? What makes us feel the opposite of what
is generally expected? Or do the opposite? Am I negativistic? Am I
a negative or positive person? Do I always see objections to things,
people, possible courses of activity? Am I a bundle of "no's" and
resistances? Am I an opposer? A rebel? A critic? Against suggestions?

9. How do wishes enter into my life? What is the function of
wishes? How do I use wishing in my life? What proportion of my
thinking is devoted to wishing? What do I do about my wishes? How
do I use them? How are wishes related to imagination? How much
wishing makes for happiness? How much wishing makes for success
and efficiency? What do wishes do to me? Do I employ them constructively? Do wishes make me unhappy? How much does a desire
for a magical solution of problems and difficulties enter into my thinking? Do I expect magic of myself, of others, of circumstances, of
doctors? Do I see the world as it is? Or as I wish it to be? Have I
been taught to see the world as it is? Have I been disillusioned by
the world, business, friends, my education? Is the world I live in a
fairy tale? Am I trying to realize a fairy tale in life? What are ideals?

What are their function? Do my ideals energize, guide, inspire, make me happy? Do they make me unhappy and distress me? Am I disappointed with life? With people? Do my principles ever interfere with others? Hurt others? Hurt myself? Do my standards ever blind me to characteristics or impulses in myself, or lead me to deny them? In difficulties what should I ask, and expect of myself? Of others? Of doctors? Of psychiatrists?

10.  Can I defer to others? Can I compromise or adjust to different points of view? Am I always right? Do I insist on others following my ideas? If they do not, do I usually withdraw? Am I tolerant? Can I give opposing ideas a fair hearing? Can I adjust to others' ideas? How do I adjust to authority? Can I work under authority? Does it irk me? Can I work with others? Do I ever rebel? How often? Has rebellion usually been successful? Has it hurt me or advanced my progress? Am I strong-minded? Do people who know me think I am obstinate, stubborn, unreasonable? Has my strong-mindedness helped me or hindered me? Have people valued my ideas and suggestions? Do I talk too much? Do I have too many suggestions? Do people resent them? Has my determination gotten me into trouble or brought me success? Do people trust me? Am I reliable? Do people impose on my good nature? Do I ever sacrifice myself for the good of others? For others' desires? Do people depend on me a great deal? Can I do things that require effort, trouble, discomfort, self-frustration, for others? Give examples. How do I stand discomfort? Pain? Have I suffered much in my life? Over what? Have I had much hard luck in life? Do things always go wrong for me? Have I had many illnesses? Many failures? Many operations? Is my body sensitive? Does it go back on me often? Does ill health interfere with my progress? Will I endure discomfort? For what? For others? For an organization? For an authority? For money? For ambition? For ideals?

11.  Have people frequently been unfair to me? Do people readily help me? Or oppose me? Or are they indifferent to me? Can I work in an organization under the authority of someone with whom I disagree? Or do not admire? Have I had to endure much disappointment? How have I dealt with it? Can I stand frustration? How have I met it? When I have had frustration, disappointment, discouragement, do I become: Anxious and apprehensive? Depressed?

Develop feelings of increased inferiority? Angry? Blame others or circumstances? Develop aches, pains, or fatigue? Rationalize the difficulties? Evade? Give up? Do difficulties challenge me to repeated efforts or new attacks? Or depress, restrain, or paralyze me? To what do I turn for support in such circumstances? Personal relationships? Physical activity? Work? Introspection? Diversions? Doctors? Philosophy? Art? Religion?

     12.   What means most to me in life? To what do I give supreme devotion? What are the last things I would give up in life?

# INDEX